INSTRUCTOR'S SOLUTIONS MANUAL

Louis L. Levy • Edward Fritz
Northland Pioneer College

A Problem Solving Approach to

MATHEMATICS
for Elementary School Teachers
FIFTH EDITION

Billstein • Libeskind • Lott

ADDISON-WESLEY PUBLISHING COMPANY
Reading, Massachusetts • Menlo Park, California • New York
Don Mills, Ontario •Wokingham, England • Amsterdam • Bonn • Sydney
Singapore • Tokyo • Madrid • San Juan • Milan • Paris

Reprinted with corrections, February 1995.

Cover art: Patchwork Sampler quilt by Margit Echols © 1983. *Photo:* Schecter Lee.

Reproduced by Addison-Wesley from camera-ready copy supplied by the author.

ISBN 0-201-52566-6

2 3 4 5 6 7 8 9 10-CRS-99 98 97 96 95

CONTENTS

CHAPTER 1 - TOOLS FOR PROBLEM SOLVING

<u>Problem</u> <u>Set</u> <u>1-1</u>

1. (a) Each figure in the sequence adds one box each to the top and bottom rows. Next would be:

    (b) Each figure in the sequence adds one upright and one inverted triangle. Next would be:

    (c) Each figure in the sequence adds one box to the base and one triangle to each row; adds one row.
         Next would be:

    (d) The figures alternate boxes and triangles, while adding one to each succeeding symbol. Next would
         be:

    (e) In a clockwise direction, the shaded area moves to a new position separated from the original by one
         open space, then two open spaces, then by three, etc. The separation in each successive step increases
         by one unit; next would be:

2. (a) The next three terms are 5×6, 6×7, and 7×8. Consecutive integers are paired and multiplied.

    (b) The next three terms are 45, 41, and 37. 4 is successively subtracted to obtain the next number in
         the pattern.

    (c) The next three terms are 15, 20, and 26. 1 is added to the first term to obtain the second; 2 is added
         to the second term to obtain the third; 3 is added to the third term to obtain the fourth; and so on.

    (d) The next three terms are 26, 37, and 50. 3 is added to the first term to obtain the second; 5 is added
         to the second term to obtain the third; 7 is added to the third term to obtain the fourth; and so on.

    (e) The next three terms are X, Y, and X. Y's separate groups of X's; the number of X's is increased by
         1 in each successive group.

    (f) The next three terms are 1, 18, and 1. 5 is added to each result, and the results are uniformly
         separated by the integer 1.

    (g) The next three terms are 34, 55, and 89. Each term is the sum of the preceeding two terms.

    (h) The next three terms are 111111, 1111111, and 11111111. Each term has the same number of 1's as
         its place in the sequence.

    (i) The next three terms are 123456, 1234567, and 12345678. Each term may be obtained by
         multiplying the previous term by 10 and then adding the number of the term in the sequence.

    (j) The next three terms are $6×2^6$, $7×2^7$, and $8×2^8$. Each consecutive positive integer is multiplied by
         the number 2 raised to the power equal to that integer.

    (k) The next three terms are 2^{32}, 2^{64}, and 2^{128}. The power to which 2 is raised in each term is twice the
         power in the preceeding term.

    (l) The three missing terms are 15, 25, and 40. Each term in the sequence is obtained by adding 5 to the
         preceeding term.

2. (m) The three missing terms are 21, 35, and 49. Each term in the sequence is obtained by adding 7 to the preceeding term.

   (n) The three missing terms are $1\frac{1}{2}$, $2\frac{1}{2}$, and $3\frac{1}{2}$. Each term in the sequence is obtained by adding $\frac{1}{2}$ to the preceeding term.

   (o) The three missing terms are 44, 88, and 110. Each term in the sequence is obtained by adding 22 to the preceeding term.

3. (a) Terms that continue a possible pattern are 11, 13, 15, ... This is an arithmetic sequence because we obtain each successive term from the previous term by the addition of the integer 2.

   (b) Terms that continue a possible pattern are 250, 300, 350, ... This is an arithmetic sequence because we obtain each successive term from the previous term by the addition of the integer 50.

   (c) Terms that continue a possible pattern are 96, 192, 384, ... This is a geometric sequence because we obtain each successive term from the previous term by multiplying by the integer 2.

   (d) Terms that continue a possible pattern are 1,000,000, 10,000,000, 100,000,000, ... This is a geometric sequence because we obtain each successive term from the previous term by multiplying by the integer 10.

   (e) Terms that continue a possible pattern are 5^7, 5^8, 5^9, ... This is a geometric sequence because we obtain each successive term from the previous term by multiplying by the integer 5 ($5^8 = 5 \cdot 5^7$, etc.).

   (f) Terms that continue a possible pattern are 66, 77, 88, ... This is an arithmetic sequence because we obtain each successive term from the previous term by the addition of the integer 11.

   (g) Terms that continue a possible pattern are 2^{11}, 2^{13}, 2^{15}, ... This is a geometric sequence because we obtain each successive term from the previous term by multiplying by the integer 2^2.

   (h) Terms that continue a possible pattern are 33, 37, 41, ... This is an arithmetic sequence because we obtain each successive term from the previous term by the addition of the integer 4.

   (i) Terms that continue a possible pattern are 216, 343, 512, ... We obtain each successive term by taking the third power of the number of the term in the sequence (i.e., the 6th term in the sequence is $6^3 = 216$). This sequence is neither arithmetic nor geometric.

4. The pattern in each is the difference 8 between successive elements on the right diagonal and the difference 6 between successive elements on the left diagonal.

   (a)

S	M	T	W	T	F	S
		1				
			9			12
	14			17		
					25	

   (b)

S	M	T	W	T	F	S
		2				
					18	
	21					

5. (a) In each step, one more row and column of dots is added to the preceeding figure. The next three terms are thus 5 rows by 6 columns = 30 dots, 6 rows by 7 columns = 42 dots, and 7 rows by 8 columns = 56 dots.

   (b) The 100th term would have 100 rows and 101 columns, or $100 \cdot 101 = 10,100$ dots.

   (c) The nth term has $n \cdot (n + 1)$ dots, or $n^2 + n$.

6. (a) The number of toothpicks in the third hexagon is 16. We can make a table:

Number of Hexagon	Number of Toothpicks
1	6
2	11
3	16
4	21
⋮	⋮
9	46
10	51

So 51 toothpicks are required for the 10th hexagon.

(b) The number of toothpicks in each hexagon form an arithmetic sequence with 1st term 6 and difference between terms 5. The number of toothpicks required to build n hexagons is thus $6 + (n - 1)5$, or $5n + 1$.

7. (a)

Number of Windmill	Number of Squares
1	5
2	9
3	13
4	17
⋮	⋮
9	37
10	41, so 41 squares are required to build the 10th windmill.

(b) The number of squares in each windmill form an arithmetic sequence with 1st term 5 and difference between terms 4. We know that the nth term in an arithmetic sequence with first term a and difference d is $a + (n - 1)d$, so the number of squares required for the nth windmill is $5 + (n - 1)4$, or $4n + 1$.

8. Ten years at 50 students per year increase gives a total of 500 new students, which added to the current enrollment gives 1200 students. Alternatively, we have an arithmetic sequence with 1st term 700 and difference 50, so the 11th term (enrollment currently plus ten more years) is $700 + (11 - 1)50 = 1200$.

9. If we make a table:

Day	Amount of Water Remaining
1	$15,360 \cdot \frac{1}{2} = 7680$ liters
2	$7680 \cdot \frac{1}{2} = 3840$ liters
⋮	⋮
9	$60 \cdot \frac{1}{2} = 30$ liters
10	$30 \cdot \frac{1}{2} = 15$ liters, so there will be 15 liters of water left in the tank after 10 days.

Alternatively, note that we have a geometric sequence with 1st term 7680 and ratio of $\frac{1}{2}$. We know that the nth term of a geometric sequence with 1st term a and ratio r is ar^{n-1}. Thus the 10th term would be $7680(\frac{1}{2})^9 = 15$ liters.

10. We can analyze this problem as follows:

Cost per foot

1st 10 feet	$10.00 + 0(0.50)$
2nd 10 feet — $10.00 + 0.50$, or	$10.00 + 1(0.50)$
3rd 10 feet — $10.00 + 0.50 + 0.50$, or	$10.00 + 2(0.50)$
4th 10 feet — $10.00 + 0.50 + 0.50 + 0.50$, or	$10.00 + 3(0.50)$
⋮
10th 10 feet — $10.00 + 0.50 + 0.50 + \cdots$, or	$10.00 + 9(0.50)$, so

10. Cost for each 10-foot section
        1st $10.00 \cdot 10.00 = 100.00$
        2nd $10.00 \cdot 10.50 = 105.00$
        3rd $10.00 \cdot 11.00 = 110.00$
        4th $10.00 \cdot 11.50 = 115.00$
        $\vdots$ $\vdots$
        10th $10.00 \cdot 14.50 = 145.00$
     Adding the cost of each 10-foot section gives a total cost of $1225.00.

11. (a)   The employee's monthly pay is $1200 the 1st month, $1220 the 2nd month, $1240 the 3rd month, and so on. This is an arithmetic sequence with 1st term 1200 and difference of 20. At the end of 24 months, therefore, the worker's monthly salary will be $1200 + (24 - 1)20 = $1660.

     (b)   After 6 months, the employee will have earned $1200 + 1220 + 1240 + 1260 + 1280 + 1300 = $7500.

     (c)   Using the general expression for the nth term of an arithmetic sequence, where the nth term is 3240, we have:
           $3240 = 1200 + (n - 1)20$
           $3240 = 1180 + 20n$
           $20n = 2060$, or $n = 103$. The employee's monthly salary will be $3240 after 103 months.

12. This is an arithmetic sequence with 1st term 1 and difference 2. The 10th term, representing the 10th stop, is thus $1 + (10 - 1)2 = 19$ people.

13. Using the general expression for the nth term of an arithmetic sequence with 1st term 24,000 and 9th term 31,680, we have:
     $31,680 = 24,000 + (9 - 1)d$
     $31,680 = 24,000 + 8d$
     $7680 = 8d$, or $d = 960$, the amount by which Joe's income increased each year. To find the year in which his income was $45,120, we then have:
     $45,120 = 24,000 + (n - 1)960$
     $45,120 = 23,040 + 960n$
     $960n = 22080$, or $n = 23$. Joe's income was $45,120 in his 23rd year.

14. (a)   We add 6 matchsticks to each figure. There are 10, 16, 22, ... matchsticks; this is an arithmetic sequence with 1st term 10 and difference 6. The 100th term is thus $10 + (100 - 1)6 = 604$, or 604 matchsticks required for the 100th figure.

     (b)   If the nth term is 500, then $500 = 10 + (n - 1)6$, or $n = 82.\bar{6}$. If $n = 82$, then, the 82nd figure will use the largest possible number of matchsticks; $10 + (82 - 1)6 = 496$ matchsticks.

     (c)   The number of squares in each figure is 3, 5, 7, 9, ... This is an arithmetic sequence with 1st term 3 and difference 2; the 82nd term will be $3 + (82 - 1)2 = 165$ squares.

15. (a)   Looking at the 3rd figure, we have $5 + 3 + 1 = 9$ triangles. The 4th figure would then have $7 + 5 + 3 + 1 = 16$ triangles. An alternative to simply adding 7, 5, 3, and 1 together is to note that $7 + 1 = 8$ and $5 + 3 = 8$. There are $\frac{4}{2} = 2$ of these sums, and $\frac{4}{2}(8) = 16$. Now see that the 100th figure would have $100 + 99 = 199$ triangles in the base, $99 + 98 = 197$ triangles in the second row, and so on until the 100th row where there would be 1 triangle. $199 + 1 = 200$; $197 + 3 = 200$; and so the sum of each pair is 200 and there are $\frac{100}{2} = 50$ of these pairs. $50 \cdot 200 = 10,000$ and so there are 10,000 triangles in the 100th figure.

     (b)   The number of triangles in the nth figure is $\frac{n}{2}$(number of triangles in base + 1). The number of triangles in the base is $n + (n - 1)$, or $2n - 1$. $(2n - 1) + 1 = 2n$. Then $\frac{n}{2}(2n) = n^2$, and there are n^2 triangles in the nth figure.

16.   (a)   Each cube adds 4 squares to the preceeding figure, or 6, 10, 14, 18, 22, 26, 30, 34, 38, 42 squares. Thus there are 42 squares to be painted in the 10th figure.

      (b)   This is an arithmetic sequence with first term 6 and difference 4. The nth term is thus: $6 + (n - 1)4$, or $4n + 2$.

17.   (a)   If the 1st difference of the sequence increases by 2 for each term, then the 5 first differences between the 1st 6 terms of the original sequence are 2, 4, 6, 8, 10. If the 1st term of the original sequence is 3, then the 1st 6 terms are 3, 5, 9, 15, 23, 33.

      (b)   If the 1st term is a, then $a + (a + 2) = 10$, or $a = 4$. Thus the 1st 6 terms of the original sequence are 4, 6, 10, 16, 24, 34.

      (c)   If the 5th term is 35, then:

The 6th term is $35 + 10 = 45$
The 4th term is $35 - 8 = 27$
The 3rd term is $27 - 6 = 21$
The 2nd term is $21 - 4 = 17$
The 1st term is $17 - 2 = 15$. Thus the sequence is 15, 17, 21, 27, 35, 45.

18.   (a)   Look for the differences:

```
5        6        14        32        64        115        191
    1        8        18        32        51        76
        7        10        14        19        25
            3        4        5        6
                1        1        1
```

It can now be seen that the 3rd difference is an arithmetic sequence with fixed difference 1. Thus the 6th term in the 2nd difference row is $25 + 7 = 32$; the 7th term in the 1st difference row is $76 + 32 = 108$; and the 8th term in the original sequence is $191 + 108 = 299$. Using the same reasoning, we find the next three terms in the original sequence to be 299, 447, 644.

      (b)   Look for the differences:

```
0        2        6        12        20        30        42
    2        4        6        8        10        12
        2        2        2        2        2
```

The 1st difference is an arithmetic sequence with fixed difference 2. Thus the 7th term in the 1st difference row is $12 + 2 = 14$; the 8th term in the original sequence is $42 + 14 = 56$. Using the same reasoning, the next three terms in the original sequence are 56, 72, 90.

      (c)   Look for the differences:

```
10        8        3        0        4        20        53
   -2       -5       -3       4        16        33
      -3        2        7        12        17
         5        5        5        5
```

The second difference is an arithmetic sequence with fixed difference 5. Thus the 6th term in the 2nd difference row is $17 + 5 = 22$; the 7th term in the 1st difference row is $33 + 22 = 55$; and the 8th term in the original sequence is $53 + 55 = 108$. Using the same reasoning, the next three terms in the original sequence are 108, 190, 304.

19. (a)   Using the general expression for the nth term of an arithmetic sequence with 1st term 51, nth term 151, and difference 1, we have:
$$151 = 51 + (n - 1)1$$
$$151 = 50 + n$$
101 = n, so there are 101 terms in the sequence.

(b)   Using the general expression for the nth term of a geometric sequence with 1st term 1, nth term 2^{60}, and ratio 2, we have:
$$2^{60} = 1(2)^{n-1}$$
$$2^{60} = 2^{n-1}$$
Since the bases, 2, are the same, then:
$60 = n - 1$, and n = 61. There are 61 terms in the sequence.

(c)   Using the general expression for the nth term of an arithmetic sequence with 1st term 10, nth term 2000, and difference 10, we have:
$$2000 = 10 + (n - 1)10$$
$$2000 = 10n$$
200 = n, so there are 200 terms in the sequence.

(d)   Using the general expression for the nth term of an arithmetic sequence with 1st term 9, nth term 353, and difference 4, we have:
$$353 = 9 + (n - 1)4$$
$$353 = 5 + 4n$$
$$348 = 4n$$
87 = n, so there are 87 terms in the sequence.

(e)   Using the general expression for the nth term of a geometric sequence with 1st term 1, nth term 1024, and ratio 2, we have:
$$1024 = 1(2)^{n-1}$$
Since $2^{10} = 1024$, then $n - 1 = 10$ and n = 11. There are 11 terms in the sequence.

(f)   This is a geometric expression with 1st term 3, nth term $3 \cdot 5^{20}$, and ratio 5. Thus in the general expression for a geometric sequence, ar^{n-1} is $3 \cdot 5^{20}$, and $n - 1 = 20$. n = 21 and there are 21 terms in the sequence.

(g)   Note that the number of each term may be obtained by subtracting 3 from the 2nd multiplicand. Then $101 - 3 = 98$ and there are 98 terms in the sequence.

20. (a)   Yes. Each successive term will still be obtained from the preceeding one by addition of a fixed number.

(b)   Yes. Each successive term will still be obtained from the preceeding one by addition of a fixed number.

21. (a)   No. Each successive term will no longer be obtained from the preceeding one by multiplying by a fixed number.

(b)   Yes. Each successive term will still be obtained from the preceeding one by multiplying by a fixed number.

22.   One may add any two arithmetic sequences and the result will always be another arithmetic sequence. The difference between terms of the new sequence will be the sum of the differences between terms of the addends.

23.   Yes, but only if the ratios of the two sequences are equal. Then the coefficients of the ratio are added to form the coefficients of the ratio of the new sequence.

24.   Yes. The products of the ratios form a new common ratio.

25.   Using the expression for the nth term of a geometric sequence with 1st term 32, nth term 162, and with 5 terms, we have:
$162 = 32r^{n-1}$
$5.0625 = r^4$
$r = 1.5$. Thus $a = 32 \cdot 1.5 = 48$; $b = 48 \cdot 1.5 = 72$; and $c = 72 \cdot 1.5 = 108$.

26.   (a)   If the 4th term is 24, the 5th term is $24 + d$, the 6th term is $24 + 2d$, the 7th term is $24 + 3d$, etc. We see that the number of d's in each case is always 4 less than the number of the term, and the 50th term is $24 + 46d$. Thus we have:
$300 = 24 + 46d$
$276 = 46d$
$d = 6$. Then the 3rd term is $24 - 6 = 18$, the 2nd term is 12, and the 1st term is 6.

      (b)   Using the above technique, we have:
$27 = 9 + 3d$
$18 = 3d$
$d = 6$, and the 2nd term is $9 - 6 = 3$; the 1st term is $3 - 6 = {}^{-}3$.

27.   (a)   1st term: $(1)^2 + 2 = 3$
          2nd term: $(2)^2 + 2 = 6$
          3rd term: $(3)^2 + 2 = 11$
          4th term: $(4)^2 + 2 = 18$
          5th term: $(5)^2 + 2 = 27$

      (b)   1st term: $5(1) - 1 = 4$
          2nd term: $5(2) - 1 = 9$
          3rd term: $5(3) - 1 = 14$
          4th term: $5(4) - 1 = 19$
          5th term: $5(5) - 1 = 24$

      (c)   1st term: $10^{(1)} - 1 = 9$
          2nd term: $10^{(2)} - 1 = 99$
          3rd term: $10^{(3)} - 1 = 999$
          4th term: $10^{(4)} - 1 = 9999$
          5th term: $10^{(5)} - 1 = 99999$

      (d)   1st term: $3(1) + 2 = 5$
          2nd term: $3(2) + 2 = 8$
          3rd term: $3(3) + 2 = 11$
          4th term: $3(4) + 2 = 14$
          5th term: $3(5) + 2 = 17$

28.   (a)   1, 1, 2, 3, 5, 8, 13, 21, 34, 55, 89, and 144

      (b)   Yes. The sum of the first four terms is one less than the sixth term; likewise for the sum of terms five and six.

      (c)   After the first two 1's, we have $2 + 3 = 5$, followed by a 5; or a pair of 5's whose sum is 10. Then we have $8 + 13 = 21$ followed by a 21; the sum of two 21's is 42. Had there been 11 terms to add, there would also have been a pair of 89's. Our sum, then, is about $2 + 10 + 42 + 89$, or 142. The exact sum is 143.

      (d)   One can continue to add sums of pairs in the sequence to find the sum of the first n terms.

29. (a)   2, 4, 6, 10, 16, 26, 42, 68, 110, 178, 288, 466.

    (b)   The sum of the first three terms is 4 less than the fifth; the sum of the first four terms is 4 less than the sixth; the sum of the first five terms is 4 less than the seventh; etc.

    (c)   The first two terms are 2 and 4, or $2 + 4 = 6$ followed by a 6. Then there is $10 + 16 = 26$ followed by a 26; $26 + 26 = 52$. Then $42 + 68 = 110$ followed by 110. Thus our sum is about $12 + 52 + 220 + 178 = 462$. The exact sum is 460.

    (d)   The sum of the first n terms equals the $(n + 2)$th term $- 4$.

30. (a)   (i)   The 100th term is $1 + (100 - 1)2 = 199$.
           (ii)   The nth term is $1 + (n - 1)2 = 2n - 1$.

    (b)   (i)   The 100th term is $0 + (100 - 1)50 = 4950$.
           (ii)   The nth term is $0 + (n - 1)50 = 50n - 50$.

    (c)   (i)   The 100th term is $3(2)^{100-1} = 3 \cdot 2^{99}$.
           (ii)   The nth term is $3(2)^{n-1} = 1.5 \cdot 2^n$.

    (d)   (i)   The 100th term is $10(10)^{100-1} = 10 \cdot 10^{99} = 10^{100}$.
           (ii)   The nth term is $10(10)^{n-1} = 10^n$.

    (e)   (i)   The 100th term is $5^2(5)^{100-1} = 5^{101}$.
           (ii)   The nth term is $5^2(5)^{n-1} = 5^{n+1}$.

    (f)   (i)   The 100th term is $11 + (100 - 1)11 = 1100$.
           (ii)   The nth term is $11 + (n - 1)11 = 11n$.

    (g)   (i)   The 100th term is $2^1(2^2)^{100-1} = 2^{199}$.
           (ii)   The nth term is $2^1(2^2)^{n-1} = 2^{2n-1}$.

    (h)   (i)   The 100th term is $9 + (100 - 1)4 = 405$.
           (ii)   The nth term is $9 + (n - 1)4 = 4n + 5$.

    (i)   (i)   The 100th term is $100^3 = 1,000,000$.
           (ii)   The nth term is n^3.

31. (a)   1st pentagon has 1 dot
           2nd pentagon has $5 = 1 + 4$ dots
           3rd pentagon has $12 = 1 + 4 + 7$ dots; analyzing the sequence, we have:
           4th pentagon has $22 = 1 + 4 + 7 + 10$ dots
           5th pentagon has $35 = 1 + 4 + 7 + 10 + 13$ dots
           6th pentagon has $51 = 1 + 4 + 7 + 10 + 13 + 16$ dots.

    (b)   The number of additional dots in each pentagon forms an arithmetic sequence with 1st term 1 and difference 3. For the 100th pentagon we would have $1 + (100 - 1)3 = 298$ additional dots. Using the technique of problem 15(a), we would have $\frac{100}{2}(1 + 298) = 50 \cdot 299 = 14,950$ dots; i.e., the 100th pentagonal number is 14,950.

32.   We find the nth term of the arithmetic sequence to be $300 + (n - 1)200 = 200n + 100$.
       We find the nth term of the geometric sequence to be $2(2)^{n-1} = 2^n$.
       Now construct a table such as:

32.

n	2^n	$200n \pm 100$
1	2	300
2	4	500
3	8	700
⋮	⋮	⋮
11	2028	2300
12	4056	2500

So we find that with the 12th term the geometric sequence is larger than the arithmetic sequence.

33. (a) Given that the scissors are small enough and sharp enough, an infinite number of pieces may be obtained.

   (b) We start with 1 peice of paper. Cutting it into five pieces gives us 5. Taking one of the pieces and cutting it into fives pieces again gives us $4 + 5 = 9$ pieces. Continuing this process, we have an arithmetic sequence: 1, 5, 9, 13, ... Thus the number of pieces after the nth experiment would be $1 + 5 + 9 + 13 + \cdots + [1 + (n - 1)4] = 1 + 5 + 9 + 13 + \cdots + (4n - 3)$. Using the technique of problem 15(a), we would have $\frac{n}{2}[1 + (4n - 3)] = \frac{n}{2}(4n - 2) = 2n^2 - n$ pieces.

34. (a)

1		8		28		56		70		56		28		8		1
1		9		36		84		126		126		84		36		9		1

   (b) 1st row: 1
   2nd row: 2
   3rd row: 4
   4th row: 8
   ⋮
   10th row: The sum should be 512. For the nth row, the sum should be 2^{n-1}.

   (c) 1st row: 0
   2nd row: 0
   3rd row: 0
   4th row: 0

   (d) Answers may vary. One example is that the numbers in each row increase to a maximum and then are the same in decreasing order.

Problem Set 1-2

1. (a) Adding "front and back" terms $(1 + 99, 2 + 98, ...)$ gives 49 pairs which add to 100, plus the single middle term 50. The sum is thus $49 \cdot 100 + 50 = 4950$.

   (b) The technique is the same as for (a). There will always be a single middle term whose value is the average of the 1st and last, or $\frac{1+n}{2}$. The number of pairs may be obtained by dividing n by 2 and rounding down, or $\frac{n}{2} - \frac{1}{2}$. The pairs will all add to $n + 1$. Thus the sum is $(\frac{n}{2} - \frac{1}{2})(n + 1) + \frac{1+n}{2}$. For example, if $n = 37$ there are $\frac{37}{2} - \frac{1}{2} = 18$ pairs, each of value $37 + 1 = 38$ and a middle term of value $\frac{1+37}{2} = 19$, so the sum is $18 \cdot 38 + 19 = 703$.

   (c) 251,001. To find the number of terms in any arithmetic sequence, subtract the 1st term from the last, divide by the common difference, and add 1 (because both ends must be accounted for). There are thus $\frac{1001-1}{2} + 1 = 501$ terms, $\frac{501}{2} - \frac{1}{2} = 250$ pairs, and one middle term $\frac{1+1001}{2} = 501$. The sum is thus (250 pairs)$\cdot$(1002 each) + 501 = 251,001.

2. This method is not equivalent to the method presented in the text. Every number is counted twice, giving double the correct sum of 5050.

3. Each consecutive L has two more squares than the previous L. The general expression for the number of squares in the nth L is then $2n - 1$ (from 1, 3, 5, ...) and there are n L's. The series for the number of squares is thus $1 + 3 + 5 + \cdots + (2n - 1)$. The result is always equal to n^2.

4. There are 13 squares of 1 unit each; 4 squares of 4 units each; and 1 square of 9 units. There are a total of 18 squares.

5. The maximum amount is $1.19, composed of:
    1 half-dollar
    1 quarter
    4 dimes
    0 nickels
    4 pennies
    Any other combination would result in less money; e.g., including a nickel would allow only one dime to keep from having change for a quarter.

6. (a)   204. Counting 1×1, 2×2, 3×3, ... squares gives 8^2 1×1 squares, 7^2 2×2 squares, 6^2 3×3 squares, ... (i.e., for 2×2 squares there are 7 pairs of consecutive squares in each column and row, or 7·7 2×2 squares, etc.). The general formula is:
    $$1^2 + 2^2 + 3^2 + \cdots + n^2 = \frac{n(n+1)(2n+1)}{6}.$$

    (b)   No. The logic is somewhat analgous to $2(n^2) \neq (2n)^2$

7. Start both the 7-minute and 11-minute timers. When the 7-minute timer stops, put the egg on. When the 11-minute timer stops, restart it. When it stops again the egg is done (4 minutes + 11 minutes).

8. 12 ways. Make a table as follows and note the pattern:

$5	$10	$20
0	1	2
2	0	2
0	3	1
2	2	1
4	1	1
6	0	1
0	5	0
2	4	0
4	3	0
6	2	0
8	1	0
10	0	0

9. 12. There are four choices for the 1st digit, then three for the 2nd (since one has already been used), two for the 3rd digit, and one final digit to finish the number. This gives $4 \cdot 3 \cdot 2 \cdot 1 = 24$ numbers, but the two nines are indistinguishable so 24 must be divided by 2, giving 12.

10. Let B be the number of boys and D be the number of dogs. Since dogs and boys each have one head, while boys have 2 feet and dogs 4, we can form the equations:
    $$B + D = 22$$
    $$2B + 4D = 68.$$
    Solving this system of equations, we find we have 10 boys and 12 dogs.

11. Let R be the cost of the ruler and C be the cost of the compass. We can then form the equations:
    $$R + C = 4.00$$
    $$C = R + 0.90$$

11. To solve, we substitute the cost of the compass, R + 0.90, into the first equation:

$$R + (R + 0.90) = 4.00$$
$$2R + 0.90 = 4.00$$
$$2R = 3.10$$
$$R = 1.55, \text{ so the cost of the ruler is } \$1.55, \text{ and}$$
$$C = 1.55 + 0.90$$
$$C = 2.45, \text{ so the cost of the compass is } \$2.45.$$

12. The cat makes one foot progress each day except for the last day when it will not slide back (because it will be out of the well). So in 15 days it will climb 15 feet; on the 16th day it will climb 3 more feet and be out of the well.

13. (a)   42, 55, 68, 81, 94, 107, 120, 133, 146, 159, 172, 185, 198

     (b)   There are 14 "spaces" between the 15 houses and a spread of $211 - 29 = 182$ to be covered. Thus each space must be $182 \div 14 = 13$. The difference could also be found by using the general expression for an arithmetic sequence, where the nth term is $a + (n - 1)d$. Let $a_{15} = 211$, $a = 29$, and $n = 15$.

14. (a)   The number of cubes in staircase $1 = 1$; in staircase 2, $2 + 1 = 3$; in staircase 3, $3 + 2 + 1 = 6$; in staircase 4, $4 + 3 + 2 + 1 = 10$; etc. Thus for staircase 25 there will be $25 + 24 + \cdots + 2 + 1$ cubes, or $\frac{25}{2}(25 + 1) = 325$ cubes.

     (b)   (*i*)   The number of squares to be painted in the 1st solid is 6; in the 2nd, 14; in the 3rd, 24; in the 4th, 36; etc. The number of <u>additional</u> squares to be painted in each succeeding solid is thus $14 - 6 = 8$, $24 - 14 = 10$, $36 - 24 = 12$; or 8, 10, 12, 14, ... This is an arithmetic sequence with 1st term 8 and difference 2. From the 1st to the 100th solid, there are 99 terms in the sequence. The number of additional squares from the 99th to the 100th solid is therefore $8 + (99 - 1)2 = 204$. The total number of additional squares, from the 1st to the 100th, is $\frac{99}{2}(8 + 204) = 10{,}494$. Finally, 6 squares to be painted in the 1st solid plus $10{,}494 = 10{,}500$ squares.

           (*ii*)   Generalizing from (*i*), the nth solid will require $n^2 + 5n$ squares to be painted.

15. If you are on the middle rung and climb up 3, you are 3 above the middle. If you then go down 5, you are 2 below the middle. Of the 10 rungs to get onto the roof, it takes 2 to get back to the middle, so there must be 8 rungs above the middle. In all, then, there must be 8 above the middle + 8 below the middle + 1 middle for a total of 17 rungs.

16. Working backwards, in the next to last step David and Judy would have 24 and Jacobo 96 marbles. Prior to that David had 12, Jacobo 48, and Judy 84. To begin with, then, Jacobo had 24, Judy 42, and David 78.

17. 732 marbles. This can best be done by working backward. (A crucial piece of the solution is in understanding that if a given number is a fraction of some original number, you must divide by the fraction to get the original; e.g., 150 is $\frac{3}{4}$ of some number, so the number is $150 \div \frac{3}{4} = 200$.) Starting with 100, add back the 20 Jacobo gave to David. The resulting 120 is $\frac{2}{3}$ of what he had before giving the $\frac{1}{3}$ to another friend. Thus he had $120 \div \frac{2}{3} = 180$. Adding back the 2 given to David yields 182, which is half the previous quantity of 364. Again adding back 2 given to David gives 366; this is half the original which then must have been 732.

18. (a)   Weigh 4 against 4 and then pick the heavier side. Then weigh 2 against 2 and again pick the heavier side. Finally, weigh 1 against 1 to determine the heaviest.

18. (b) Weigh 3 against 3, laying 2 aside. If the groups of three balance, weigh the remaining 2 to find the heavier. If not, of the three from the heavier side, weigh 1 against 1, laying one aside; either the heavier marble will be indicated by the scale tipping or the marble left off is heaviest. (Up to 3^n marbles can be sorted with this setup, using n weighings.)

19. (a) 11 coins. He must have 5 pennies to make an even $1.00. The minimum number of coins would have as many quarters as possible, or 3 quarters. The remaining $0.20 must consist of at least one dime and one nickel; the only possibility is one dime and two nickels. Thus the minimum coins are 5 pennies, 2 nickels, 1 dime, and 3 quarters.

    (b) 63 coins. The maximum number of coins is achieved by having as many pennies as possible. It is a requirement to have 1 quarter, 1 dime, and 1 nickel = $0.40, so there may then be 60 pennies.

20. The perimeter of a rectangle is twice the length plus twice the width, or P = 2L + 2W. If the length is 80 feet more than the width, then L = 80 + W. The perimeter is 1080 feet, or:
$$2(80 + W) + 2W = 1080.$$
Solving, we find W = 230 feet, and L then is 230 + 80 or 310 feet.

21. Adding the numbers gives 99. This tells you that each row, diagonal, and column must add to $99 \div 3 = 33$. Place the center number in a sequence in the center square, then add numbers until achieving the desired result. One possible solution is:

17	7	9
3	11	19
13	15	5

22. The sum is not divisible by 3; thus it is impossible to split the numbers into three groups of three with equal sums.

23. (a) If both numbers were less than or equal to 9, then their product would be less than $9 \times 9 = 81$, which is not greater than 82.

    (b) See (a).

24. (a) See problem 1.(c) above. There are $\frac{1020-2}{2} + 1 = 510$ terms. There are $\frac{510}{2} = 255$ pairs which add to $2 + 1020 = 1022$. The sum is thus $255 \cdot 1022 = 260,610$.

    (b) There are $\frac{1001-1}{5} + 1 = 201$ terms. The sum is thus $\frac{201}{2}(1 + 1001) = 100,701$.

    (c) There are $\frac{403-3}{4} + 1 = 101$ terms. The sum is thus $\frac{101}{2}(3 + 403) = 20,503$.

25. Each of the 20 people shook hands with 17 others after dinner. Multiplying, $20 \cdot 17 = 340$. This counts each handshake twice, however (i.e., Mary was one of the 17 Joe shook with and Joe was one of the 17 Mary shook with). Thus there were $340 \div 2 = 170$ handshakes.

26. Yes. She can use the $8\frac{1}{2}$-inch side twice to get 17 inches and then use the 11-inch side to get back to 6 inches.

27. This problem may be solved in two ways:

    (i) Working backwards, Jose must have had $6000 before buying the house, $12,000 before losing half, and $13,500 before spending $1500 getting married.

    (ii) Algebraically, if we let A be the amount of money Jose started with, then:
$$A - 1500 - \tfrac{1}{2}(A - 1500) - \tfrac{1}{2}[\tfrac{1}{2}(A - 1500)] = 3000$$
(simply translating the wording of the problem into an algebraic statement).
Solving, $A - 1500 - \tfrac{1}{4}A + 375 = 3000$, and A = $13,500.

28. $78, $42, and $24. See problem 16 above; the reasoning is the same.

29. (a) As each line is added, it can cross each of the previous lines. Making a table, we would thus have:

Nr. of Lines	Nr. of Intersections
1	0
2	1
3	$3 = 2 + 1$
4	$6 = 3 + 2 + 1$
5	$10 = 4 + 3 + 2 + 1$
$\vdots$	$\vdots$
20	$19 + 18 + 17 + \cdots + 2 + 1$

Using Gauss' technique, $19 + 18 + \cdots + 2 + 1 = \frac{19}{2}(19 + 1) = 190$ intersection points.

(b) The maximum number of points is $(n - 1) + (n - 2) + (n - 3) + \cdots + 2 + 1 = \frac{n-1}{2}[(n - 1) + 1]$ $= \frac{1}{2}(n^2 - n)$.

30. 35 moves. This can be done manually using drawings or objects such as coins. An easier way to project the number of moves is to first solve simpler problems; for example:

    One on each side - 3 moves.

    Two on each side - 8 moves.

    Three on each side - 15 moves.

The number of moves required for n women on each side is $(n + 1)^2 - 1$. For this problem,

    $(5 + 1)^2 - 1 = 35$.

31. (a) 21, 24, 27 (adding 3 to each term to obtain the subsequent term).

(b) 243, 2, 729 (Multiplying every other term by 3 with 2's in between).

32. The nth term is $22 + (n - 1)10 = 10n + 12$.

33. See problem 1.(c) above. There are $\frac{83-3}{4} + 1 = 21$ terms. Alternatively, use the expression for the nth term of an arithmetic sequence:

    $83 = 3 + (n - 1)4$

    $80 = (n - 1)4$

    $20 = n - 1$

    $21 = n$

Note that we have used the same operations.

34. $\frac{21}{2}(3 + 83) = 903$.

Problem Set 1-3

1. (a) The largest 3- and 2-digit numbers are the 700's and 50's or the 500's and 70's. Using the calculator to try various combinations, we find $\boxed{5}\boxed{4}\boxed{1} \boxed{\times} \boxed{7}\boxed{2} = 38,952$, which is the greatest possible product. For the largest quotient, we want the smallest divisor, or 12, and the largest divident, or 754. We thus find that $\boxed{7}\boxed{5}\boxed{4} \boxed{\div} \boxed{1}\boxed{2} = 62.8\overline{3}$, which is the greatest possible quotient.

(b) The least possible product is $\boxed{2}\boxed{5}\boxed{7} \boxed{\times} \boxed{1}\boxed{4}$. The least possible quotient is $\boxed{1}\boxed{2}\boxed{4} \boxed{\div} \boxed{7}\boxed{5}$.

2. (a) $10 \cdot 365$ days $= 3650

(b) $120 \cdot 52$ weeks $= 6240 (this plan yields the greatest amount of money.)

(c) $0.25 \cdot 24$ hours per day $\cdot 365$ days $= 2190

2.   (d) $0.01·60 minutes·24 hours·365 days = $5256

3.   Vera bought items costing $3.99 + $5.87 + $6.47 = $16.33.

4.   Try 7: 7·259 = 1813; 1813·429 = 777777. Try 9: 9·259 = 2331; 2331·429 = 999999. This works because 259·429 = 111111, and any single-digit number multiplied by 111111 gives a corresponding series of that number.

5.   There is a difference of 7 between each term of the sequence. Enter [7][+][K] in your calculator; then enter [1] to place a 1 in the display. Now count the number of times [=] must be depressed to arrive at 113 in the display. You will find that there are 17 terms in the sequence.

6.   [.][2][×][2][2][EE][9][=] gives $4.4×10^9$ ounces of catsup needed.
   [÷][1][6][=] gives $2.75×10^8$ (or 275,000,000) catsup bottles.

7.   Try multiplying 5,230,010 by the natural numbers until your result exceeds eight digits (because most calculators have an eight-digit display). You will find that 5,230,010·19 has eight digits; 5,230,010·20 has nine digits. 5,230,010·20 and all larger multipliers must therefore be displayed in scientific notation.

8.   (a)   Add 500 + 200 + 56 + 100 + 60 + 20 + 3.

      (b)   Subtract 31 from 155 and subsequent remainders until you have a remainder of less than 31. Count the number of times you have subtracted 31.

9.   Enter [1][0][0][−][2][6][−][1][=] to obtain a display of 73.

10.   (a)   Multiply 7×7×7 to obtain 343. Then subtract 7 six times to display 301.

      (b)   Multiply eleven 2's together to obtain 2048.
            Then add the product of ten 2's to obtain 3072.
            Then add the product of seven 2's to obtain 3200.
            Then add the product of five 2's to obtain 3232.
            Then add the product of three 2's to obtain 3240.
            Then add three 2's.

11. $10·60 minutes·24 hours·365 days = $5,256,000 per year.

12.   Assume a pulse rate of 72. Then:

      (a)   Your heart would beat 72 times.

      (b)   Your heart would beat 72·60 = 4320 times.

      (c)   Your heart would beat 4320·24 = 103,680 times.

      (d)   Your heart would beat 103,680·7 = 725,760 times.

      (e)   Your heart would beat $103,680·365\frac{1}{4}$ = 37,869,120 times.

13.   Let n be the number for which we are looking. Then $\left(\frac{n}{25} - 18\right)37 = 259$. Solving, we have:
$$\frac{n}{25} - 18 = 7$$

$$\frac{n}{25} = 25, \text{ and } n = 625.$$

14.   10! = 3,628,800.

15.   (a)   For example:

$$11 \cdot 99 = 1089$$
$$37 \cdot 99 = 3663$$
$$54 \cdot 99 = 5346$$

The 1st and 3rd digits add to 9; the 2nd and 4th digits also add to 9.

    (b)   For example:

$$11 \cdot 999 = 10989$$
$$23 \cdot 999 = 22977$$
$$46 \cdot 999 = 45954$$

The middle digit is always 9; the sum of the 1st and 4th digits is 9; the sum of the 2nd and 5th digits is also 9.

16. $1 \div 30 = 0.0333333$ on the calculator.

17.   40,000 kilometers is 40,000,000 meters. If we assume the distance from fingertip to fingertip of the average person is about 2 meters, then $40,000,000 \div 2 = 20,000,000$ people holding hands.

18. $5459 = 53 \cdot 103$. Try dividing 5459 by the prime numbers.

19.   Play second and make sure that the sum showing when you hand the calculator to your opponent is a multiple of 3.

20.   Play first and press 4. Then make sure that the sum showing when you hand the calculator to your opponent is 1 less that a multiple of 5.

21.   Play first and press 3. Then make sure that the sum showing when you hand the calculator to your opponent is 3 more than a multiple of 10.

22.   Play second and make sure that the sum showing when you hand the calculator to your opponent is a multiple of 3.

23.   Play second and make sure that the sum showing when you hand the calculator to your opponent is a multiple of 4.

24.   Play first and press 5. Then make sure that the sum showing when you hand the calculator to your opponent is 2 less than a multiple of 10.

25.   (a) $1 + 2 + 2^2 + 2^3 + 2^4 + 2^5 = 2^6 - 1$, since:

$$\begin{aligned}(1 + 2 + 2^2 + 2^3 + 2^4) + 2^5 &= 2^5 - 1 + 2^5 \\ &= (2^5 + 2^5) - 1 \\ &= 2 \cdot 2^5 - 1 \\ &= 2^6 - 1\end{aligned}$$

    (b)   The sum in the nth row of the pattern is $2^n - 1$.

    (c)   If $n = 15$, then $2^n - 1 = 2^{15} - 1 = 32,768 - 1 = 32,767$

26.   (a) $\ldots, 35, 42, 49, \ldots$

    (b) $\ldots, 1, 16, 1, 20, \ldots$

27.   We have an arithmetic sequence with 1st term 12 and difference 20. Thus the nth term is:

$$12 + (n - 1)20 = 12 + 20n - 20 = 20n - 8.$$

28. $86 = 6 + (n - 1)4$
     $86 = 6 + 4n - 4$
     $84 = 4n$
     $n = 21$, so there are 21 terms in the sequence.

29. There are nine ways of making change:

Pennies	Nickels	Dimes
1	4	0
1	2	1
1	0	2
6	3	0
6	1	1
11	2	0
11	0	1
16	1	0
21	0	0

Chapter 1 Test

1. (a) 15, 21, 28 (add 1 to the difference each time between terms; e.g., $10 + 5$, $15 + 6$, ...)

    (b) 32, 27, 22 (subtract 5 from each term to obtain the subsequent term)

    (c) 400, 200, 100 (each term is half the previous term)

    (d) 21, 34, 55 (each term is the sum of the previous two terms - this is the Fibonacci sequence)

    (e) 17, 20, 23 (add 3 to each term to obtain the subsequent term)

    (f) 256, 1024, 4096 (multiply each term by 4 to obtain the subsequent term)

    (g) 16, 20, 24 (add 4 to each term to obtain the subsequent term)

    (h) 125, 216, 343 (each term is the 3rd power of the counting numbers - 1^3, 2^3, 3^3, etc.)

2. (a) Neither.

    (b) Arithmetic.

    (c) Geometric.

    (d) Neither.

    (e) Arithmetic.

    (f) Geometric.

    (g) Arithmetic.

    (h) Neither.

3. (a) The nth term is $5 + (n - 1)3 = 3n + 2$.

    (b) The nth term is n^3 (third powers of the counting numbers).

3.   (c)   The nth term is 3^n (each term is the nth power of 3).

4.   (a) $3(1) + 2 = 5$
               $3(2) + 2 = 8$
               $3(3) + 2 = 11$
               $3(4) + 2 = 14$
               $3(5) + 2 = 17$

      (b) $1^2 + 1 = 2$
               $2^2 + 2 = 6$
               $3^2 + 3 = 12$
               $4^2 + 4 = 20$
               $5^2 + 5 = 30$

      (c) $4(1) - 1 = 3$
               $4(2) - 1 = 7$
               $4(3) - 1 = 11$
               $4(4) - 1 = 15$
               $4(5) - 1 = 19$

5.   (a)   There are $\frac{200-2}{2} + 1 = 100$ terms. The sum is $\frac{100}{2}(2 + 200) = 10{,}100$.

      (b)   There are $\frac{151-51}{1} + 1 = 101$ terms. The sum is $\frac{101}{2}(51 + 151) = 10{,}201$.

6.   (a)   To obtain the nth term, add the units digit of n to the end of the previous term:
               1, 12, 123, 1234, 12345, ...

      (b)   1234567890. Only the units digit is added to the end of the previous term.

7.   Given row 1, all rows, columns, and diagonals must add to 34. First complete those with one missing, then two, etc., to work through the square:

16	3	2	13
5	10	11	8
9	6	7	12
4	15	14	1

8.   89 days. Remember that dates skip from 1 BC to 1 AD.

9.   10 days. On the 9th day it reaches as high as 19 cm before sliding back to 18 cm. On the 10th day it climbs out before sliding back.

10.   26 people.   The 10 middle tables will hold 2 each and the 2 end tables will hold 3 each.

11. $2.00 - subtract the extra cost and divide by 2. Or, algebraically, if S is the cost of the shirt and T is the cost of the tie, then:
     $S + T = 9.50$
     $S = T + 5.50$
     $(T + 5.50) + T = 9.50$
     $2T + 5.50 = 9.50$
     $2T = 4.00$
     $T = 2.00$, so the cost of the tie is $2.00.

12.   21 posts. $100 \div 5 = 20$ plus 1 because both ends must be counted.

13.   128 matches. The rounds proceed as follows:
        64 matches - 1 bye
        32 matches - 1 bye
        16 matches - 1 bye
        8 matches - 1 bye
        4 matches - 1 bye
        2 matches - 1 bye
        1 match - 1 bye
        <u>1 match</u>
      128 matches

14.   3, 5, 9, 11, 13, since 19,305 is not divisible by 7.

15.   44,000,000 turns:
      1 mile = 5280 feet
      $5280 \div 6 = 880$ turns to travel 1 mile
      (880 turns per mile)(50,000 miles) = 44,000,000.

16.   20 students. There are 9 students between 7 and 17 (8 - 16). There must be 9 between them in both directions, since they are direct opposites. Thus $9 + 9 + 2 = 20$.

17.   3 large + (3 large)(2 medium in each) + (3·2 medium)(5 small in each)
    3 large +   6 medium   +   30 small   = 39 boxes.

18.   <u>Pointing up</u>   <u>Pointing down</u>
      1×1: $1 + 2 + 3 + 4 + 5$ 1×1: $1 + 2 + 3 + 4$
      2×2: $1 + 2 + 3 + 4$ 2×2: $1 + 2$
      3×3: $1 + 2 + 3$ Total: 13
      4×4: $1 + 2$
      5×5: 1
      Total: 35
      There are $35 + 13 = 48$ triangles in the figure.

19.   Observe that the power of 10 in the expression is always one greater than the highest power of 10 in the sum.

    (a) $\dfrac{10^{13} - 1}{9}$

    (b) $\dfrac{10^{n+1} - 1}{9}$

    (c) $\dfrac{10^{n} - 1}{9}$

20.   9 hours. Since the return trip took 4 hours at 20 kph, the distance between homes is $4 \cdot 20 = 80$ km. Then (80 km uphill)$\div$(16 kph uphill) = 5 hours to Larry's. The total trip was 5 hours + 4 hours = 9 hours.

21.   The perimeter, P, of a rectangle is twice the length plus twice the width, or $P = 2W + 2L$. If the length, L, is $2W + 4$, then:
    $2W + 2(2W + 4) = 68$
    $2W + 4W + 8 = 68$
    $6W = 60$
    $W = 10$, so the width is 10 feet
    $L = 2W + 4$
    $L = 2 \cdot 10 + 4 = 24$, so the length is 24 feet.

CHAPTER 2 - SETS, FUNCTIONS, AND LOGIC

Problem Set 2-1

1. (a) "Wealthy" is not defined; thus the set is not well defined.

    (b) "Great" books is not defined; thus the set is not well defined.

    (c) Since we can tell if any given number is or is not in the set, it is well defined.

    (d) There is a defined group of subsets, so this set is well defined.

2. (a) {m, a, t, h, e, i, c, s} or {x|x is a letter in the word *mathematics*}

    (b) {Alabama, Arizona, ... , Wisconsin, Wyoming}, or {x|x is a state in the continental United States}.

    (c) {January, June, July} or {x|x is a month whose name begins with J}

    (d) {21, 22, 23, 24, ... } or {x|x is a natural number greater than 20} or {x|x ∈ N and x > 20}

    (e) {Alabama, Alaska, ... , Wyoming} or {x|x is a state in the United States}

    (f) ∅ or {} or {x|x is a day in the week starting with the letter P}

    (g) {Alaska, California, Hawaii, Oregon, Washington} or {x|x is a state in the United States that borders the Pacific Ocean}

3. (a) B = {x, y, z, w}

    (b) 3 ∉ B

    (c) {1, 2} ⊂ {1, 2, 3, 4}

    (d) D ⊈ E

    (e) A ⊄ B

    (f) 0 ∉ ∅

    (g) {0} ≠ ∅

4. (a) Answers may vary. Three might be: {x|x is a college student} or {x|x is a female (or male)} or {x|x is a person with (color) eyes}.

    (b) Answers may vary. Three might be: {x|x is an infant who drives an automobile legally} or {x|x is a U.S. citizen who lives on Jupiter} or {x|x is a prime number less than 2}.

5. (a) Yes, because {1, 2, 3, 4, 5} ~ {m, n, o, p, q}

    (b) No, because {m, a, t, h} ≁ {f, u, n}

    (c) Yes, because {a, b, c, d, e, f, ... , m} ~ {1, 2, 3, 4, 5, 6, ... , 13}

5.   (d)   No, because {x|x is a letter in the word *mathematics*} $\not\sim$ {1, 2, 3, 4, ... , 13}. Note that there are only eight unduplicated letters in the word *mathematics*.

     (e)   No, because {○, △} $\not\sim$ {2}

6.   1 ↔ a, 1 ↔ b, 2 ↔ a, 2 ↔ b.

7.   (a)   24. The 1st element of the 1st set can be paired with any of the four in the 2nd set, leaving three possible pairings for the 2nd element, two for the 3rd, and one for the 4th. There are thus $4 \cdot 3 \cdot 2 \cdot 1 = 24$ possible one-to-one correspondences.

     (b)   There are $5 \cdot 4 \cdot 3 \cdot 2 \cdot 1 = 120$ possible one-to-one correspondences.

     (c)   There are $n \cdot (n - 1) \cdot (n - 2) \cdot \ \cdots \ \cdot 2 \cdot 1 = n!$ possible one-to-one correspondences.

8.   Answers may vary; e.g., there are subsets containing professors who are (*i*) male, (*ii*) female, (*iii*) over 40, (*iv*) under 40, or (*v*) associates.

9.   A, C, and D are equal; note that the order of the elements is immaterial. E and H are equal; they are both the null set.

10. $\overline{A}$ = {x|x is a college student who does not have a straight-A average}

11. (a)   7 elements. A proper subset must have at least one less element than the set.

     (b)   1 element. Then B, to be a proper subset, would have no elements; i.e., it would be the null set.

12. (a)   5.

     (b)   C = D.

13. No. It is not a proper subset of itself, since it is equal to itself.

14. (a) $\in$

     (b) $\notin$

     (c) $\notin$

     (d) $\notin$

     (e) $\notin$

15. (a) $\not\subseteq$. 3 is not a set and thus cannot be a subset.

     (b) $\not\subseteq$. 0 is not a set and thus cannot be a subset of ∅, the null set.

     (c) $\subseteq$. {1} is actually a proper subset of {1,2}

     (d) $\subseteq$.

     (e) $\subseteq$.

16. A $\not\subseteq$ B does not imply that B $\subseteq$ A; A and B may have no elements in common.

17. (a)   True.

17. (b)   False. A could equal B; then A would be a subset but not a proper subset of B.

    (c)   True.

    (d)   False. A could be any of the proper subsets of B, thus not equal to B.

18. (a)   Let A = {a, b} and let B = {x, y, z, w}. {a, b} ~ {x, y}, a proper subset of {x, y, z, w}. Thus since $n(A) = 2$ and $n(B) = 4$, $2 < 4$.

    (b)   {a, b, c} ~ {1, 2, 3} and {1, 2, 3} ⊂ {1, 2, 3, $\cdots$, 100}, so $3 < 100$.

    (c)   { } ⊂ {1, 2, 3}, so $0 < 3$.

19. For natural numbers a and b, a is less than or equal to b if and only if, for sets A and B with $n(A) = a$ and $n(B) = b$, there exists a subset of B equivalent to A. (I.e., simply change from "proper subset" to "subset" to include equality.)

20. (a)   There are $2^6 = 64$ subsets of A. There are $2^6 - 1 = 63$ proper subsets, because the subset equal to A is not a proper subset of A.

    (b)   B has $2^n - 1$ proper subsets.

21. If order were important in the subcommittees (i.e., if there were to be a chairman, vice-chairman, and secretary) there would be seven ways of choosing a chairman, six ways of choosing a vice-chairman, and five ways of choosing a secretary, or $7 \cdot 6 \cdot 5 = 210$ different subcommittees. The subcommittee does not have any particular order, though, so we must divide 210 by the number of different possible groupings of three: $3 \cdot 2 \cdot 1 = 6$. $210 \div 6 = 35$, so there are 35 possible subcommittee groupings.

Problem Set 2-2

1. (a) $A \cap B = \{t, i, e\}$. $B \cap A = \{t, i, e\}$. The sets are therefore equal. In other words: $A \cap B = \{x | x \in A \text{ and } x \in B\} = B \cap A$, so the sets are equal.

    (b) $A \cup B = \{l, i, t, e\} = B \cup A$, so the sets are equal.

    (c) $B \cup C = \{t, i, e, q, u\}$; $A \cup (B \cup C) = \{l, i, t, e, q, u\}$.
    $A \cup B = \{l, i, t, e\}$; $(A \cup B) \cup C = \{l, i, t, e, q, u\}$.
    The sets are therefore equal.

    (d) $A \cup \emptyset = \{l, i, t, e\} = A$. The sets are therefore equal.

    (e) $A \cap A = \{l, i, t, e\}$. $A \cap \emptyset = \emptyset$. The sets are therefore not equal.

    (f) $C = \{q, u, e\}$. $\overline{C} = \{a, l, i, t, y\}$. $\overline{\overline{C}} = \{q, u, e\}$. C and $\overline{\overline{C}}$ are therefore equal.

2. (a)   True.

    (b)   False. A = {1, 2}; B = {2, 3}. A - B = {1}; B - A = {3}.

    (c)   True.

    (d)   False. U = {1, 2}; A = {1}, B = {2}. $\overline{A \cap B} = \{1, 2\}$; $\overline{A} \cap \overline{B} = \emptyset$.

    (e)   True.

2. (f)   True.

    (g)   True.

3. (a)   If B ⊆ A, all elements of B must also be elements of A, so A ∩ B = B.

    (b)   B ⊆ A implies that A is either equal to or larger than B, so A ∪ B = A.

4. (a)   (b)

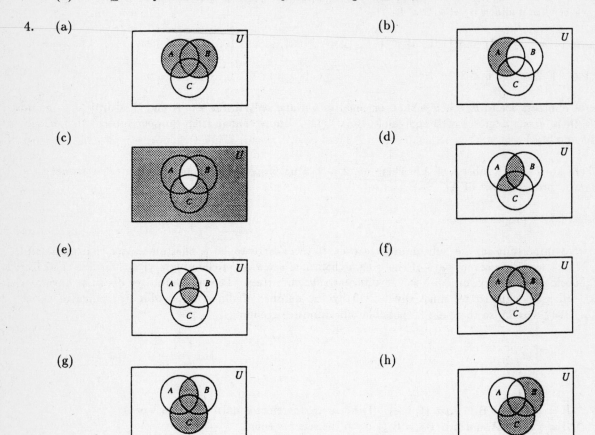

    (c)   (d)

    (e)   (f)

    (g)   (h)

5. (a) $\bar{S}$ is the set of all elements in U that are not in S. S ∪ $\bar{S}$, therefore, is the set of all elements within the universe, or U.

    (b)   S ∪ U = {x|x ∈ S or x ∈ U} = U; i.e., S can add nothing more to the whole universe.

    (c)   ∅ ∪ S = {x|x ∈ ∅ or x ∈ S} = S; i.e., ∅ has nothing to add to S.

    (d)   If U is the universe, the complement of U can have no elements, thus $\bar{U}$ = ∅.

    (e)   S ∩ U = {x|x ∈ S and x ∈ U} = S; i.e., all elements of S must be in U.

    (f)   If the null set has no elements, the complement of the null set must have all elements; thus $\bar{\emptyset}$ = U.

    (g)   There are no elements common to S and $\bar{S}$; thus S ∩ $\bar{S}$ = ∅.

    (h)   Since there are no elements common to S and $\bar{S}$, S − $\bar{S}$ = S.

    (i)   U ∩ $\bar{S}$ = $\bar{S}$.

    (j) $\bar{\bar{S}}$ is the complement of $\bar{S}$; thus, $\bar{\bar{S}}$ = S.

5. (k)   Since there are no elements in the null set there are none common to it and S; thus $\emptyset \cap S = \emptyset$.

    (l) $U - S = \bar{S}$. Taking the elements of S from U leaves only $\bar{S}$.

6. (a)   Yes. $a \in (A \cap B)$ implies that a is in both A and B, so certainly it is in their union.

    (b)   No. To be in $A \cup B$, a must be in only one of A or B; thus it is not forced to be in both.

7. (a)   If $A \cap B = \emptyset$, then A and B are disjoint sets; thus anything in A is <u>not</u> in B. Therefore,
           $A - B = \{x | x \in A \text{ and } x \notin B\} = A$.

    (b)   Since $B = U$, there can be no elements in A which are not in B. Thus $A - B = \emptyset$.

    (c)   Since A and B are equal, there can be nothing in one set that is not in the other. Thus $A - B = \emptyset$.

    (d)   If A is a subset of B, then all elements of A must be in B; so an element cannot be in A and not be in
           B at the same time. I.e., $A - B = \{x | x \in A \text{ and } x \notin B\} = \emptyset$.

8. (a) $B \cap \bar{A}$ (b) $\overline{A \cup B}$

    (c) $A \cap B \cap C$ (d) $A \cap B$

    (e) $\bar{B} \cap (A \cap C)$ (f) $[(A \cup C) \cap \bar{B}] \cup (A \cap B \cap C)$

9. (a)   A is shaded except for set B.

    (b)   The union of A and B is contained within A. Its complement is the universe outside A.

    (c)   The intersection of A and B is contained within B. The complement of A is the total region outside
           A. Their union is the shaded area.

    (d)   A - B is the set of all elements in A that are not in B.

10. (a)   False   (b)   False

(c)   False   (d)   False

(e)   False

11. (a)   (*i*)   The greatest number of elements in A ∪ B would occur if A and B were disjoint sets. In that case, $n(A ∪ B) = 5$

(*ii*)   The greatest number of elements in A ∩ B would occur if B were a subset of A. In that case, $n(A ∩ B) = B = 2.$

(b)   (*i*)   As in (a), the greatest number of elements in A ∪ B would occur if A and B were disjoint sets. Then $n(A ∪ B) = m + n.$

(*ii*)   The maximum number would occur when either of the sets was a subset of the other. Then $n(A ∩ B)$ would be the smaller of *m* or *n*.

12. (a)   Red only.   (b)   Purple, made of blue and red.

(c)   Blue only.   (d)   Orange, made of red and yellow.

(e)   Brown, made of red, blue, and yellow.   (f)   Green, made of blue and yellow.

(g)   Yellow only.

13. (a)   All natural numbers.

(b)   ∅. Evens and odds have no numbers in common.

(c)   E. Every even number is not in the set of odds.

(d)   O. Every odd number is not in the set of evens.

14. (a)   (b)

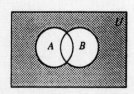   

(c)   Let U = {1, 2, 3, 4}; A = {1, 2}; B = {2, 4}

For (a), A ∪ B = {1, 2, 4}; $\overline{A∪B}$ = {3}.
$\overline{A}$ = {3, 4}; $\overline{B}$ = {1, 3}; $\overline{A} ∩ \overline{B}$ = {3} = $\overline{A∪B}$

For (b), A ∩ B = {2}; $\overline{A∩B}$ = {1, 3, 4}
$\overline{A}$ = {3, 4}, $\overline{B}$ = {1, 3}; $\overline{A} ∪ \overline{B}$ = {1, 3, 4} = $\overline{A∩B}$

15. A and B are equal. They have in common everything they both contain, which means they must both contain the same elements.

16. (a)   The set of college basketball players/students who are more than 200 cm tall.

(b)   The set of all humans who either are not college students or are less than 200 cm tall.

16. (c)   The set of all college students more than 200 cm tall or who are college basketball players.

(d)   The set of all humans who are neither college basketball players nor those who are neither students nor more than 200 cm tall.

(e)   The set of all non-basketball-playing college students taller than 200 cm.

(f)   The set of all college basketball players less than or equal to 200 cm tall.

17. (a)   Students in band only.   (b)   Students in both band and choir.

(c)   Students in choir only.   (d)   Students in neither band nor choir.

18.   There were $3 + 4 + 5 + 1 + 1 + 2 + 2 = 18$ who played one or more of the three sports.

19.   From the diagram below, there were 4 members who took biology but not mathematics.

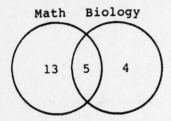

20.

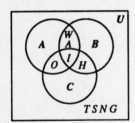

21. (a)   20 bikes. This occurs if all bikes needing new tires also need gear repairs; symbolically, if TIRES $\subset$ GEARS then TIRES $\cap$ GEARS = 20.

(b)   10 bikes. Adding the separate repairs gives $20 + 30 = 50$. This indicates that at least 10 bikes were counted twice; i.e., needed both repairs.

(c)   10 bikes. This occurs if the maximum number of bikes received both repairs, as in (a). All 20 that received tires were among the 30 having gear work, leaving 10 that required no service.

22. (a)   False. Let A = {1, 2} and B = {3, 4}. The sets are equivalent but not equal.

(b)   False. Let A = B.

(c)   False. Let $n(A) < n(B)$.

(d)   True.

(e)   True, unless A and B are infinite sets; e.g., A = {2, 4, 6, ... } and B = {1, 2, 3, ... }.

(f)   False. Let A = {1, 2} and B = {4, 5, 6}.

23. Cowboys vs Giants, Vikings vs Packers, Redskins vs Bills, and Jets vs Steelers. All picked the Cowboys to win their game, so the opponent cannot be among any of the choices. The only team not picked was the Giants. Phyllis and Paula both picked the Steelers, so their opponent cannot be among their other choices. This leaves the Jets. Phyllis and Rashid both picked the Vikings which leaves the Packers as the only possible opponent. The Redskins and Bills are left as opponents by elimination.

24. (a)   {(x, a), (x, b), (x, c), (y, a), (y, b), (y, c)}

(b)   {(a, x), (a, y), (b, x), (b, y), (c, x), (c, y)}

(c)   ∅. There are no elements in ∅ to have a cross-product with.

(d)   {(0,0)}

(e)   ∅

(f)   {(x, a), (x, b), (x, c), (x, 0), (y, a), (y, b), (y, c), (y, 0)}

(g)   {(x, 0), (y, 0), (a, 0), (b, 0), (c, 0)}

(h)   {x, y, (a, 0), (b, 0), (c, 0)}

25. (a)   No. The elements of the ordered pairs are reversed by reversing the order of the sets in the product.

(b)   No. The parentheses would be oriented differently; e.g., if A = {a}, B = {b}, and C = {c}, then (A × B) × C = {(a, b), c} while A × (B × C) = {a, (b, c)}.

26. (a)   C = {a}, D = {b, c, d, e}.

(b)   C = {1, 2}, D = {1, 2, 3}.

(c)   C = {0, 1}, D = {0, 1}.

27. (a) $5 \cdot 4 = 20$ elements. Each of the five in A are paired with each of the four in B.

(b) $m \cdot n$ elements.

(c) $m \cdot n \cdot p$ elements. A × B has $m \cdot n$ elements, each of which is paired with the p elements in C.

28. (a) $3 \cdot 0 = 0$ elements.

(b) $1 \cdot 0 = 0$ elements.

(c) $0 \cdot 0 = 0$ elements.

29. If $n[(A \cup B) \times B] = 24$, then $n(A \cup B) = \frac{24}{3} = 8$. If $A \cap B = \emptyset$, then A and B are disjoint sets. Thus if $n(B) = 3$ then $n(A) = 8 - 3 = 5$.

30. Yes.

31. 30 games. This is equivalent to the number in the Cartesian product of the two sets of teams; i.e., $6 \cdot 5 = 30$.

32. This is equivalent to the cross product of {SLACKS}, {SHIRTS}, and {SWEATERS}. Thus the number of elements in the cross product is $n(\text{SLACKS}) \cdot n(\text{SHIRTS}) \cdot n(\text{SWEATERS}) = 4 \cdot 5 \cdot 3 = 60$, or 60 different combinations.

33. We are given:
    26 British females
    17 American women
    17 American males
    29 girls
    44 British citizens
    29 women
    24 British adults

Thus:
    29 women − 17 American women = 12 British women
    26 British females − 12 British women = 14 British girls
    29 girls − 14 British girls = 15 American girls

And so:

British women=12	American males=17
British men=12	American women=17
British girls=14	American girls=15
British boys=6	
Total British=44	Total American=49

There were 44 + 49 = 93 people in the group.

34. Teachers in all grades shared a fundamental knowledge base. In grades 5-8 and 9-12, some of this knowledge overlapped. There was a knowledge base in grades 9-12 not shared by the other grades.

35. Representing the data by a Venn diagram shows:

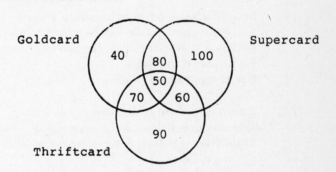

Totaling all areas gives 40 + 100 + 90 + 80 + 60 + 70 + 50 = 490 students. Either the editor was right in that an error must have been made because there was not a total of 500 students, or the editor was wrong by not realizing that the "missing" ten students could have had credit cards other than the three shown.

36. { }, {a}, {b}, {c}, {a, b}, {a, c}, {b, c}, {a, b, c}

37. Yes. If the numbers are all natural numbers, then 2n is always an even number.

38. {p}, {q}, {r}, {s}, {p, q}, {p, r}, {p, s}, {q, r}, {q, s}, {r, s}, {p, q, r}, {p, q, s}, {p, r, s}, {q, r, s}.

39. (a)   {Maine, Maryland, Massachusetts, Michigan, Minnesota, Mississippi, Missouri, Montana}

     (b)   {x|x is the name of a state in the United States which starts with the letter *M*}.

Problem Set 2-3

1.   (a)   The second element is the square of the first element. Thus (5, 25) and (6, 36) are two more pairs.

     (b)   The second element is the husband of the first element. Thus (Hillary, Bill) and (Barbara, George) are two more pairs.

1. (c) The second element is the capitalization of the first element. Thus (e, E) and (f, F) are two more pairs.

   (d) The second element is the cost of the first element (at $3\frac{1}{3}$ ¢ each). Thus (9 candies, 30 ¢) and (12 candies, 40 ¢) are two more pairs.

2. (a) *a* is the tallest of the students. *b* is the shortest. From tallest to shortest, the students are *a, c, n, m,* and *b*.

   (b) *c* is the tallest. In order, they are *c, n, a, b,* and *m*.

3. Answers may vary. (Fluffy, Sue), (Jinx, Mary), and (Garfield, Jon) are three examples.

4.

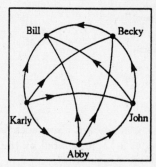

5. (a) Not reflexive — a person cannot be a parent to him/herself.
   Not symmetric — John can be a parent to Jane, but Jane cannot be a parent to John.
   Not transitive — If John is the parent of James and James is the parent of Joseph, John is not the parent of Joseph.
   Not an equivalence relation.

   (b) Reflexive — Juan is the same age as Juan.
   Symmretic — If Juan is the same age as Juanita, then Juanita is the same age as Juan.
   Transitive — If Juan is the same age as Jose and Jose is the same age as Victor, Juan is the same age as Victor.
   An equivalence relation (because the relation is reflexive, symmetric, and transitive).

   (c) Reflexive — Jo Ann has the same last name as herself.
   Symmetric — If Jo Ann has the same last name as Cheryl, then Cheryl has the same last name as Jo Ann.
   Transitive — If Jo Ann has the same last name as Cheryl and Cheryl has the same last name as Penelope, then Jo Ann has the same last name as Penelope.
   An equivalence relation.

   (d) Reflexive — Vicky is the same height as herself.
   Symmetric — If Barbara is the same height as Margarita, then Margarita is the same height as Barbara.
   Transitive — If Willy is the same height as Billy and Billy is the same height as Don, then Willy is the same height as Don.
   An equivalence relation.

   (e) Not reflexive — Cindy cannot be married to herself.
   Symmetric — If Arnold is married to Pam, then Pam is married to Arnold.
   Not transitive — If John is married to Clara and Clara is married to James, then John is not married to James.
   Not an equivalence relation.

5. (f)   Reflexive — Peter lives within 10 miles of himself.
           Symmetric — If Jon lives within 10 miles of Evangeline, the Evangeline lives within 10 miles of Jon.
           Not transitive — If Fred lives within 10 miles of Jim and Jim lives within 10 miles of Herb, then Fred
                does not necessarily live within 10 miles of Herb.
           Not an equivalence relation.

    (g)   Not reflexive — Juan cannot be older than himself.
           Not symmetric — If Jose is older than Mireya then Mireya cannot be older than Jose.
           Transitive — If Jean is older than Mike and Mike is older than Cybil, then Jean is older than Cybil.
           Not an equivalence relation.

6. (a)   Reflexive, symmetric, and transitive; thus is an equivalence relation.

    (b)   Transitive.

    (c)   Symmetric.

7. (a)   Multiply the given number by 3 and subtract 1 (or 3n - 1).

    (b)   Square the given number and add 1 (or $n^2 + 1$)

    (c)   Square the given number and add the given number to that result (or $n^2 + n$).

8. (a) $f(x) = 2x$

    (b) $f(x) = x - 2$

    (c) $f(x) = x + 6$

    (d) $f(x) = x^2 + 1$

9. (a)   Not a function. The element 1 is paired with both *a* and *d*.

    (b)   Not a function. The element 2 is not paired with any element from the set {a, b, c, d}.

    (c)   A function.

    (d)   Not a function. 1 is paired to more than one element from the set {a, b, c, d}, while 2 and 3 are not
           paired at all.

10. W(Normal Car) = 4

11. Yes. Each element of a set is mapped to a single element of a 2nd set (it in fact is a very special function,
    called one-to-one and onto).

12. This diagram does define a function. Every element from A is paired and each is associated with only one
    element from B.

13. (a) $g(0) = 3(0) + 5 = 5$.

    (b) $g(2) = 3(2) + 5 = 11$.

    (c) $g(10) = 3(10) + 5 = 35$.

    (d) $g(a) = 3(a) + 5 = 3a + 5$.

14. (a)

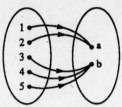

(b)   32. Each of the five elements in the domain have two choices for a pairing, which implies $2^5 = 32$ possible functions.

15. (a)

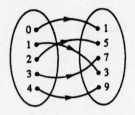

(b)   {(0, 1), (1, 3), (2, 5), (3, 7), (4, 9)}

(c)

x	f(x)
0	1
1	3
2	5
3	7
4	9

(d)

16. (a) $(g \circ f)(0) = 7(0) - 5 = {}^-5$

(b) $(g \circ f)(3) = 7(3) - 5 = 16$

(c) $(g \circ f)(10) = 7(10) - 5 = 65$

17. Assume 29 cents for the first ounce plus 20 cents for each additional ounce. Then:

(a) $0.29 + 0.20(n - 1)$ is the cost in dollars for an n-ounce letter.

(b) $0.29 + 0.20(3 - 1) = 0.29 + 0.40 = \$0.69$ for a 3-ounce letter.

18. (a)   If $T = 70$, then $C = 70 - 40 = 30$ chirps per 15 seconds, or 2 chirps each second.

(b)   40 chirps per minute is 40 chirps per 60 seconds = 10 chirps per 15 seconds. Therefore $10 = T - 40$, so $T = 10 + 40 = 50°$ F.

19. (a)   Two miles is $\frac{1}{2}$ mile plus six $\frac{1}{4}$-mile segments. The fare is thus $2.50 + 6(0.50) = \$5.50$.

19.   (b)   0.50 for each $\frac{1}{4}$ mile gives 2.00 for each mile beyond the first $\frac{1}{2}$ mile. This gives a cost of
              2.50 + 2.00(n miles - first $\frac{1}{2}$ mile) = 2.50 + 2.00n - 1.00 = \$2.00n + \$1.50 for an *n*-mile trip.

20.   A rule is divide by 8; B rule is add 2.

21.   (a)   The score made most often is 51; its frequency is 7.

      (b)   The highest score obtained was 56.

      (c)   Two girls scored 54.

22.   (a)   5n - 2.

      (b) 3^n

      (c)   2n

23.   (a)   Yes. The set of all people has exactly one mother (assuming biological mothers only) each. More or
              less than one is not possible.

      (b)   No. Some elements of the set of all boys do not have a brother.

24.   (a)

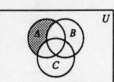 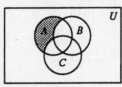

$$A - (B \cup C) = (A - B) \cap (A - C)$$

      (b)

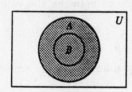

$$A \cup B = B$$

25.   Not a well-defined set; the word "rich" is not defined.

26.   (a) $\{x \mid x \in 2n$ for $n > 6$ and $n \in N\}$

      (b) $\{x \mid x < 14$ and $x \in N\}$

27.   (a)   A = {a, b, c}. $\overline{B}$ = {a, d}. A $\cup \overline{B}$ = {a, b, c, d} = U.

      (b)   A $\cap$ B = {b, c}. $\overline{A \cap B}$ = {a, d}.

      (c)   Since there are no elements in $\emptyset$, A $\cap \emptyset = \emptyset$.

      (d)   Since there are no elements common to B and C, B $\cap$ C = $\emptyset$.

      (e)   B - A = $\{x \mid x \in$ B and $x \notin$ A}. There are no elements in this set, so B - A = $\emptyset$.

28. $A = \{a, b, c\}$. $N = \{1, 2, 3\}$
     $a \leftrightarrow 1$
     $b \leftrightarrow 2$
     $c \leftrightarrow 3$

29. $\{a, b, c, d\}$ is an equivalent set; the number of elements is the same.

30. (a)   There are $3 \cdot 2 \cdot 1 = 6$ one-to-one correspondences between 3-element sets.

     (b)   There are $3 \cdot 3 = 9$ elements in $A \times B$.

31. We need to show that $(A \cup B) \cup C = A \cup (B \cup C)$:
     $A \cup B = \{h, e, l, p, m\}$; $B \cup C = \{m, e, n, o, w\}$
     $(A \cup B) \cup C = \{h, e, l, p, m, n, o, w\} \leftrightarrow A \cup (B \cup C) = \{h, l, p, m, e, n, o, w\}$

Problem Set 2-4

1.   (a)   False statement (a statement is a sentence that is either true or false, but not both).

     (b)   Not a statement.

     (c)   False statement.

     (d)   Not a statement (i.e., it can be either true or false).

     (e)   Not a statement.

     (f)   Not a statement (truth cannot be determined without knowing the value of x).

     (g)   True statement.

     (h)   Not a statement (could be either true or false depending upon the value of x).

     (i)   Not a statement. (This is a paradox. If it is true, it must be false, but then it isn't true ... .)

     (j)   Not a statement.

2.   (a)   There exists a natural number $x = 3$ such that $x + 8 = 11$.

     (b)   For all natural numbers x, $x + 0 = x$.

     (c)   There exists a natural number x such that $x^2 = 4$.

     (d)   There exists no natural number x such that $x + 1 = x + 2$.

3.   (a)   For all natural numbers x, $x + 8 = 11$.

     (b)   There is no natural number x such that $x + 0 = x$.

     (c)   For all natural numbers x, $x^2 = 4$.

     (d)   There exists a natural number x, such that $x + 1 = x + 2$.

4.   (a)   The book does not have 500 pages.

      (b)   Six is not less than eight.

      (c) $3 \cdot 5 \neq 15$.

      (d)   No people have blond hair.

      (e)   There exists a dog that does not have four legs.

      (f)   All cats have nine lives.

      (g)   There exists a square that is not a rectangle.

      (h)   All rectangles are squares.

      (i)   There exists a natural number x such that $x + 3 \neq 3 + x$.

      (j)   For all natural numbers x, $3 \cdot (x + 2) = 12$.

      (k)   There exists a counting number that is not divisible by itself and 1.

      (l)   All natural numbers are divisible by 2.

      (m)   There exists a natural number x such that $5x + 4x \neq 9x$.

5.   (a)

p	~p	~(~p)
T	F	T
F	T	F

      (b)

p	~p	p∨~p	p∧~p
T	F	T	F
F	T	T	F

      (c)   Yes   (d)   No

6.   (a) $q \wedge r$

      (b) $r \vee \sim q$

      (c) $\sim(q \wedge r)$

      (d) $\sim q$

7.   (a)   False (true if and only if both p and q are true).

      (b)   True (false if both p and q are false; true otherwise).

      (c)   True (negation of p).

      (d)   False.

      (e)   False [analgous to -(-x) = x]

      (f)   True (both $\sim$p and q are true).

7. (g)   False (both are false).

    (h)   False (p ∨ q is true).

    (i)   False (~p ∧ q is true).

    (j)   False.

8. (a)   False.   (b)   False

    (c)   True   (d)   True

    (e)   False   (f)   True

    (g)   False   (h)   True

    (i)   True   (j)   True

9. (a)

p	q	~p	~q	~p ∨ ~q	~(p ∨ q)
T	T	F	F	F	F
T	F	F	T	T	F
F	T	T	F	T	F
F	F	T	T	T	T

Since the truth table for ~p ∨ ~q is not the same as for ~(p ∨ q), the statements are not logically equivalent.

    (b)

p	q	~p	~q	p ∨ q	~(p ∨ q)	~p ∧ ~q
T	T	F	F	T	F	F
T	F	F	T	T	F	F
F	T	T	F	T	F	F
F	F	T	T	F	T	T

Since the truth table for ~(p ∨ q) is the same as for ~p ∧ ~q, the statements are logically equivalent.

    (c)

p	q	~p	~q	p ∧ q	~(p ∧ q)	~p ∧ ~q
T	T	F	F	T	F	F
T	F	F	T	F	T	F
F	T	T	F	F	T	F
F	F	T	T	F	T	T

Since the truth table for ~(p ∧ q) is not the same as for ~p ∧ ~q, the statements are not logically equivalent.

    (d)

p	q	~p	~q	p ∧ q	~(p ∧ q)	~p ∨ ~q
T	T	F	F	T	F	F
T	F	F	T	F	T	T
F	T	T	F	F	T	T
F	F	T	T	F	T	T

Since the truth table for ~(p ∧ q) is the same as for ~p ∨ ~q, the statements are logically equivalent.

10. (a)   ~(p ∨ q) is logically equivalent to ~p ∧ ~q.
           ~(p ∧ q) is logically equivalent to ~p ∨ ~q.

10. (b)   Operations on sets are equivalent to operations on logical statements, where the symbol "~" represents a complement, ∨ represents a union, and ∧ represents an intersection.

11.

p	q	~p	~q	~p ∨ q
T	T	F	F	T
T	F	F	T	F
F	T	T	F	T
F	F	T	T	T

12. (a)   This statement is equivalent to ~(W ∧ J). DeMorgan's equivalent is ~W ∨ ~J. Today is not Wednesday or this is not the month of June.

   (b)   This statement is equivalent to ~(B ∧ T). DeMorgan's equivalent is ~B ∨ ~T. Yesterday I didn't eat breakfast or I didn't watch television.

   (c)   This statement is equivalent to ~R ∨ ~J. DeMorgan's equivalent is ~(R ∧ J). It is not true that it is both raining and the month is July.

Problem Set 2-5

1. (a)   p → q.

   (b)   ~p → q.

   (c)   p → ~q.

   (d)   p → q.

   (e)   ~q → ~p.

   (f)   p ↔ q.

2. (a)   Converse: If you are good in sports, then you eat Meaties.
          Inverse: If you do not eat Meaties, then you are not good in sports.
          Contrapositive: If you are not good in sports, then you do not eat Meaties.

   (b)   Converse: If you do not like mathematics, then you do not like this book.
          Inverse: If you like this book, then you like mathematics.
          Contrapositive: If you like mathematics, then you like this book.

   (c)   Converse: If you have cavities, then you do not use Ultra Brush toothpaste.
          Inverse: If you use Ultra Brush toothpaste, then you do not have cavities.
          Contrapositive: If you do not have cavities, then you use Ultra Brush toothpaste.

   (d)   Converse: If your grades are high, then you are good at logic.
          Inverse: If you are not good at logic, then your grades are not high.
          Contrapositive: If your grades are not high, then you are not good at logic.

3. (a)

p	q	p ∨ q	p → (p ∨ q)
T	T	T	T
T	F	T	T
F	T	T	T
F	F	F	T

3.   (b)

p	q	p ∧ q	(p ∧ q) → q
T	T	T	T
T	F	F	T
F	T	F	T
F	F	F	T

     (c)

p	~p	~(~p)	p ↔ ~(~p)
T	F	T	T
F	T	F	T

     (d)

p	q	p → q	~(p → q)
T	T	T	F
T	F	F	T
F	T	T	F
F	F	T	F

4.   (a)   T   (b)   T

     (c)   F   (d)   F

     (e)   T   (f)   F

5.   (a)   ~p is T; ~q is T; so ~p → ~q is T.

     (b)   (p → q) is T; so ~(p → q) is F.

     (c)   (p ∨ q) is F; (p ∧ q) is F; so (p ∨ q) → (p ∧ q) is T.

     (d)   p is F; ~p is T; so p → ~p is T.

     (e)   (p ∨ ~p) is T; p is F; so (p ∨ ~p) → p is F.

     (f)   (p ∨ q) is F; (p ∧ q) is F; so (p ∨ q) ↔ (p ∧ q) is T.

6.   Yes. Any contradictory statement would satisfy this condition; e.g., if it is red, then it is blue; or if a person is five years old she is old enough to vote.

7.   No. If it does not rain, then Iris can either go to the movies or not without making her statement false.

8.   (a)   No (inverse).

     (b)   Yes (contrapositive).

     (c)   No (converse).

9.   The contrapositive is logically equivalent: "If a number is not a multiple of 4, then it is not a multiple of 8."

10. (a)

p	q	r	p → q	p ∧ r	(p ∧ r) → q	(p → q) → [(p ∧ r) → q]
T	T	T	T	T	T	T
T	T	F	T	F	T	T
T	F	T	F	T	F	T
T	F	F	F	F	T	T
F	T	T	T	F	T	T
F	T	F	T	F	T	T
F	F	T	T	F	T	T
F	F	F	T	F	T	T

Since (p → q) always implies [(p ∧ r) → q], it is a tautology.

(b)

p	q	p → q	(p → q) ∧ r	[(p → q) ∧ p] → q
T	T	T	T	T
T	F	F	F	T
F	T	T	F	T
F	F	T	F	T

Since [(p → q) ∧ p] always implies q, it is a tautology

(c)

p	q	p → q	~q	(p → q) ∧ ~q	~p	[(p → q) ∧ ~q] → ~p
T	T	T	F	F	F	T
T	F	F	T	F	F	T
F	T	T	F	F	T	T
F	F	T	T	T	T	T

Since [(p → q) ∧ ~q] always implies ~p, it is a tautology.

(d)

p	q	r	p → q	q → r	(p → q) ∧ (q → r)	p → r	[(p → q) ∧ (q → r)] → (p → r)
T	T	T	T	T	T	T	T
T	T	F	T	F	F	F	T
T	F	T	F	T	F	T	T
T	F	F	F	T	F	F	T
F	T	T	T	T	T	T	T
F	T	F	T	F	F	T	T
F	F	T	T	T	T	T	T
F	F	F	T	T	T	T	T

Since [(p → q) ∧ (q → r)] always implies (p → r), it is a tautology.

11. (a) p → q is analogous to {p|p ∈ P and p ∈ Q}. q ⇸ p is analogous to {q|q ∈ Q and q ∉ P}.
Therefore they are analgous to the relationship P ⊂ Q.

(b) p → q is analogous to {p|p ∈ P and p ∈ Q}. q → p is analogous to {q|q ∈ Q and q ∈ P}.
Therefore they are analgous to the relationship P = Q.

(c) A ⊆ B is analogous to p → q. A̅ ⊆ B̅ is analgous to ~p → ~q.
A ⊆ B = {x|x ∈ A and x ∈ B}. A̅ ⊆ B̅ = {x|x ∉ A and x ∉ B}.
Which is true only if A = B.

12. (a) Using the chain rule, our statement is p → s. The logical equivalent is the contrapositive, or
~s → ~p. Therefore p is false.

(b) If r is false, we have the contrapositive ~r → ~(p ∧ q). If q is true, then (p ∧ q) can be false only if
p is false.

12. (c)   Yes, if p is false. In fact, q must be true in order for q → p to be false.

13. (a)   Let p = Mary's little lamb follows her to school.
           q = It will break the rules.
           r = Mary will be sent home.
           Then p → (q ∧ r).

    (b)   Let p = Jack is nimble.
           q = Jack is quick.
           r = Jack makes it over the candlestick.
           Then ~(p ∧ q) → ~r.

    (c)   Let p = The apple hit Newton on the head.
           q = The laws of gravity were discovered.
           Then ~p → ~q.

14. (a)   Valid.

    (b)   Valid.

    (c)   Valid (although it doesn't directly follow).

    (d)   Invalid.

15. (a)   Let p = Helen is a college student.
           q = All college students are poor.
           Then we have p → q, or if Helen is a college student she is poor.
                        p is true, she is a college student.
           So q is true, Helen is poor.

    (b)   Let p = Some freshmen like math.
           q = All who like math are intelligent.
           Then p → q, or some freshmen are intelligent.

    (c)   Let p = I study for the final.
           q = I pass the course.
           r = I look for a teaching job.
           Then p → q, if I study for the final I pass the course.
                q → r, if I pass the course I look for a teaching job.
                p → r, if I study for the final I will look for a teaching job.

    (d)   Let p = Equilateral triangle.
           q = Isosceles triangle.
           Then p → q
                ~p → ~q, or, there may exist triangles that are not equilateral.

16. (a)   If a figure is a square, then it is a rectangle.

    (b)   If a number is an integer, then it is a rational number.

    (c)   If a figure has exactly three sides, then it may be a triangle.

    (d)   If it is raining, then it is cloudy.

1.   A = {x|x is a letter of the Greek alphabet}.

2.   {m, a, t, h}, {m, a, t}, {m, a, h}, {m, t, h}, {a, t, h}, {m, a}, {m, t}, {m, h}, {a, t}, {a, h}, {t. h}, {m},
     {a}, {t}, {h}, { }.

3.   (a)   A person younger than 30 living in Montana.

     (b)   A person 30 or older living in Montana who owns a pickup.

     (c)   A person living in Montana.

     (d)   A person living in Montana who does not own a pickup.

     (e)   A person living in Montana who is younger than 30 or does not own a pickup.

     (f)   A person living in Montana who is 30 or older and does not own a pickup.

4.   (a)   {r, a, v, e}.

     (b)   {l, e}.

     (c)   {u, n, i, v, r}.

     (d)   {r, v}.

     (e)   {u, v, s}.

     (f)   {a, l, e}.

     (g)   {i, n}.

     (h)   {e}.

     (i)   5.

     (j)   16 (each of the four elements in C can be paired with each of the four in D ⇒ 4·4 = 16 in C × D).

5.   (a)   A ∩ (B ∪ C):

     (b)   ($\overline{A \cup B}$) ∩ C:

6.   (a)   {(i, s), (i, e), (i, t), (d, s), (d, e), (d, t), (e, s), (e, e), (e, t), (a, s), (a, e), (a, t)}.

     (b)   {(s, s), (s, e), (s, t), (e, s), (e, e), (e, t), (t, s), (t, e), (t, t)}.

6.   (c)   0. Since ∅ has no elements, it is not possible to make an ordered pair using an element from it.

      (d)   3. There are 3 elements in B that are not in A: {i, d, a}.

7.   5040, assuming that all 7 letters are distinct. Consider seven "slots" in which to put the letters; there are 7 letters which could go in the 1st slot, then 6 left which could go in the 2nd slot, and so on. The number of possible words is then $7 \cdot 6 \cdot 5 \cdot 4 \cdot 3 \cdot 2 \cdot 1 = 7! = 5040$.

8.   (a)   Answers may vary. One possible correspondence is t ↔ e, h ↔ n, and e ↔ d.

      (b) $3 \cdot 2 \cdot 1 = 6$ correspondences are possible.

9.   A ∩ (B ∪ C)   (A ∩ B) ∪ C

10.   (a)   B ∪ (A ∩ C)   (b)   B − C

11.   (a)   The associative property states that (A ∩ B) ∩ C = A ∩ (B ∩ C).
             (A ∩ B) ∩ C = {2, 3} ∩ {3, 4, 5, 6, 7} = {3}.
             A ∩ (B ∩ C) = {1, 2, 3} ∩ {3, 4, 5} = {3}.
             Both expressions yield {3} and are thus equal.

      (b)   The commutative property states that A ∪ B = B ∪ A.
             A ∪ B = {1, 2, 3} ∪ {2, 3, 4, 5} = {1, 2, 3, 4, 5}.
             B ∪ A = {2, 3, 4, 5} ∪ {1, 2, 3} = {1, 2, 3, 4, 5}.
             Both expressions yield {1, 2, 3, 4, 5} and are thus equal.

12.   (a)   False. Sets A and B could be disjoint.

      (b)   False. It is not a proper subset of itself.

      (c)   False. A ∼ B only requires the same number of elements - not necessarily the same elements.

      (d)   False. The set increases without limit.

      (e)   False. Infinite sets are equivalent to proper subsets of themselves.

      (f)   False. Let A = {1, 2, 3, 4, ...) and let B = {1}.

      (g)   True.

      (h)   False. The sets may be   disjoint but not empty.

13.   (a)   17, if P = Q.

      (b)   34, if P and Q are disjoint.

      (c)   0, if P and Q are disjoint.

      (d)   17, if P = Q.

14. 7. n(Crew) + n(Swimming) + n(Soccer) = 57. The two lettering in all three sports are counted 3 times, so subtract 2 twice, giving 53. n(Awards) = 46, thus 53 - 46 = 7 were counted twice; i.e., 7 lettered in exactly two sports.

15. Three questions would accomplish this:
    (*i*)   Is it above the Canada-U.S. border?
    (*ii*)   Does its name begin with a vowel?
    (*iii*)   Is it inland?

16. (a)   36 students were in the survey.

    (b)   6 students liked only mathematics.

    (c)   5 students liked English and mathematics but not history.

17. (a)   Yes.

    (b)   No. *a* and *b* both correspond to two components of the range.

    (c)   Yes.

18. (a) $f(0) = 3(0) + 7 = 7$.

    (b) $f(8) = 3(8) + 7 = 31$.

    (c) $f(10) = 3(10) + 7 = 37$.

19. (a)   Pair each post office with the zip code it serves.

    (b)   Let A = $\{x|x$ is a digit from 0 to 9$\}$ = One of 10 sets of states.
    B = $\{x|x$ is a digit from 00 to 99$\}$ = One of 100 geographic areas in each element of A.
    C = $\{x|x$ is a digit from 00 to 99$\}$ = One of 100 local delivery areas in each element of A $\cap$ B.
    Then 59801 = 5 $\in$ A;
    $$98 \in \{A \cap B\};$$
    $$01 \in \{A \cap B \cap C\}.$$

20. (a) $\{3, 4, 5, 6\}$.

    (b) $\{14, 29, 44, 59\}$.

    (c) $\{0, 1, 4, 9, 16\}$.

    (d) $\{5, 9, 15\}$.

21. (a)   Reflexive (Joe belongs to the same club as himself).
    Symmetric (if Joe belongs to the same club as Mary, then Mary belongs to the same club as Joe).
    Transitive (if Joe belongs to the same club as Mary, and Mary belongs to the same club as Sam, the Joe may belong to the same club as Sam).

    (b)   Transitive only.

    (c)   Symmetric only.

    (d)   Is neither reflexive, symmetric, nor transitive.

22. (a)   Yes.

     (b)   Yes.

     (c)   No (unless the value of x is determined).

     (d)   Yes.

23. (a)   No women smoke.

     (b) $3 + 5 \neq 8$.

     (c)   Some heavy metal rock is not loud.

     (d)   Beethoven wrote some non-classical music.

24. (a)

p	q	~q	p ∨ ~q	(p ∨ ~q) ∧ p
T	T	F	T	T
T	F	T	T	T
F	T	F	F	F
F	F	T	T	F

     (b)

p	q	~q	p → ~q	(p → ~q) ∨ q
T	T	F	F	T
T	F	T	T	T
F	T	F	T	T
F	F	T	T	T

     (c)

p	q	~q	p → ~q	~q → p	(p → ~q) ∧ (~q → p)
T	T	F	F	T	F
T	F	T	T	T	T
F	T	F	T	T	T
F	F	T	T	F	F

     (d)

p	q	~p	~q	~p ∨ ~q	q ∧ p	(~p ∨ ~q) → (q ∧ p)
T	T	F	F	F	T	T
T	F	F	T	T	F	F
F	T	T	F	T	F	F
F	F	T	T	T	F	F

25. (a)

p	q	r	q ∨ r	p ∧ (q ∨ r)	p ∧ q	p ∧ r	(p ∧ q) ∨ (p ∧ r)
T	T	T	T	T	T	T	T
T	T	F	T	T	T	F	T
T	F	T	T	T	F	T	T
T	F	F	F	F	F	F	F
F	T	T	T	F	F	F	F
F	T	F	T	F	F	F	F
F	F	T	T	F	F	F	F
F	F	F	F	F	F	F	F

Since the truth tables for p ∧ (q ∨ r) and (p ∧ q) ∨ (p ∧ r) are the same, the two statements are logically equivalent.

25. (b)

p	q	p → q	q → p
T	T	T	T
T	F	F	T
F	T	T	F
F	F	T	T

Since the truth tables for p → q and q → p are not the same, the two statements are not logically equivalent.

26. Converse: If someone will faint, we are having a rock concert.
Inverse: If we do not have a rock concert, no one will faint.
Contrapositive: If no one will faint, we are not having a rock concert.

27. (a) Joe Czernyu loves Mom and apple pie.

(b) The structure of the Statue of Liberty will eventually rust.

(c) Albertina will pass Math 100 (she had two options; since she did not fulfill one, she must do the other).

28. (a) Let f = fair-skinned; s = sunburned; d = went to the dance; w = parents ask why.
Then f → s
s → ~d
~d → w
The final argument is ~w → ~f, which is valid. (Consider the contrapositives of the first three arguments from bottom to top.)

29. (a) Valid. In statement 3, "ridiculous diets" is redundant because of statement 1; it can thus be reduced to statement 2.

(b) Valid.

(c) Valid.

CHAPTER 3 - NUMERATION SYSTEMS AND WHOLE NUMBERS

1. (a) $\overline{\overline{\text{M}}}$CDXXIV. The double bar over the M represents 1000·1000·1000, while a single bar over the M represents only 1000·1000.

   (b) 46,032. The 46 in 46,032 means $4 \cdot 10^4 + 6 \cdot 10^3$, while 46 in 4632 represents $4 \cdot 10^3 + 6 \cdot 10^2$.

   (c) < ▼▼ . The space between < and ▼▼ represents 10·60 rather than 10.

   (d) 𓆼𓎆𓏺 . 𓆼 has a place value of 1000, while 𓍢 has a place value of only 100.

   (e)  .  represents three groups of 20 plus zero 1's;  means three 5's and three 1's, or 15.

2. (a) MCMXLIX represents 1949; thus one more is 1950, or MCML; one less is 1948, or MCMXLVIII.

   (b) $\overline{\text{M}}$I represents 1000·1000 + 1, or 1,000,001; thus one more is $\overline{\text{M}}$II; one less is $\overline{\text{M}}$.

   (c) CMXCIX is 999; one more is M; one less is CMXCVIII.

   (d) << <▼ is 20·60 + 11 = 1211; thus one more is 1212, or << <▼▼ ; one less is 1210, or << <.

   (e) 𓆼𓍢𓍢 is 1200; one more is 1201, or 𓆼𓍢𓍢𓏺 ; one less is 1199, or 𓆼𓍢𓎆𓎆𓎆𓎆𓎆𓎆𓎆𓎆𓎆𓏺𓏺𓏺𓏺𓏺𓏺𓏺𓏺𓏺.

   (f)  is 7·20 + 13·1 = 153; thus one more is 154, or  ; one less is 152, or  .

3. MCMXXII is 1000 + 900 + 22, or the year 1922.

4. (a) Use place value in columns as done in the Hindu-Arabic system. Group the numerals in each column; trade symbols and shift columns if necessary.

   (b) Group by symbol; trade symbols as necessary.

5. Group by symbol. Then borrow one heel bone and add ten vertical staffs; subtract 5 vertical staffs from 13 vertical staffs to record 8 vertical staffs. Borrow one scroll and add ten heel bones; subtract 4 heel bones from 11 heel bones to record 7 heel bones. The difference is thus 𓎆𓎆𓎆𓎆𓎆𓎆𓎆𓏺𓏺𓏺𓏺𓏺𓏺𓏺𓏺.

6. (a) CXXI (b) XLII

   (c) LXXXIX (d) $\overline{\text{M}}$CCLXXXII

7. (a) 𓎆𓎆𓎆𓎆𓎆𓏺𓏺 (b) 𓍢𓏺𓏺𓏺

   (c) 𓏺𓏺𓏺 (d) 𓎆𓎆𓎆𓏺𓏺𓏺𓏺𓏺𓏺𓏺𓏺

8.

Hindu-Arabic	Babylonian	Egyptian	Roman	Mayan
72	▼ <▼▼	𓎆𓎆𓎆𓎆𓎆𓎆𓎆𓏺𓏺	LXXII	
602	< ▼▼	𓍢𓍢𓍢𓍢𓍢𓍢𓏺𓏺	DCII	
1223	<< <<▼▼▼	𓆼𓍢𓍢𓎆𓎆𓏺𓏺𓏺	MCCXXIII	

9.   Answers may vary. Three examples are in dates, paragraph numbering, and super bowl names.

10.   Zero is a number with place value; nothing means the total absence of any number.

11.   (a)   With no place values, listing the symbols can become cumbersome.

      (b)   Place values of 60 are awkward; numbers can be ambiguously written.

      (c)   Arithmetic operations are difficult.

12.   (a)   Systems may vary. One such could derive from a world in which people have only one arm with five fingers; thus place value will be in powers of 5 rather than 10. In this system, $\mathcal{O} = 0$, $\mathcal{A} = 1$, $\mathcal{B} = 2$, $\mathcal{C} = 3$, and $\mathcal{D} = 4$. A number such as $\mathcal{BDO}$, then, would mean $2 \cdot 25 + 4 \cdot 5 + 0 = 70$ in the Hindu-Arabic system. All arithmetic operations would be similar to those in the Hindu-Arabic system, except for the place values.

      (b)

H-A	Yours	H-A	Yours
1	$\mathcal{A}$	100	$\mathcal{DOO}$
5	$\mathcal{AO}$	5000	$\mathcal{ACOO}$
10	$\mathcal{BO}$	10000	$\mathcal{CAOO}$
50	$\mathcal{BOO}$	15280	$\mathcal{DDBAAO}$

13.   (a)   Hundreds (from the decimal point left: units → tens → hundreds)

      (b)   Tens (units → tens)

      (c)   Thousands (units → tens → hundreds → thousands)

      (d)   Hundred thousands (units → tens → hundreds → thousands → ten thousands → hundred thousands)

14.   (a) $3,000,000 + 4,000 + 5 = 3,004,005.$

      (b) $20,000 + 1 = 20,001.$

      (c) $3000 + 500 + 60 = 3560.$

      (d) $9,000,000 + 90 + 9 = 9,000,099.$

15.   To separate groupings of hundreds, thousands, millions, billions, etc.

16.   (a) $3 \cdot 25 + 2 \cdot 5 + 1 \cdot 1 = 86.$

      (b) $1 \cdot 8 + 0 \cdot 4 + 1 \cdot 2 + 1 \cdot 1 = 11.$

17.   The number could be either 811 or 910. They satisfy the conditions that the hundreds digit must be 8 or 9, the tens digit must be odd, and the sum of the digits must equal 10.

18.   Answers may vary. One might argue that if no changes have been made in 600 years, the system must be serving its purpose well.

19.   After setting 9 as the constant in your calculator's memory, enter 9 and then depress the ⊟ key six times. Your result should be 4,782,969.

20.   (a)   If your calculator has an eight-digit display, the largest possible number using these keys only once would be 98,765,432.

20. (b)   12,345,678.   (c)   99,999,999.

    (d)   11,111,111.

21. (a)   We need to subtract a number with a 2 in the thousands place and a 2 in the tens place, or 2020.
           Thus 32,420 − 2020 = 30,400.

    (b)   67,357 − 50 = 67,307.

Problem Set 3-2

1. (a)   5 is less than 7 if and only if there exists a natural number k such that $5 + k = 7$. In this case, k = 2
           (a natural number).

    (b)   6 is greater than 3 if and only if there exists a natural number k such that $3 + k = 6$. k = 3.

2. No. If k = 0, we would have k = 0 + k, implying k > k.

3. Suppose A and B were not disjoint; let A = {1, 2, 3} and B = {3, 4, 5}. Then A $\cup$ B = {1, 2, 3, 4, 5} and
    n(A $\cup$ B) = 5. But n(A) + n(B) = 3 + 3 = 6; thus sets must be disjoint to define addition.

4. (a)

    (b)

5. (a)   Using the missing-addend model, 2 + (7 − 2) = 7. Thus $\boxed{5}$ + 2 = 7.

    (b)   (6 − 4) + 4 = 6; thus $\boxed{2}$ + 4 = 6.

    (c)   Whole numbers which can make this statement true are $\boxed{0}$, $\boxed{1}$, and $\boxed{2}$.

    (d)   Any whole number larger than or equal to $\boxed{3}$ will make this statement true.

6. (a)   3 is the number which must be added to 5 to obtain 8, so 8 − 5 = $\boxed{3}$.

    (b) $\square$ is the number which results when 4 is added to 9, or $\boxed{13}$ − 4 = 9.

    (c)   0 is the identity element, so   a − 0 = $\boxed{a}$.

    (d)   a − $\boxed{0}$ = a.

    (e)   The whole numbers which make this true are $\boxed{9}$, $\boxed{8}$, $\boxed{7}$, $\boxed{6}$, $\boxed{5}$, $\boxed{4}$, and $\boxed{3}$. Numbers less than 3 will
           result in a non-whole number result.

    (f)   Whole numbers greater than $\boxed{9}$ will make this statement true.

7. (a)   Closed.   (b)   Closed.

7.   (c)   Closed.   (d)   Not closed. $3 + 7 \notin \{3, 5, 7\}$.

     (e)   Closed.

8.   (a) $x = 213 + 119$ (b) $119 + x = 213$

     (c) $213 = x + 119$

9.   (a)   Commutative property of addition of whole numbers.

     (b)   Associative property of addition of whole numbers.

     (c)   Commutative property of addition [i.e., $(6 + 3) = (3 + 6)$].

10.   (a) $3280 < 3802$, 3820, or $8023 < 8032$.

     (b) $2803 < 2830$, 3028, 3082, 3208, 3280, or $3802 < 3820$.

11.   (a)   Each term is found by adding 5 to the previous term, so the next three are $28 + 5 = \underline{33}$, $33 + 5 = \underline{38}$, and $38 + 5 = \underline{43}$.

     (b)   Each term is found by subtracting 7 from the previous term, so the next three are $63 - 7 = \underline{56}$, $56 - 7 = \underline{49}$, and $49 - 7 = \underline{42}$.

12.   (a)

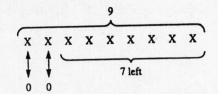

     (b)

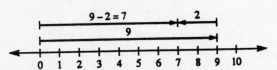

13.   Let A = $\{1, 2, 3\}$ and B = $\{1, 2, 3, 4, 5\}$; so $n(A) = 3$ and $n(B) = 5$. Then B $-$ A $= \{4, 5\}$ and $n(B - A) = 2$, corresponding to $n(B) - n(A) = 5 - 3 = 2$.

14.   (a) $5 - 3 \neq 3 - 5$

     (b) $(8 - 3) - 2 \neq 8 - (3 - 2)$

     (c) $4 - 0 \neq 0 - 4$ and $0 - 4 \neq 4$

15.   (a)   9. A number greater than 9 would have two digits.

     (b)   8. If A were larger, C must be larger than 9.

     (c)   3. A and B must be 1 and 2; no smaller single digit numbers are available.

     (d)   6 or 8. A and B must be 2 and 4 or 2 and 6.

     (e)   5. If B + A = A + 5 = C, then B must be 5 for the equation to be true.

     (f)   4 or 8. B could be 1 and A then must be 3; or B could be 2 and then A must be 6.

15. (g) 9. B must be 2 and A must be 7.

16. (a) C = 1. Addition of no two single-digit numbers will result in a sum greater than 18.

     (b) No, because C = 1.

     (c) A can be 8 or 9.

     (d) D can only be 2.

17. Note that even rows sum to 0, while odd rows sum to 1. Since row 50 is even, its sum is 0.

18. (a)

8	1	6
3	5	7
4	9	2

     (b)

17	10	15
12	14	16
13	18	11

19. Assign letters to each of the blanks, as below:

a	b
c	d

We can then write equations: $a + b = 11$; $a + c = 12$; and $b + c = 7$.
Solving this system of equations, we find: $a = 8$, $b = 3$, and $c = 4$. Substituting these values for a, b, and c, then d must equal 12, and so our squares are:

8	3
4	12

20. We first look at sums:

1	5	3	→	9
6	7	2	→	15
8	9	4	→	21

        ↓   ↓   ↓
       15 21   9

Noting that the sums are correct in the 1st column and 2nd row, there is a difference of 6 from 15 in all other rows and columns. Since $9 - 3 = 6$, it can be seen that the 9 (row 3, column 2) and 3 (row 1, column 3) should be switched. Doing so then gives:

1	5	9
6	7	2
8	3	4

and all rows and columns sum to 15.

21. First decide on three combinations that total 13 as a sum. Then arrange them so that the middle numbers fit the "across" boxes:

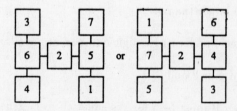

22.

	44	12
61		

23. (a)   Answers may vary.

1	2
3	5
4	6

1	3
2	5
4	6

(b)   Yes, for example:

1	4
2	5
3	6

24.   28 dominos.

25.   If Millie and Samantha both start with $0, then Millie's savings will be $3, $6, $9, ... and Samantha's will be $5, $10, $15, ... After five months Millie will have $15 and Samantha will have $25.

26.   Look for a pattern:

   2 nails on each axis → 1 intersection
   3 nails on each axis → 3 intersections → 2 new ones
   4 nails on each axis → 6 intersections → 3 new ones
   5 nails on each axis → 10 intersections → 4 new ones

   $\vdots$

   6 nails → 15 intersections
   7 nails → 21 intersections
   8 nails → 28 intersections
   9 nails → 36 intersections
   10 nails → 45 intersections

27.   We can treat this problem as an arithmetic sequence: $1 + 3 + 5 + 7 + \ldots$. Using the methods of Chapter 1, to find the number of guests arriving on the 20th ring we would have:
   20th term $= 1 + (20 - 1) \cdot 2 = 39$.
   The sum of all 20 arrival groups would be:
   Sum $= \frac{20}{2} \cdot (1 + 39) = 400$ guests.

28.   Answers may vary. One reason is that the "counting on" strategy can be made simpler in some cases by using the commutative property.

29.   Answers may vary. One reason is that no one strategy best fits all addition/subtraction problems.

30.   Yes. Answers may vary, but one reason is that answers taken at face value from the display of a calculator may be wrong if the wrong keys have been used.

31.   Change the problem to $9 + 3$ and then use the "counting on" strategy.

32.   (a) $7 \cdot 10 = 70$ (b) $9 \cdot 1000 = 9000$

      (c) $11 \cdot 100 = 1100$ (d) $56 \cdot 10 = 560$

32. (e) $347 \cdot 10 = 3470$

33. Calculators may vary; some systems are shown below:

(a)   Enter $\boxed{1}\boxed{+}$ as the constant. Enter $\boxed{1}$ and then depress $\boxed{=}$ 100 times.

(b)   Enter $\boxed{2}\boxed{+}$ as the constant. Enter $\boxed{2}$ and then depress $\boxed{=}$ 50 times.

(c)   Enter $\boxed{5}\boxed{+}$ as the constant. Enter $\boxed{5}$ and then depress $\boxed{=}$ 20 times.

34. Calculators may vary; some systems are shown below:

(a)   Enter $\boxed{1}\boxed{\times}$ as the constant. Enter $\boxed{2}\boxed{7}$ and then depress $\boxed{=}$ 27 times.

(b)   Enter $\boxed{3}\boxed{\times}$ as the constant. Enter $\boxed{2}\boxed{7}$ and then depress $\boxed{=}$ 9 times.

(c)   Enter $\boxed{9}\boxed{\times}$ as the constant. Enter $\boxed{2}\boxed{7}$ and then depress $\boxed{=}$ 3 times.

35. Start with $\boxed{2}\boxed{+}\boxed{2}$, or two 2's. Keep adding by 2, counting each time. After the 13th operation, the calculator will display 26.

36. (a)   Subtracting 1 from 10 (or X), we have CMLIX.

(b)   Subtracting 1 from 9 (or IX), we have XXXVIII.

37. There are fewer symbols to remember and place value is used.

38. $5286 = 5 \cdot 10^3 + 2 \cdot 10^2 + 8 \cdot 10 + 6$

Problem Set 3-3

1.

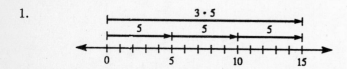

2. $5 \cdot 2 + 5 \cdot 5 = 10 + 25 = \$35$

3. (a)   Closed. $0 \cdot 0 = 0$, $0 \cdot 1 = 0$, $1 \cdot 0 = 0$, and $1 \cdot 1 = 1$ are all products contained in $\{0, 1\}$.

(b)   Closed. $0 \cdot 0 = 0$, and $0 \in \{0\}$.

(c)   Closed. The product of any two even numbers is also an even number.

(d)   Closed. The product of any two odd numbers is also an odd number.

(e)   Closed. If we multiply any two terms in the sequence, we will still have an arithmetic sequence with 1st term 1 and difference 3.

(f)   No. $2 \cdot 2 = 4 \notin \{0, 1, 2\}$.

4. (a)   No. $2 + 3 = 5$.

(b)   Yes. There will be no products equal to 5.

4. (c)   (*i*)   No. $2 + 4 = 6.$

         (*ii*)   No. $2 \cdot 3 = 6.$

5.   This is false; consider the set A = {1}.

6. $8 \cdot 3 = (6 + 2) \cdot 3 = 6 \cdot 3 + 2 \cdot 3 = 18 + 6 = 24.$

7.   (a)   Commutative property of multiplication of whole numbers.

     (b)   Associative property of multiplication of whole numbers.

     (c)   Commutative property of addition of whole numbers. Note that the order of multiplication is unchanged.

     (d)   Zero multiplication property.

     (e)   Identity property of multiplication of whole numbers.

     (f)   Commutative property of multiplication of whole numbers.

     (g)   Distributive property of multiplication over addition.

     (h)   Distributive property of multiplication over addition.

8.   (a) $3 \cdot \boxed{5} = 15$ (b) $18 = 6 + 3 \cdot \boxed{4}$

     (c) $\boxed{x} \cdot (5 + 6) = \boxed{x} \cdot 5 + \boxed{x} \cdot 6$, where x may be any whole number.

9.   (a)   Given $(a + b)(c + d)$ and applying the distributive property twice, we have:
           $$a(c + d) + b(c + d)$$
           $$= ac + ad + bc + bd$$

     (b) $3 \cdot x + 3 \cdot y + 3 \cdot 5 = 3x + 3y + 15$

     (c) $\square \cdot \triangle + \square \cdot \circ$

     (d) $x(x + y + z) + y(x + y + z)$
           $= xx + xy + xz + yx + yy + yz$
           $= xx + xy + xy + xz + yy + yz$
           $= x^2 + 2xy + xz + y^2 + yz$

10. (a)   Using the order of operations, $2 \cdot 3 + 5 = 6 + 5 = 11.$

     (b) $2(3 + 5) = 2 \cdot 3 + 2 \cdot 5 = 6 + 10 = 16.$

     (c) $2 \cdot 3 + 2 \cdot 5 = 6 + 10 = 16.$

     (d) $3 + 10 = 13.$

11. (a) $4 + (3 \times 2) = 14$ (Parentheses are unneeded if the order of operations is observed.)

     (b) $(9 \div 3) + 1 = 4$ (Parentheses unneeded)

     (c) $(5 + 4 + 9) \div 3 = 6$

11. (d) $(3 + 6 - 2) \div 1 = 7$ (Parentheses unneeded)

12. $a(b + c + d) = a[[(b + c) + d] = a(b + c) + ad = ab + ac + ad.$

13. (a)   True (associative property of multiplication).

    (b)   False; a misstatement of the distributive property.

    (c)   False; a misstatement of the distributive property.

    (d)   False; a misstatement of the distributive property.

14. $(m + n)(x + y) = m(x + y) + n(x + y) = mx + my + nx + ny.$ This is the product obtained with the FOIL method.

15. (a) $18 \div 3 = \boxed{6}$ (b) $\boxed{0} \div 76 = 0$

    (c) $28 \div \boxed{4} = 7$

16. (a)

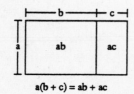

    $a(b + c) = ab + ac$

    (b)

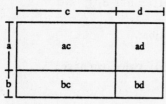

    $(a + b)(c + d) = ac + ad + bc + bd$

17. (a) $40 = 8 \cdot 5$ (b) $326 = 2 \cdot x$

    (c) $48 = 16 \cdot x$ (d) $x = 5 \cdot 17$

18. (*i*)   The original number is returned.   (*ii*)   Yes.

    (*iii*) Multiplication by 2 and division by 2 essentially cancel. Addition of 2 and then division by 2 leaves a number 1 more than the original, which is then returned by subtracting 1.

19. (a) $(5 \otimes 2) \oplus 6 = 16$)   (b) $(5 \oplus 3) \otimes 5 = 40$

    (c) $(15 \oslash 3) \ominus 4 = 1$ (where $\oslash$ is $\div$ in the circle)   (d) $(6 \oslash 3) \otimes (5 \ominus 3) = 4$

20. (a) $2 \div 1 \neq 1 \div 2$

    (b) $(8 \div 4) \div 2 \neq 8 \div (4 \div 2)$

    (c) $8 \div (2 + 2) \neq (8 \div 2) + (8 \div 2)$

    (d) $3 \div 4 \notin W.$

21. $\$160 \div 5$ months $= \$32$ per month.

22. $17 \div 7 = 2$ whole sandwiches for each person. $17 - 2 \cdot 7 = 3$ sandwiches that were left over.

23. A log (of any length) cut into ten pieces means nine cuts. Nine cuts at 1 minute per cut = 9 minutes.

24. (a) Look for all possible combinations of numbers that will make the equation true:

□	△
0	34
1	26
2	18
3	10
4	2

(b) Using the proper order of operations, $\triangle = 64 + 2 = 66$.

25. Sequentially divide 36 by all whole factors: We find 1 and 36, 2 and 18, 3 and 12, 4 and 9, and 6 and 6.

26. There are $4 \cdot 3 = 12$ different possible color schemes.

27. Since Tony has 6 ways to continue after each of the 5 ways to the park, his total choices are $5 \cdot 6 = 30$.

28. Since $8 \cdot 9 = 72$ players, then $72 \div 6 = 12$ new teams.

29. Division is multiplication by the reciprocal of the divisor.

30. Arbitrarily, let a = 4 and b = 5. Then $3(4 \cdot 5) = 3(20) = 60$. Sue's technique (a misstatement of the distributive property) would result in $3(4) \cdot 3(5) = 12 \cdot 15 = 180$. She is inserting an additional factor of 3.

31. (a) Yes. The system is closed because the result of any operation is in the set S.

(b) Yes. It is commutative because $a \odot b = b \odot a$, $a \odot c = c \odot a$, and $b \odot c = c \odot b$.

(c) Yes. The identity is *a* because $a \odot a = a$, $a \odot b = b$, and $a \odot c = c$.

(d) Yes. For example, $(a \odot b) \odot c = a \odot (b \odot c)$ ·

32. (a) $28 \div 5 = 5.6$; $5 \cdot 5 = 25$; $28 - 25 = 3$, the remainder.

(b) $32 \div 10 = 3.2$; $10 \cdot 3 = 30$; $32 - 30 = 2$, the remainder.

(c) $29 \div 3 = 9.\bar{6}$; $3 \cdot 9 = 27$; $29 - 27 = 2$, the remainder.

(d) $41 \div 7 = 5.\overline{857142}$; $7 \cdot 5 = 35$; $41 - 35 = 6$, the remainder.

(e) $49,382 \div 14 = 3527.285714$; $14 \cdot 3527 = 49,378$; $49,382 - 49,382 = 4$, the remainder.

33. (a)
$3 = 1 + 9 - 7$
$4 = 1^7 + \sqrt{9}$
$5 = 7 - \sqrt{9} + 1$
$6 = 7 - 1^9$
$7 = 7 \cdot 1^9$
$8 = 7 + 1^9$
$9 = 1^7 \cdot 9$
$10 = 1^7 + 9$
$11 = 7 + 1 + \sqrt{9}$

$12 = 19 - 7$
$13 = 91 \div 7$
$14 = 7(\sqrt{9} - 1)$
$15 = 7 + 9 - 1$
$16 = (7 + 9) \cdot 1$
$17 = 7 + 9 + 1$
$18 = \sqrt{9}(7 - 1)$
$20 = 7\sqrt{9} - 1$

34. Egyptian: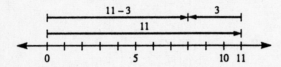
     Roman: LXXV
     Babylonian: ▼ ∠▼▼▼▼▼

35. $35,206 = 3 \cdot 10^4 + 5 \cdot 10^3 + 2 \cdot 10^2 + 0 \cdot 10^1 + 6 \cdot 1$

36. $\{1, 2\}: 1 + 2 = 3 \notin \{1, 2\}.$

37. Subtraction is not commutative. For example, $3 - 2 \neq 2 - 3.$

38.

```
            |--------11 - 3-------->|<----3---->|
            |                       |           |
            |----------11----------------------->|
      <--+---+---+---+---+---+---+---+---+---+---+--->
         0               5                 10  11
```

Problem Set 3-4

1. (a)   Scratch   Conventional
          ^{1}3 ^{2}7 ^{1}8 9   1   2   1
           $\not{9}_3$ $\not{2}_1$ $\not{9}_8$ $\not{6}_5$ 3   7   8   9
          + 6   8 $\not{4}_2$ 3   9   2   9   6
          ‾‾‾‾‾‾‾‾‾‾‾‾‾‾‾‾‾‾   + 6   8   4   3
           1   9   9   2   8   ‾‾‾‾‾‾‾‾‾‾‾‾‾‾‾‾
                                                     1   9   9   2   8

     Estimating, by rounding to the nearest thousand, $4000 + 9000 + 7000 = 20,000$, so the answers are
     reasonable.

    (b)   Scratch   Conventional
          ^{1}5 ^{2}2 4   1   2
           3   2 $\not{6}_2$ 5   2   4
           $\not{5}_4$ $\not{6}_2$ 7   3   2   8
          + 1   3 $\not{5}_4$ 5   6   7
          ‾‾‾‾‾‾‾‾‾‾‾‾   + 1   3   5
           1   5   5   4   ‾‾‾‾‾‾‾‾‾‾‾‾
                                                     1   5   5   4

     Estimating, by rounding to the nearest hundred, $500 + 300 + 600 + 100 = 1500$, so the answers are
     reasonable.

2. The "scratch marks" represent the conventional "carries."

3. The columns separate place value and show that $7 + 8 = 15$ and $20 + 60 = 80$. Finally, $15 + 80 = 95$.

4. (a)   9 8 1   (b)   2 0 2 5
          +4 2 1   1 1 9 6
          ‾‾‾‾‾‾‾‾   + 3 1 4 8
           1 4 0 2   ‾‾‾‾‾‾‾‾‾‾
                                                6 3 6 9

    (c)   1 0 6 9   (d)   2 9 1
           2 0 9 4   4 5 1
           9 5 4 6   + 5 8 4
           9 0 0 3   ‾‾‾‾‾‾‾‾
          +7 0 6 4   1 3 2 6
          ‾‾‾‾‾‾‾‾‾‾
           2 8 7 7 6
```
```

5.   (a)
```
  8 7 6 9 3
- 4 6 4 1 4
-----------
  4 1 2 7 9
```
     (b)
```
  8 1 3 5
- 4 6 8 2
---------
  3 4 5 3
```

   (c)
```
  3 8 3
- 1 5 9
-------
  2 2 4
```
     (d)
```
  1 3 2 9 6
-   8 3 0 9
-----------
    4 9 8 7
```

6.   (a)
```
  [7][6][2]
+ [8][5][3]
-----------
  1 6 1 5
```
     (b)
```
  [2][6][7]
+ [3][5][8]
-----------
    6 2 5
```

7.   (a)
```
  [8][7][6]
- [2][3][5]
-----------
    6 4 1
```
     (b)
```
  [6][2][3]
- [5][8][7]
-----------
      3 6
```

8. $125 + 137 + 238 = 500$ books were added. Thus there were $15,282 + 500 = 15,782$ at year's end.

9.   (a)   Each term of the sequence is found by adding 5 to the preceding term; thus the next three are: $29 + 5 = \underline{34}$; $34 + 5 = \underline{39}$; $39 + 5 = \underline{44}$.

     (b)   Each term of the sequence is found by subtracting 3 from the preceding term; thus the next three are: $85 - 3 = \underline{82}$; $82 - 3 = \underline{79}$; and $79 - 3 = \underline{76}$.

10.   Marie spends $25 + 15 + 17 = 57¢$. $87 - 57 = 30¢$ left.

11.   By dinner time Tom had consumed $90 + 120 + 119 + 185 + 110 + 570 = 1194$ calories. Subtracting from 1500: $1500 - 1194 = 306$. Tom may have steak or salad, but not both.

12. $170 - 115 = 55$ pounds; this is Molly's weight.
$115 - 65 = 50$ pounds; this is Karly's weight.
65 pounds is Samantha's weight.

13.   Wally's income was $150 + 54 + 260 = \$464$. His expenses were $22 + 60 + 15 + 58 + 185 = \$340$. Wally's savings were $464 - 340 = \$124$.

14.
```
  [3][4][2][8]
+ [5][6][3][1]
-------------
  9 0 5 9
```

15.   (a)   (i)   Clustering can be used when a group of numbers cluster around a common value. In case (i), the numbers are at wide variance, so clustering would not be a good strategy.

         (ii)   These numbers cluster around 500, so the strategy would be a good one.

     (b)   (i)   Case (i): Total value of lead digits is $1000 + 3000 = 3000$. $64 + 445$ is about 500. $474 + 467$ is about 900. The estimate is about $3000 + 500 + 900 = 4400$. (The exact sum is 4450.)

           Case (ii): Total value of lead digits is $400 + 400 + 500 + 500 + 500 = 2300$. $83 + 28$ is about 100. $75 + 30$ is about 100. 3 may be disregarded. The estimate is about $2300 + 100 + 100 = 2500$. (The exact sum is 2519.)

15. (b) (*ii*) Case (*i*): 64 + 2445 is about 2500. 1467 + 474 is about 1900. The estimate is about 2500 + 1900 = 4400.

   Case (*ii*): 503 is about 500. 528 + 475 is about 1000. 530 + 483 is about 1000. The estimate is about 500 + 1000 + 1000 = 2500.

   (*iii*) Case (*i*): 474 rounds to 500; 1467 rounds to 1500; 64 rounds to 100; 2445 rounds to 2400. The estimate is 500 + 1500 + 100 + 2400 = 4500.

   Case (*ii*): 483 rounds to 500; 475 rounds to 500; 530 rounds to 500; 503 rounds to 500; 528 rounds to 500. The estimate is 5·500 = 2500.

16. Her estimate is too high. 38 + 74 is about 100; 92 + 17 is about 100. If we add 100 + 100 + 130, we get an estimate of about 330 (the exact sum is 351).

17. (a) 2 years is 104 weeks; 4 months is about 16 weeks; 9 days is about 1 week. Lewis and Clark spent about 104 + 16 + 1 = 121 weeks in the Northwest.

   (b) $1126 \div 365$ is slightly over 3 years.

   (c) There are 365 days per year·24 hours per day·60 minutes per hour·60 seconds per minute = 31,536,000 seconds per year.

   (d) There are 365·24·60 = 525,600 minutes per year. If your average pulse is 72, your heart will beat 72·525,600 = 37,843,200 times per year.

18.

Hawks	15	32	40	33	120
Warriors	20	25	47	39	131

19. Algorithms are step-by-step systematic procedures for performing operations. They are taught to give students the tools necessary for solving problems in their disciplines.

20. The lead digits sum only to their respective place values. Smaller place values are ignored.

21. Answers may vary. One situation might lie in estimating your time of arrival from an automobile trip.

22. (a) (*i*)
```
    6 8 7
  + 5 4 9
  ───────
      1 6
    1 2
  1 1
  ───────
  1 2 3 6
```
   (*ii*)
```
    3 5 9
  + 6 7 3
  ───────
      1 2
    1 2
    9
  ───────
  1 0 3 2
```

   (b) Placing partial sums under their addends maintains place value.

23. Easier to keep partial sums in proper order; time-consuming.

24. (a) The tens digit was not carried.

   (b) Partial sums are not in the correct place value position.

   (c) The units minuend is subtracted from the subtrahend; thus borrowing is not accomplished.

   (d) 1 should have been borrowed from the 5 in the minuend's ten position.

25. (a)   (*i*) $93 + 39 = 132$; $132 + 231 = 363$, which is a palindrome.

    (*ii*) $588 + 885 = 1473$; $1473 + 3741 = 5214$; $5214 + 4125 = 9339$, which is a palindrome.

    (*iii*) $2003 + 3002 = 5005$, which is a palindrome.

    (b)   569,327

26. We want to work around $700 + 300$, since that sum is the closest to the 1111 for which we are trying:

    0 0 0
    7 7 0
    0 0 0
    3 3 0
    0 1 1
    ‾‾‾‾‾
    1 1 1 1

27. Trial and error (preferably with a calculator) will yield $8 + 8 + 8 + 88 + 888 = 1000$. The starting point would be 888, since that is close to but not over 1000; the other values come with the remaining five 8's.

28. (a)

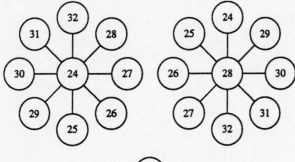

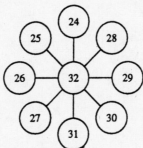

    (b)   Three (24, 28, or 32).

29. It appears that the second number was being entered twice: $8 + 6 + 6 = 20$; $5 + 4 + 4 = 13$; $15 - 3 - 3 = 9$.

30. (a)   Each sums to 34.   (b)   The sum is 34.

    (c)   The sum is 34.

    (d)   Yes. All rows, columns, and diagonals still total the same number (78).

    (e)   Yes. All rows, columns, and diagonals still total the same number (1).

31. $5 \cdot 10^3 + 2 \cdot 10^2 + 8 \cdot 10^1 + 0 \cdot 1$

32. Answers may vary: $3 + (4 + 5) = (3 + 4) + 5$ is one example.

33.

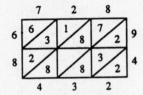

34. $\overline{M}$ indicates $1000 \cdot 1000$, so $\overline{M}CDX = 1,000,410$.

35.   (a) $ax + a = a(x + 1)$

       (b) $3(x + y) + a(x + y) = (3 + a)(x + y)$

36.   5 shirts with each of 3 pants is $3 \cdot 5 = 15$ combinations.

Problem Set 3-5

1.   (a)   (i)   Conventional

$$
\begin{array}{r}
7\ 2\ 8 \\
\times\quad 9\ 4 \\
\hline
2\ 9\ 1\ 2 \\
6\ 5\ 5\ 2 \\
\hline
6\ 8\ 4\ 3\ 2
\end{array}
$$

       (ii)   Lattice

       (b)   (i)   Conventional

$$
\begin{array}{r}
3\ 0\ 6 \\
\times\quad 2\ 4 \\
\hline
1\ 2\ 2\ 4 \\
6\ 1\ 2 \\
\hline
7\ 3\ 4\ 4
\end{array}
$$

       (ii)   Lattice

2.   Diagonals separate place values as placement does in the conventional algorithm.

3.   (a)   Start with multiplication of 4 _ 6 by 3. The _ must be 2, since we have carried 1 from $3 \cdot 6$, and only $3 \cdot 2 + 1 = 7$. Similar reasoning gives:

$$
\begin{array}{r}
4\ \underline{2}\ 6 \\
\times\ \ 7\ 8\ 3 \\
\hline
1\ \underline{2}\ 7\ 8 \\
3\ 4\ 0\ 8 \\
\underline{2}\ 9\ 8\ 2\ \ \ \ \\
\hline
3\ 3\ 3\ 5\ \underline{5}\ 8
\end{array}
$$

     (b)

$$
\begin{array}{r}
3\ 2\ 7 \\
\times\ \ 9\ \underline{4}\ 1 \\
\hline
3\ 2\ 7 \\
1\ \underline{3}\ 0\ 8 \\
\underline{2}\ 9\ \underline{4}\ 3\ \ \ \ \\
\hline
3\ 0\ \underline{7}\ \underline{7}\ 0\ 7
\end{array}
$$

4.   (a)   Answers may vary. Assume one shower, six toilet flushes, three face/hand washings, five drinks, two teeth brushings, three dish washes, and two cookings (we'll have cold cereal for breakfast). Then $1 \cdot 75 + 6 \cdot 22 + 3 \cdot 7 + 5 \cdot 1 + 2 \cdot 1 + 3 \cdot 30 + 2 \cdot 18 = 361$ liters.

     (b)   The hypothetical person in (a) uses more water than average.

     (c)   About $215{,}000{,}000 \cdot 200 = 43{,}000{,}000{,}000$ liters per day.

5.   (a)   There are $7 + 12 = 19$ factors of 5, so $5^7 \cdot 5^{12} = 5^{7+12} = 5^{19}$.

     (b) $6^{10} \cdot 6^2 \cdot 6^3 = 6^{10+2+3} = 6^{15}$

     (c) $10^{296} \cdot 10^{17} = 10^{296+17} = 10^{313}$

     (d) $2^7 \cdot 10^5 \cdot 5^7 = 2^7 \cdot 5^7 \cdot 10^5 = (2 \cdot 5)^7 \cdot 10^5 = 10^7 \cdot 10^5 = 10^{7+5} = 10^{12}$

6.   (a) 2^{100} is greater. $2^{80} + 2^{80} = 2^{80}(1 + 1) = 2 \cdot 2^{80} = 2^{81}$

     (b) 2^{102} is greatest. $2^{101} = 2 \cdot 2^{100}$; $3 \cdot 2^{100} = 3 \cdot 2^{100}$; and $2^{102} = 2^2 \cdot 2^{100}$

7.   (a)

$$6 \cdot 23 = 6 \cdot (20 + 3) = 6 \cdot 20 + 6 \cdot 3$$

7. (b)

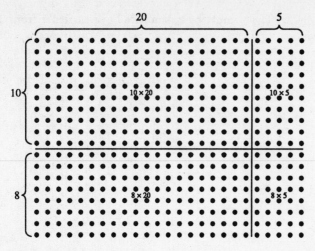

$$18 \cdot 25 = (20 + 5) \cdot (10 + 8) = 20 \cdot 10 + 20 \cdot 8 + 5 \cdot 10 + 5 \cdot 8$$

8. (a)
```
        4 7 6
    ×   2 9 3
    ─────────
      1 4 2 8
    4 2 8
    9 5 2
    ─────────
  1 3 9 4 6 8
```

(b) Placement still indicates place values.

(c)
```
      3 6 3
    ×   8 4
    ─────────
    2 9 0 4   │ (8·363)
    1 4 5 2   │ (4·363)
    ─────────
  3 0 4 9 2
```

9.
```
  →  1 7  ×      6 3
        8      1 2 6
        4      2 5 2
        2      5 0 4
  →     1    1 0 0 8      and 63 + 1008 = 1071
```

10. (a) $300 \div 14 = 21$ with a remainder of 6. We can discard the remainder, since we are looking only for a whole number. Thus $14 \cdot 21 = 294 < 300$; $n = 21$.

(b) $7459 \div 21 = 355$ with a remainder of 4. Thus $21 \cdot 355 = 7455 \leq 7459$; $n = 355$.

(c) $2134 \div 7 = 304$ with a remainder of 6. Thus $7 \cdot 304 = 2128 \leq 2134$; $n = 304$.

(d) $79,485 \div 483 = 164$ with a remainder of 273. Thus $483 \cdot 164 = 79,212 < 79,485$; $n = 164$.

11. (a) $300 \div 14 = 21$ plus a remainder. To find the least number greater than 300 we round up; $n = 22$.

(b) $4369 \div 23 = 189$ plus a remainder; $n = 190$.

(c) $782 \div 183 = 6$ plus a remainder; $n = 7$.

(d) $8654 \div 222 = 38$ plus a remainder; $n = 39$.

12. (a) $15 \cdot 12 = (10 + 5) \cdot 12 = 10 \cdot 12 + 5 \cdot 12 = 120 + 60 = 180$.

12.   (b) $14 \cdot 102 = 14 \cdot (100 + 2) = 14 \cdot 100 + 14 \cdot 2 = 1400 + 28 = 1428.$

     (c) $30 \cdot 99 = 30 \cdot (100 - 1) = 30 \cdot 100 - 30 \cdot 1 = 3000 - 30 = 2970.$

13.   Use division to reverse multiplication and subtraction to reverse addition. We thus find:

a	b	a·b	a + b
6 7	5 6	3 7 5 2	1 2 3
3 2	7 8	2 4 9 6	1 1 0
1 5	1 8	2 7 0	3 3

14.   (a) $3 \cdot 444 = 1332$ calories.

     (b)   Jane: $2 \cdot 462 = 924$ calories.
            Carolyn: $3 \cdot 198 = 594$ calories.
            Jane burned more, by $924 - 594 = 330$ calories.

     (c)   Lyle: $3 \cdot 708 = 2124$ calories.
            Maurice: $5 \cdot 444 = 2220$ calories.
            Maurice burned more, by $2220 - 2124 = 96$ calories.

15. $2 \cdot 666 = 1332$ calories per day expended in swimming.
      $1500 - 1332 = 168$ calories per day increased intake.
      $168 \cdot 14 = 2352$ excess calories consumed in the 14 days. Since $2352 < 3500$, he gained less than 1 pound.

16. $24 \cdot 30 = \$720$ total premiums. $720 \div 12 = \$60$ per month.

17.   (a)   (*i*)   <u>Repeated Subtraction</u>

```
8 | 6 2 3
    5 6 0      7 0  eights
    ─────
      6 3
      5 6        7  eights
      ───      ───
        7      7 7  remainder 7
```

        (*ii*)   <u>Familiar</u>

```
      7 7      remainder 7
  8 | 6 2 3
      5 6
      ───
        6 3
        5 6
        ───
          7
```

     (b)   (*i*)   <u>Repeated Subtraction</u>

```
3 6 | 2 9 8
      2 8 8      8  36's
      ─────    ───
        1 0      8  remainder 10
```

        (*ii*)   <u>Familiar</u>

```
            8    remainder 10
  3 6 | 2 9 8
        2 8 8
        ─────
          1 0
```

17. (c)   (i)   Repeated Subtraction

$$
\begin{array}{r}
3\ 9\ 1\ \overline{\big)\ 4\ 0\ 0\ 1} \\
3\ 9\ 1\ 0 \\
\hline
9\ 1
\end{array}
\quad
\begin{array}{l}
10 \\
\hline
10
\end{array}
\quad
\begin{array}{l}
391\text{'s} \\
\text{remainder } 91
\end{array}
$$

(ii)   Familiar

$$
\begin{array}{r}
1\ 0 \qquad \text{remainder } 91 \\
3\ 9\ 1\ \overline{\big)\ 4\ 0\ 0\ 1} \\
3\ 9\ 1 \\
\hline
9\ 1
\end{array}
$$

18. (a) $3\overline{\big)\ 8\ 7\ 6}$

(b) $8\overline{\big)\ 3\ 6\ 7}$

19. (a) $450 \cdot 24$ months $= \$10,800$; $10,800 + 1500 = \$12,300$ total price if paid monthly.
Thus the monthly payment option is the more expensive.

(b) $12,300 - 8600 = \$3700$ more expensive if paid monthly.

20. $64 \cdot 1024 = 65,536$ bits.

21. Reversing the operation, $300 \div 10 = 30$. Then $30 \div 10 = 3$, the correct answer.

22. Income: $245 \cdot 2 = \$490$ from washing cars $+ \$490$ in school matching funds $= \$960$.
Expenses: $350 \cdot 0.72 = \$252$ bus rent $+ 2 \cdot 20 \cdot 5 = \$200$ dorm fees $+ 20 \cdot 28 = \$560$ meals is $\$1012$.
Since total expected expenses are greater than income, the band has not yet raised enough money.
$\$1012 - 980 = \$32$ still needed; at $\$2$ per car plus $\$2$ matching from the school, $32 \div 4 = 8$ cars.

23. When given an input, perform operations as noted on the function machines. When given an output, reverse
the operations. Thus:

In	Out
2	11
4	15
0	7
6	19
12	31

24. (a)   Choose 3, 6, and 7. Possible numbers are 36, 37, 67, 63, 73, and 76.

(b)   Sum $= 352$ (c)   Sum $= 16$

(d) $352 \div 16 = 22$

(e)   Numbers may vary. One set is 4, 5, and 9, from which 45, 49, 59, 54, 94, and 95 may be formed.
Sum of the two-digit numbers is 396; sum of the one-digit numbers is 18. $396 \div 18 = 22$.

(f)   Yes. Let the numbers be represented by a, b, and c. Then the possible two-digit numbers are:
$10a + b$, $10a + c$, $10b + c$, $10b + a$, $10c + a$, and $10c + b$.
Their sum is: $a(10 + 10 + 1 + 1) + b(10 + 10 + 1 + 1) + c(10 + 10 + 1 + 1)$
$= 22a + 22b + 22c = 22(a + b + c)$. Dividing by $(a + b + c)$ always gives 22.

25. (a)   Examples may vary. One such is: $36 \cdot 84 = 3024$; $63 \cdot 48 = 3024$.

25. (b)   Let the digits of the two numbers be *a, b, c,* and *d.* Then if ab·cd = ba·dc, a·c must equal b·d. Thus in the example above, 3·8 = 6·4 = 24.

26.   Pages with 1 digit: 9.
Pages with 2 digits: 10-19, 20-29, ... , 90-99; 90 pages·2 digits = 180 digits.
Pages with 3 digits: 100-109, 110-119, ... , 190-199, 200-299, ... , 990-999; 900 pages·3 digits = 2700 pages.
9 + 180 + 2700 = 2889; there are 2981 − 2889 = 92 digits remaining.
92 digits ÷ 4 digits per number = 23 pages. So there are 9 + 90 + 900 + 23 = 1022 pages in the book.

27. (a)   Numbers may vary; pick 7. 2·7 = 14; 14·3 = 42; 42 + 24 = 66; 66 ÷ 6 = 11; 11 − 7 = 4.

   (b)   Let *n* be the chosen number. Then the operations result in: $[3(2n) + 24] \div 6 - n$ = (6n + 24) ÷ 6 − n = n + 4 − n = 4. Thus, regardless of the value of *n.* the result will always be 4.

28.   Molly reads at the rate of 160 pages ÷ 4 hours = 40 pages per hour. She will finish the book in 200 ÷ 4 = 5 hours. Karly reads at the rate of 100 pages ÷ 4 hours = 25 pages per hour. She will finish the book in 200 ÷ 25 = 8 hours, 3 hours more than for Molly.

29.   Sami's exact collections are 12·38 = $456, so her estimate is high; she probably multiplied 15·40 for her $600 guess. She would have had a closer estimate if she'd rounded 12 to 10 and 38 to 40, or 10·40 = $400.

30. (a)   Digits were not carried; place value was not observed.

   (b)   5 was multiplied by 6 to get 30; the 3 was carried, but then 3 was multiplied by 2 instead of 6 again.

   (c)   4 was multiplied by 6, but then 6 and 3 were added instead of being multiplied.

   (d)   When 1 was brought down, the quotient of 0 was not recorded.

31.   The cat must make up 100 feet with a speed differential of 30 − 20 = 10 ft/sec. 100 ft ÷ 10 ft/sec = 10 seconds to catch the dog.

32.   Let *n* be the number of weeks. Then:
356 + 30n = 980
30n = 624
n = 20.8, so it will take Mira about 21 more weeks to buy the computer.

33.   1672 students ÷ 29 students per bus = 57.7 buses. 58 buses will be needed, but not all will be full.

34.   Jerry used 40 − 4 = 36 L; $\frac{396\ km}{36\ liters}$ = 11 km/L.

35.   The two digits of the number are repeated in the product; i.e., 25·101 = 2525. If we let the two digits be designated by *a* and *b,* then:

```
    1 0 1
×     a b
  ─────────
    b 0 b
  a 0 a
  ─────────
  a b a b
```
   Note that no partial products are greater than 9, so no carrying is involved.

36. (a)   (*i*)   She saves (200 + 80 + 20 + 100) − 330 = $70.

   (*ii*)   She saves (25 + 0 + 5 + 10) − 30 = $10.

   (b) $330 cost to buy ÷ $30 cost per trip to rent = 11 trips to break even. She will save on the 12th trip and beyond.

37. (a) (*i*) $27 \times 198 = 5346$; all digits are used.   (*ii*) $48 \times 159 = 7632$; all digits are used.

(*iii*) $39 \times 186 = 7254$; all digits are used.

(b)   Use trial and error with digits not in the given factor:

(*i*) $1963 \times 4 = 7852$; all digits are used.   (*ii*) $483 \times 12 = 5796$; all digits are used.

(*iii*) $297 \times 18 = 5346$; all digits are used.

(c)   1. Any factor times 1 would give that factor in return; it would thus be used more than once.

38. (a)   For the greatest product, we need the largest multiplicands which can be formed using the four

$$\begin{array}{r} \boxed{7}\ \boxed{6}\ \boxed{3} \\ \times \quad \boxed{8} \end{array}$$

numbers. 8×763 is greater than 7×863 because $8 \times 700 = 7 \times 800$, but 8×63 is greater than 7×63.

(b)   For the least product, we need the smallest multiplicands which can be formed using the four

$$\begin{array}{r} \boxed{6}\ \boxed{7}\ \boxed{8} \\ \times \quad \boxed{3} \end{array}$$

numbers. 3×678 is smaller than 6×378 because $3 \times 600 = 6 \times 300$, but 3×78 is smaller than 6×78.

39. (a)   For the greatest product, we need the largest multiplicands which can be formed using the five

$$\begin{array}{r} \boxed{7}\ \boxed{6}\ \boxed{2} \\ \times \quad \boxed{8}\ \boxed{3} \end{array}$$

numbers. 83×762 is greater than 82×763 because $80 \times 700 = 70 \times 800$, but 3×62 is greater than 2×63

(b)   For the least product, we need the smallest multiplicands which can be formed using the five

$$\begin{array}{r} \boxed{3}\ \boxed{7}\ \boxed{8} \\ \times \quad \boxed{2}\ \boxed{6} \end{array}$$

numbers. 26×378 is smaller than 36×278 because $20 \times 300 = 30 \times 200$, but 26×78 is smaller than 36×78.

40. $700 \cdot 4 = 2800$ Quarter Pounders per cow.
$21,000,000,000 \div 2800 = 7,500,000$ cows for 21 billion Quarter Pounders.

41. (a) $3 \cdot 37 = 111$, the first partial product. $40 \cdot 37 = 1480$, the second partial product. We have:

$$\begin{array}{r} 3\ 7 \\ \times \quad 4\ 3 \\ \hline 1\ 1\ 1 \\ 1\ 4\ 8\ 0 \\ \hline 1\ 5\ 9\ 1 \end{array}$$

(b) $558 \div 6 = 93$, so the missing multiplicand is 93. $30 \times 93 = 2790$, the 2nd partial product. We have:

$$\begin{array}{r} 9\ 3 \\ \times \quad 3\ 6 \\ \hline 5\ 5\ 8 \\ 2\ 7\ 9\ 0 \\ \hline 3\ 3\ 4\ 8 \end{array}$$

(c)   The only quotient of 12 which could leave a remainder of 3 is 9; $9 \times 1 = 9$. Thus:

$$\begin{array}{r} 1\ 3 \\ 9\overline{)1\ 2\ 3} \\ 9 \\ \hline 3\ 3 \\ 2\ 7 \\ \hline 6 \end{array}$$

42. (a) $1 \times 1 = 1$
            $11 \times 11 = 121$
            $111 \times 111 = 12321$
            $1111 \times 1111 = 1234321$
            Without multiplying, the next product should be 123454321.

     (b) $99 \times 99 = 9801$
            $999 \times 999 = 998001$
            $9999 \times 9999 = 99980001$
            Without multiplying, the next product should be 9999800001

43. \$1 per second·60 seconds = \$60 per minute.
     \$60 per minute·60 minutes = \$3600 per hour.
     \$3600 per hour·24 hours = \$86,400 per day.
     \$86,400 per day·7 days = \$604,800 per week.
     \$86,400 per day·30 days = \$2,595,000 per month (assuming a 30-day month).
     \$86,400 per day·365 days = \$31,536,000 per year (assuming a non-leap year).
     \$31,536,000·20 = \$630,720,000 in 20 years.

44. The number 375,000 is midway between 250,000 and 1,000,000. If you ask, "Is the number less than 375,000?", the yes or no answer gives you a new range. By continually narrowing the range in this manner, you will find that 19 questions are needed.

45. ꝯꝯꝯꝯꝯꝯꓵꓵꓵꓵꓵꓵꓵꓵ|||||

46. 300,260

47. Numbers may vary. One example is: $5 + 0 = 5 = 0 + 5$.

48. (a) $x(a + b + 2)$ (b) $(3 + x)(a + b)$

49. $59,260 - 52,281 = 6,979$ miles traveled.

50. There were $192 + 215 + 317 = 724$ people at the conference.

Problem Set 3-6

1. (a)   Remember that place values represent powers of 2; i.e.,
                $1 = 1 \cdot 2^0$
                $10 = 1 \cdot 2^1 + 0 \cdot 2^0$
                $100 = 1 \cdot 2^2 + 0 \cdot 2^1 + 0 \cdot 2^0$, etc. Thus the first 15 counting numbers are:
           $(1, 10, 11, 100, 101, 110, 111, 1000, 1001, 1010, 1011, 1100, 1101, 1110, \text{ and } 1111)_{two}.$

    (b) $(1, 2, 10, 11, 12, 20, 21, 22, 100, 101, 102, 110, 111, 112, 120)_{three}.$

    (c) $(1, 2, 3, 10, 11, 12, 13, 20, 21, 22, 23, 30, 31, 32, 33)_{four}.$

    (d) $(1, 2, 3, 4, 5, 6, 7, 10, 11, 12, 13, 14, 15, 16, 17)_{eight}.$

2. One digit is needed for each of the units; 20 digits (including zero) would be needed in base 20.

3. $2032_{four} = (2 \cdot 10^3 + 0 \cdot 10^2 + 3 \cdot 10 + 2)_{four}$

4. (a)   1 is the largest units digit; thus the largest three-digit number is 111_{two}

4. (b) 555_{six} (c) 999_{ten}

    (d) EEE_{twelve}

5. (a) $EE0_{twelve} = (11 \cdot 10^2 + 11 \cdot 10 + 0)_{twelve}.$
          Thus $EE0_{twelve} - 1 = (11 \cdot 10^2 + 10 \cdot 10 + 11)_{twelve} = ETE_{twelve}$, and
          $EE0_{twelve} + 1 = (11 \cdot 10^2 + 11 \cdot 10 + 1)_{twelve} = EE1.$

    (b) $100000_{two} - 1 = 11111_{two}$, and $100000_{two} + 1 = 100001_{two}$

    (c) $555_{six} - 1 = 554_{six}$, and $555_{six} + 1 = 1000_{six}$

    (d) $100_{seven} - 1 = 66_{seven}$, and $100_{seven} + 1 = 101_{seven}$

    (e) $1000_{five} - 1 = 444_{five}$, and $1000_{five} + 1 = 1001_{five}$

    (f) $110_{two} - 1 = 101_{two}$, and $110_{two} + 1 = 111_{two}$

6. (a)   4 is not a valid digit in base four; the numerals are 0, 1, 2, and 3.

    (b)   There are no numerals 6 or 7 in base five.

    (c)   There is no digit T in base three.

7. (a)   There are 3 groups of 125 in 432, with remainder 57.
          There are 2 groups of 25 in 57, with remainder 7.
          There is 1 group of 5 in 7, with remainder 2.
          Thus $432_{ten} = 3212_{five}$

    (b)   There is 1 group of 1728 in 1963, with remainder 235.
          There is 1 grouuup of 144 in 235, with remainder 91.
          There are 7 groups of 12 in 91, with remainder 7.
          Thus $1963_{ten} = 1177_{twelve}$

    (c)   There is 1 group of 256 in 404, with remainder 148.
          There are 2 groups of 64 in 148, with remainder 20.
          There is 1 group of 16 in 20, with remainder 4.
          There is 1 group of 4 in 4, with remainder 0.
          Thus $404_{ten} = 12110_{four}$

    (d)   There is 1 group of 32 in 37, with remainder 5.
          There are 0 groups of 16 in 5, with remainder 5.
          There are 0 groups of 8 in 5, with remainder 5.
          There is 1 group of 4 in 5, with remainder 1.
          There are 0 groups of 2 in 1, with remainder 1.
          Thus $32_{ten} = 100101_{two}$

    (e) $(4 \cdot 10^4 + 3 \cdot 10^2)_{ten} = 40300_{ten}$
          There is 1 group of 20736 in 40300, with remainder 19564.
          There are 11 groups of 1728 in 19564, with remainder 556.
          There are 3 groups of 144 in 556, with remainder 124.
          There are 10 groups of 12 in 124, with remainder 4.
          Thus $40300_{ten} = 1E3T4_{twelve}$

8. $42_{eight} = 4 \cdot 8 + 2 = 34_{ten}$
There is 1 group of 32 in 34, with remainder 2.
There are 0 groups of 16 in 2, with remainder 2.
There are 0 groups of 8 in 2, with remainder 2.
There are 0 groups of 4 in 2, with remainder 2.
There is 1 group of 2 in 2, with remainder 0.
Thus $42_{eight} = 34_{ten} = 100010_{two}$

9. (a) $432_{five} = 4 \cdot 5^2 + 3 \cdot 5 + 2 = 100 + 15 + 2 = 117_{ten}$

   (b) $101101_{two} = 1 \cdot 2^5 + 1 \cdot 2^3 + 1 \cdot 2^2 + 1 = 32 + 8 + 4 + 1 = 45_{ten}$

   (c) $92E_{twelve} = 9 \cdot 12^2 + 2 \cdot 12 + 11 = 1296 + 24 + 11 = 1331_{ten}$

   (d) $T0E_{twelve} = 10 \cdot 12^2 + 11 = 1440 + 11 = 1451_{ten}$

   (e) $111_{twelve} = 1 \cdot 12^2 + 1 \cdot 12 + 1 = 144 + 12 + 1 = 157_{ten}$

   (f) $346_{seven} = 3 \cdot 7^2 + 4 \cdot 7 + 6 = 147 + 28 + 6 = 181_{ten}$

10. $2 \cdot 25 + 4 \cdot 5 + 2 \cdot 1 = 72¢.$
There are 2 groups of 25 in 72, with remainder 22.
There are 4 groups of 5 in 22, with remainder 2.
Thus the fortune is $242_{five}¢$.

11. To give the fewest number of prizes, the dollar amount of each must be maximized. Thus $900 =:
   1 prize at $625 with $275 left over.
   2 prizes at $125 with $25 left over.
   1 prize at $25 with nothing left over; thus no $5 or $1 prizes awarded.

12. 3 quarters, with 22¢ left over; 4 nickels, with 2¢ left over; and 2 pennies.

13. (a) There are 8 groups of 7 days (1 week), with 2 days left over, so 58 days = 8 weeks and 2 days.

   (b) There are 4 groups of 12 months (1 year), with 6 months left over, so 54 months = 4 years and 6 months.

   (c) There is 1 group of 24 hours (1 day), with 5 hours left over, so 29 hours = 1 day and 5 hours.

   (d) There are 5 groups of 12 (5 feet), with 8 inches left over, so 68 inches = 5 feet 8 inches.

14. $Pencils_{twelve} = 11 \cdot 12^2 + 6 \cdot 12 + 6 = E66_{twelve}$. $Pencils_{ten} = 11 \cdot 144 + 6 \cdot 12 + 6 = 1662_{ten}$.

15. (a) There are 6 groups of 7 in 44, so b = 6.

   (b) There are 5 groups of 144 in 734, with remainder 14. There is 1 group of 12 in 14, so b = 1.

   (c) There must be 2 groups of b in 23, with remainder 5; thus $2b + 5 = 23 \Rightarrow 2b = 18 \Rightarrow b = 9$.
   Thus $23_{ten} = 25_{nine}$.

16. 75 minutes + 18 minutes + 45 seconds + 30 seconds = 93 minutes + 75 seconds
   = 93 minutes + 1 minute + 15 seconds = 1 hour + 33 minutes + 1 minutes + 15 seconds.
   George's meal took 1 hour 34 minutes 15 seconds of cooking time.

17. A minimum of four weights are needed to check from 1 through 15 ounces: one each of 8, 4, 2, and 1 ounce.
   For 32 ounces, the inspector would need one each of 16, 8 4, 2, and 1 ounce.

18. (a)   The minimum number of coins totaling 117 pennies is 4 quarters, 3 nickels, and 2 pennies.

(b)   2 quarters → 50 pennies; 4 nickels → 20 pennies; thus she will have $50 + 20 + 3 = 73$ pennies.

19. (a)

$$\begin{array}{r} 1 \\ 4\ 3 \\ +\ 2\ 3 \\ \hline 1\ 2\ 1_{five} \end{array}$$

Note that in the units column, $(3 + 3)_{five} = 11_{five}$; in the fives column, $(1 + 4 + 2)_{five} = 12_{five}$.

(b)

$$\begin{array}{r} 4\ 3 \\ -\ 2\ 3 \\ \hline 2\ 0_{five} \end{array}$$

We need no borrowing, since we are not subtracting any number from one smaller than itself.

(c)

$$\begin{array}{r} 1\ 1 \\ 4\ 3\ 2 \\ +\ \ 2\ 3 \\ \hline 1\ 0\ 1\ 0_{five} \end{array}$$

In the units column, $(2 + 3)_{five} = 10_{five}$; in the fives column $(1 + 3 + 2)_{five} = 11_{five}$; and in the 25's column $(1 + 4)_{five} = 10_{five}$.

(d)

$$\begin{array}{r} 3\ \ 12 \\ \cancel{4}\ \cancel{2} \\ -\ 2\ 3 \\ \hline 1\ 4_{five} \end{array}$$

10_{five} was borrowed from the fives column to make $(10 + 2)_{five} = 12_{five}$ in the units column; $(12 - 3)_{five} = 4_{five}$.

(e)

$$\begin{array}{r} 1 \\ 1\ 1\ 0 \\ +\ \ 1\ 1 \\ \hline 1\ 0\ 0\ 1_{two} \end{array}$$

In the twos (i.e., 10_{two}) column, $(1 + 1)_{two} = 10_{two}$. In the fours column, $(1 + 1)_{two} = 10_{two}$.

(f)

$$\begin{array}{r} 1\ \ \ 1 \\ \cancel{1}\cancel{0}\ \cancel{1}\cancel{0}\ 10 \\ \cancel{1}\ \cancel{0}\ \cancel{0}\ \cancel{0}\ 1 \\ -\ \ \ \ 1\ 1\ 1 \\ \hline 1\ 0\ 1\ 0_{two} \end{array}$$

We had to borrow 10_{two} from the 16's, eights, and fours columns in order to subtract $(10 - 1)_{two}$.   Further subtraction required no more borrowing.

20. (i)   Addition:

+	0	1	2	3	4	5	6	7
0	0	1	2	3	4	5	6	7
1	1	2	3	4	5	6	7	10
2	2	3	4	5	6	7	11	12
3	3	4	5	6	7	10	11	12
4	4	5	6	7	10	11	12	13
5	5	6	7	10	11	12	13	14
6	6	7	10	11	12	13	14	15
7	7	10	11	12	13	14	15	16

Base Eight

(*ii*)   Multiplication:

×	0	1	2	3	4	5	6	7
0	0	0	0	0	0	0	0	0
1	0	1	2	3	4	5	6	7
2	0	2	4	6	10	12	14	16
3	0	3	6	11	14	17	22	25
4	0	4	10	14	20	24	30	34
5	0	5	12	17	24	31	36	43
6	0	6	14	22	30	36	44	52
7	0	7	16	25	34	43	52	61

Base Eight

21. (a)   Note that in performing these calculations we are working with base 60. Thus if we carry forward we carry forward in sixties rather than in tens.

```
   1                1
   3 hours     36 minutes     58 seconds
 + 5 hours     56 minutes     27 seconds
  ─────────────────────────────────────────
   9 hours     33 minutes     25 seconds
```

(In each operation, we carry forward; e.g., 58 seconds + 27 seconds = 85 seconds; we put down 25 seconds and carry 60 seconds = 1 minute

(b)   Note that in performing these calculations we are working with base 60. Thus if we must borrow, we borrow 60 rather than 10 as we would in base 10.

```
                   95
   4                ⅗⅝               98
   ⅝ hours     ⅛⅝ minutes     ⅛⅝ seconds
 - 3 hours     56 minutes     58 seconds
  ─────────────────────────────────────────
   1 hour      39 minutes     40 seconds
```

(We first borrowed 60 seconds from 36 minutes, then borrowed 60 minutes from 5 hours)

22. (a)
```
   1              1
   1 quart     1 pint      1 cup
 +             1 pint      1 cup
  ──────────────────────────────────
   2 quarts    1 pint      0 cups
```

(b)
```
                  2
   1 quart                 1 cup
 -             1 pint      1 cup
  ──────────────────────────────────
               1 pint
```

(c)
```
                  6
   0              ⅞              5
   1 gallon     ⅜ quarts     1 cup
 -             4 quarts     2 cups
  ──────────────────────────────────
               2 quarts     3 cups, or 2 quarts, 1 pint, 1 cup.
```

23.   20 friends·2 cups each = 40 cups needed. There are 2 cups per pint·2 pints per quart·4 quarts per gallon, or 16 cups per gallon. 40 cups needed ÷ 16 cups per gallon = 2.5 gallons; she would have to buy 3 gallons to have enough.

24.

$$
\begin{array}{r}
3 \\
\cancel{3}_1\ \ 2 \\
1\ -\ \cancel{3}_0 \\
2\ \ \ 2 \\
\cancel{4}_3\ \ \cancel{3}_0 \\
\cancel{2}_0\ \ 3 \\
+\ \ 1\ \ \cancel{2}_0 \\
\hline
3\quad 1\quad 0_{five}
\end{array}
$$

25. In these operations, we are borrowing and carrying, respectively, in 12's:

(a)

	15	
3	$\cancel{5}$	18
$\cancel{4}$ gross	$\cancel{4}$ dozen	$\cancel{6}$ ones
−		
	5 dozen	9 ones
3 gross	10 dozen	9 ones

(b)

1	1	
2 gross	9 dozen	7 ones
+ 3 gross	5 dozen	9 ones
6 gross	3 dozen	4 ones

26. (a) If each student receives 1 cup, then there were:
  1 pint = 2 cups
  1 quart = 2 pints = 4 cups
  1 gallon = 4 quarts = 8 pints = 16 cups. There were 2 + 4 + 16 = 22 cups, or 22 students.

  (b) 31 students = 31 cups
  There is 1 group of 16 (1 gallon) in 31 cups, with 15 cups left over.
  There are 3 groups of 4 (3 quarts) in 15 cups, with 3 cups left over.
  There is 1 group of 2 (1 pint) in 3 cups, with 1 cup left over.
  Thus it was necessary to buy 1 gallon, 3 quarts, 1 pint, and 1 cup for the 31 students.

27. (a) $3 \cdot 20 + 10 = 70$ (b) $4 \cdot 20 + 7 = 87$

28. There is no digit 5 in base five.

29. (a) Work backwards to fill in the blanks. For example, in the units column, $(10 - 2)_{five} = 3_{five}$. Remember to borrow when working backward in the $(10)_{five}$ column. Thus:

$$
\begin{array}{r}
2\ \ 3\ \ \underline{0} \\
-\quad 2\ \ 2 \\
\hline
\underline{2}\ \ 0\ \ 3_{five}
\end{array}
$$

  (b) In the units column (working backward), $(1 + 2)_{three} = 10_{three}$. We would have had to borrow in the $(10)_{three}$ column; now $(1 + 2)_{three} = (10)_{three}$. Continuing to work backward:

$$
\begin{array}{r}
2\ \ 0\ \ 0\ \ 1\ \ 0 \\
-\quad 2\ \ \underline{0}\ \ 2\ \ 2 \\
\hline
1\ \ \underline{0}\ \ 2\ \ \underline{1}\ \ 1_{three}
\end{array}
$$

30. (a)

$$
\begin{array}{r}
1 \\
3\ \ 2 \\
\times\quad 4 \\
\hline
2\ \ 3\ \ 3_{five}
\end{array}
$$

  When we multiplied 2_{five} by 4_{five}, we obtained one 5 and three 1's, or 13_{five}. We put down the 3 and carried the 1. When we multiplied 3_{five} by 4_{five} and added 1_{five}, we obtained two 5's and three 1's, or 23_{five}. The procedure is the same as in base ten, except that we are carrying partial products in base five.

30. (b)

$$4 \overline{\smash{)}\begin{array}{c} 4_{five} \\ 3\ \ 2 \\ 3\ \ 1 \\ \hline 1 \end{array}}$$

Thus the quotient is 4_{five} with remainder 1.

(c)

$$\begin{array}{r} 4\ 3 \\ \times\ \ 2\ 3 \\ \hline 2\ 3\ 4 \\ 1\ 4\ 1 \\ \hline 2\ 1\ 4\ 4_{five} \end{array}$$

(d)

$$3 \overline{\smash{)}\begin{array}{c} 3\ \ 1_{five} \\ 1\ 4\ 3 \\ 1\ 4 \\ \hline 0\ 3 \\ 0\ 3 \\ \hline 0 \end{array}}$$

(e) $13_{eight} \cdot 5_{eight} = 67_{eight}$

(f) $67_{eight} \div 4_{eight} = 15_{eight}$ with remainder 3

(g) $10010_{two} \div 11_{two} = 110_{two}$

(h) $10110_{two} \cdot 101_{two} = 1101110_{two}$

31. (a)   The base must be nine, since in the units column $(3 + 8)_{nine} = 12_{nine}$.

(b)   The base must be four, since in the units column $(3 + 3)_{four} = 12_{four}$.

(c)   The base must be six, since in the units column $(2 \cdot 3)_{six} = 10_{six}$.

(d)   Any base greater than or equal to 2.

32. $323_{five} \cdot 42_{five} = 30221_{five}$.

33. If we let *a* be the base a and let *b* be the base b, then:
        $3a + 2 = 2b + 3$
        $3a - 2b = 1$
and the smallest numbers *a* and *b* for which this is true are a = 3 and b = 4. Thus $32_{three} = 23_{four}$.

34. Answers may vary; two examples are that we measure time in base 60 and we measure some volumes in bases two and four.

Chapter 3 Test

1.   (a) $\overline{\text{CDXLIV}} = 1000 \cdot \text{CD} + \text{XLIV} = 1000 \cdot 400 + 40 + 4 = 400{,}044$

(b) $4 \cdot 5^2 + 3 \cdot 5 + 2 = 117_{ten}$

(c) $11 \cdot 12^2 + 10 \cdot 12 + 0 = 1704_{ten}$

(d) $1 \cdot 2^3 + 0 \cdot 2^2 + 1 \cdot 2 + 1 = 11_{ten}$

1. (e) $4 \cdot 7^3 + 1 \cdot 7^2 + 3 \cdot 7 + 6 = 1448_{ten}$

2. (a)   CMXCIX

    (b)   ∩ ∩ ∩ ∩ ∩ ∩ ∩ ∩ IIIII

    (c) $\overset{\bullet}{\underset{\bullet\,\bullet\,\bullet}{\rule{1em}{0.4pt}}}$

    (d)   2 groups of 125 + 3 groups of 25 + 4 groups of 5 + 1 = 2341_{five}

    (e)   1 group of 1728 = 1000_{twelve}

    (f)   1 group of 16 + 1 group of 8 + 0 groups of 4 + 1 group of 2 + 1 = 11011_{two}

    (g)   1 group of 729 + 2 groups of 81 + 4 groups of 9 + 1 = 1241_{nine}

    (h) $13_{eight} = 11_{ten}$
           1 group of 8 + 0 groups of 4 + 1 group of 2 + 1 = 1011_{two}

3. (a) $3^{4+7+6} = 3^{17}$ (b) $2^{10+11} = 2^{21}$

    (c) $3^4(1 + 2) = 3 \cdot 3^4 = 3^5$ (d) $2^{80}(1 + 3) = 2^2 \cdot 2^{80} = 2^{82}$

4. (a)   Distributive property of multiplication over addition.

    (b)   Commutative property of addition.

    (c)   Identity property of multiplication.

    (d)   Distributive property of multiplication over addition.

    (e)   Commutative property of multiplication.

    (f)   Associative property of multiplication.

5. (a)   3 < 13 if and only if there exists a number k such that 3 + k = 13. If k = 10, then 3 + 10 = 13, and
           3 < 13.

    (b)   12 > 9 if and only if there exists a number k such that 13 − k = 9. If k = 3, then 12 − 3 = 9, and
           12 > 9.

6. $1000 \cdot 483 = 10^3(4 \cdot 10^2 + 8 \cdot 10^1 + 3 \cdot 1) = 4 \cdot 10^5 + 8 \cdot 10^4 + 3 \cdot 10^3$
    $= 4 \cdot 10^5 + 8 \cdot 10^4 + 3 \cdot 10^3 + 0 \cdot 10^2 + 0 \cdot 10^1 + 0 \cdot 1 = 483,000$

7. (a)   <u>Scratch</u>   <u>Traditional</u>

    ```
        1                                                  1
      3 1 6                                              3 1 6
     7₁1 2                                               7 1 2
   +  9₁1                                             +   9 1
   ─────────                                          ─────────
    1 1 1 9                                            1 1 1 9
    ```

    (b)   <u>Scratch</u>   <u>Traditional</u>

    ```
      3 1 6                                              3 1 6
      7 1 2                                              7 1 2
   + 9₇1 3                                             + 9 1 3
   ──────────                                          ──────────
    1 7 3 E_twelve                                      1 7 3 E_twelve
    ```

8.　(a)　60,074　　　　　　　　　　　　　　(b)　14150_{eight}

9.　(a)　<u>Repeated</u> <u>Subtraction</u>

$$9\ 1\ 2\ \overline{)\ 4\ 8\ 0\ 3}$$
$$\underline{4\ 5\ 6\ 0}\quad 5 - 912\text{'s}$$
$$2\ 4\ 3\quad \overline{5 - 912\text{'s}}\quad \Rightarrow 5,\ \text{remainder } 243$$

<u>Conventional</u>

$$\begin{array}{r}5 \\ 9\ 1\ 2\ \overline{)\ 4\ 8\ 0\ 3} \\ \underline{4\ 5\ 6\ 0} \\ 2\ 4\ 3\end{array}\quad \Rightarrow 5,\ \text{remainder } 243$$

　(b)　<u>Repeated</u> <u>Subtraction</u>

$$1\ 1\ \overline{)\ 1\ 0\ 1\ 1}$$
$$\underline{9\ 9\ 0}\quad 90 - 11\text{'s}$$
$$2\ 1$$
$$\underline{1\ 1}\quad 1 - 11$$
$$1\ 0\quad \overline{91 - 11\text{'s}}\quad \Rightarrow 91,\ \text{remainder } 10$$

<u>Conventional</u>

$$\begin{array}{r}9\ 1 \\ 1\ 1\ \overline{)\ 1\ 0\ 1\ 1} \\ \underline{9\ 9} \\ 2\ 1 \\ \underline{1\ 1} \\ 1\ 0\end{array}\quad \Rightarrow 91,\ \text{remainder } 10$$

　(c)　<u>Repeated</u> <u>Subtraction</u>

$$2\ 3\ \overline{)\ 3\ 3\ 1\ 2}$$
$$\underline{2\ 3\ 0\ 0}\quad (100 - 23\text{'s})_{five}$$
$$1\ 0\ 1\ 2$$
$$\underline{1\ 0\ 1\ 0}\quad (20 - 23\text{'s})_{five}$$
$$2\quad \overline{(120 - 23\text{'s})_{five}}\quad \Rightarrow 120_{five},\ \text{remainder } 2_{five}$$

<u>Conventional</u>

$$\begin{array}{r}1\ 2\ 0_{five} \\ 2\ 2\ \overline{)\ 3\ 3\ 1\ 2} \\ \underline{2\ 3} \\ 1\ 0\ 1 \\ \underline{1\ 0\ 1} \\ 0\ 2\end{array}\quad \Rightarrow 120_{five},\ \text{remainder } 2_{five}$$

9.　(d)　<u>Repeated</u> <u>Subtraction</u>

$$1\ 1\ \overline{)\ 1\ 0\ 1\ 1}$$
$$\underline{1\ 1\ 0}\quad (10\ \text{elevens})_{two}$$
$$1\ 0\ 1$$
$$\underline{1\ 1}\quad (1\ \text{eleven})_{two}$$
$$1\ 0\quad \overline{(11\ \text{elevens})_{two}}\quad \Rightarrow 11_{two},\ \text{remainder } 10_{two}$$

9.   (d).   Conventional

$$\begin{array}{r} 1\ 1_{two} \\ 1\ 1\ \overline{)\ 1\ 0\ 1\ 1\ } \\ 1\ 1 \\ \hline 1\ 0\ 1 \\ 1\ 1 \\ \hline 1\ 0 \end{array}$$ $\Rightarrow 11_{two}$, remainder 10_{two}

10.   (a) $5 \cdot 912 + 243 = 4803$ (b) $91 \cdot 11 + 10 = 1011$

     (c) $(120 \cdot 23)_{five} + 2_{five} = 3312_{five}$ (d) $(11 \cdot 11)_{two} + 10_{two} = 1011_{two}$

11.   (a)   Tens   (b)   Thousands

     (c)   Hundreds

12.   (a) $\boxed{9 < \text{whole numbers} < 16}$ (b) $\boxed{10}$

     (c) $\boxed{\text{Any whole number}}$ (d) $\boxed{\text{Whole numbers} \le 26}$

13.   (a)

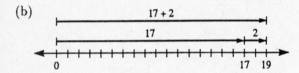

     (b)

     (c) 14_{five} (d) 21_{three}

14.   (a) $(3 + 7 + 5)a = 15a$ (b) $(3 + 7 - 5)x^2 = 5x^2$

     (c) $ax + bx + yx$ (d) $(3 + y)(x + 5)$

15.   (a) $2 + 4 + C = 7 \Rightarrow C = 1$ (b) $D = 6$ (i.e., $1 + 2 + 3$)

     (c)   If $A = 1$ and $C = 5$, then $B = 3$ and $D = 9$. Any other values would result in non-whole numbers or
          $D > 9$.

16. $720 - 162 - 158 - 33 + 28 = \$395$ balance.

17. $320 \cdot 6 + 410 \cdot 6 = \$4380$ total earnings.

18. $15,600 \div 24 = 650$ cases per hour; $650 \cdot 4 = 2600$ cases in four hours.

19. $461,040 \div 120 = \$3842$ per investor.

20.   (a)
     $$\begin{array}{r} \boxed{2}\ \boxed{9}\ \boxed{6} \\ + \boxed{5}\ \boxed{4}\ \boxed{1} \\ \hline \boxed{8}\ \boxed{3}\ \boxed{7} \end{array}$$

20. (b)   Several solutions are possible. For example:

$$\begin{array}{r} \boxed{5}\,\boxed{6}\,\boxed{9} \\ +\ \boxed{2}\,\boxed{1}\,\boxed{4} \\ \hline \boxed{7}\,\boxed{8}\,\boxed{3} \end{array}$$

21. Let m be the number of miles on the 1st day. Then $m + (m + 30) + (m + 60) + \cdots = 2040$
    This is an arithmetic sequence with 1st term m and difference 30; thus:
    On the 10th day he drove $m + (10 - 1)30 = m + 270$ miles.
    And $2040 = \frac{10}{2}[m + (m + 270)]$
    $\qquad\quad 2040 = 10m + 1350$
    $\qquad\quad 10m = 690 \Rightarrow m = 69$ miles the first day.

22. $60 \cdot 8 = 480$ ounces required; $480 \div 12 = 40$ 12-ounce cans.

23. 2 slacks$\cdot$3 blouses$\cdot$2 sweaters $= 12$ outfits.

24.
+	5	7	9
8	13	15	17
11	16	18	20
21	26	28	30

25. Let n be the whole number. Then $[12(\frac{n}{13}) - 20] + 89 = 93$
    $\frac{12n}{13} + 69 = 93$
    $12n = 312$, and the number $= 26$

26. There are 8 groups of 3 in 24 apples; $8 \cdot 69 = \$5.52$ on sale.
    $32 \cdot 24 = \$7.68$ regular price.
    So $7.68 - 5.52 = \$2.16$ saved.

27. \$6000.

28. Let B be the number of bicycles and T be the number of tricycles.
    Then $2B + 3T = 126$ wheels
    $\qquad \underline{2B + 2T = 108}$ pedals
    $\qquad\qquad\quad T = 18$ tricycles
    $\qquad\quad 2B + 3(18) = 126$
    $\qquad\qquad\quad B = 36$ bicycles

29. $30 \cdot 5 + 8 \cdot 8 = \$214$ earned.

30. Let q be the amount from the first question. Then we have $q + 2q + 4q + \cdots$
    which is a geometric sequence with 1st term q, ration 2, and number of terms 5. Thus:
    $6400 = q(2)^{5-1} = 16q$
    and $q = \$400$.

CHAPTER 4 - THE INTEGERS

1. (a) If 2 is an integer, then the unique integer ⁻2 is called the opposite of 2. The opposite of an integer is the integer of the opposite sign.

   (b) 5. The opposite of a negative number is a positive number.

   (c) ⁻m. The opposite of a variable is the variable with the opposite sign, just as with integers (or any real number).

   (d) 0. Since zero is neither positive nor negative, it is its own opposite.

   (e) m.

   (f) ⁻a + ⁻b

2. (a) ⁻(⁻2) means the opposite of ⁻2, or 2.

   (b) m.   (c)   0.

3. (a) Absolute value is the distance on a number line between 0 and a specified number. The distance between 0 and ⁻5 is 5 units, or |⁻5| = 5.

   (b) 10. Remember that absolute value does not mean opposite sign; rather, the distance from 0 on a number line.

   (c) ⁻|⁻5| means the opposite of the absolute value of ⁻5. Since |⁻5| = 5, its opposite is ⁻5.

4. (a)

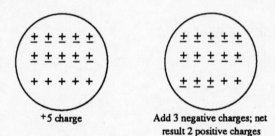

+5 charge   Add 3 negative charges; net
                         result 2 positive charges

   (b)

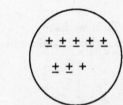

−2 charge   Add 3 positive charges; net
                         result 1 positive charge

   (c)

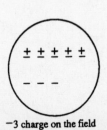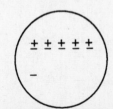

−3 charge on the field   Take away 2 negative charges; net
                         result 1 negative charge

4.   (d)

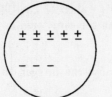

−3 charge on the field   Add 2 negative charges; net
                                result 5 negative charges

5.   Black chips represent positive numbers; white chips represent negative numbers. Thus:

      (a)

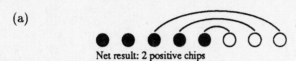

Net result: 2 positive chips

      (b)

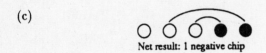

Net result: 1 positive chip

      (c)

Net result: 1 negative chip

      (d)

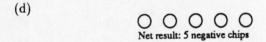

Net result: 5 negative chips

6.   (a)

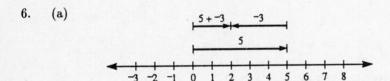

      (b)

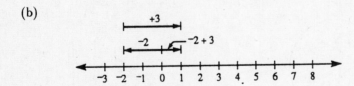

      (c)

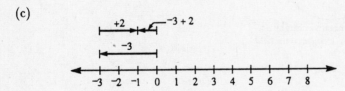

      (d)

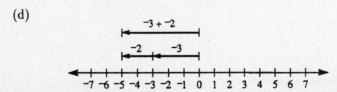

7. To add integers with unlike signs, subtract the lesser of the two absolute values (e.g., |10| = 10, |‾3| = 3) from the greater. The sum of the two integers will be that difference with the same sign as the integer with the greater absolute value.

    (a) 10 + ‾3 = |10| − |‾3| = 10 -- 3 = 7. The sign is positive because the integer 10 has the greater absolute value.

    (b) ‾2. |‾12| − |10| = 2; the sign is negative because 12 has the larger absolute value and it is negative.

    (c) If two integers with unlike signs have equal absolute value, their sum is 0. Thus,
         10 + ‾10 = |10| − |‾10| = 10 − 10 = 0.

    (d) 0

    To add integers with like signs, add the absolute values of the integers. The sum will have the same sign as the integers.

    (e) ‾10. ‾2 + ‾8 = |‾2| + |‾8| = 2 + 8; the sign will be negative because the integers are both negative.

    (f) (‾2 + ‾3) + 7 = ‾5 + 7 = 2.

    (g) ‾2 + (‾3 + 7) = ‾2 + 4 = 2.

8. (a) 7 points down. ‾17 + 10 = ‾7.

    (b) ‾2° C. ‾10 + 8 = ‾2.

    (c) 4900 feet. 5000 + ‾100 = 4900.

    (d) $150 less. ‾200 + 100 + ‾50 = ‾150.

    (e) 3 yard loss. ‾2 + 7 + 0 + ‾8 = ‾3.

9. (a) ‾45 + ‾55 + ‾165 + ‾35 + ‾100 + 75 + 25 + 400 = ‾400 + 500 = 100.

    (b) $400. $300 (beginning) + $100 (net result of transactions from a)

10. (a)

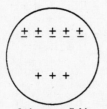   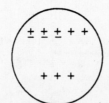

3 charge on field   Take away 2 negative charges; net
                                 result 5 positive charges on the field

    (b)

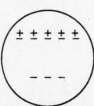   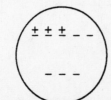

−3 charge on field   Take away 2 positive charges; net
                                 result 5 negative charges on the field

10. (c)

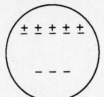 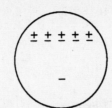

⁻3 charge on field   Take away 2 negative charges; net
                            result 1 negative charge on the field

11. (a) The car starts at 0 and backs up 4 units. It then turns around and faces in the negative direction (to indicate subtraction) and backs up 1 unit (for ⁻1). Thus:

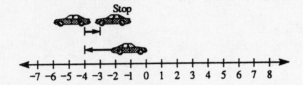

(b)

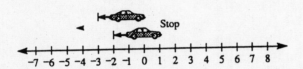

12. (a) Start with subtraction that we already know how to do. Thus:
⁻4 − 2 = ⁻6
⁻4 − 1 = ⁻5
⁻4 − 0 = ⁻4; so, since the next value in the pattern is ⁻3,
⁻4 − ⁻1 = ⁻3

(b) ⁻2 − 4 = ⁻6
⁻2 − 3 = ⁻5
⁻2 − 2 = ⁻4
⁻2 − 1 = ⁻3

13. (a) ⁻1   (b) 1

(c) 3

14. (a) For the integers 2 and 11, $2 - 11$ is the unique integer n such that $2 = 11 + n$. Thus: $2 = 11 + {}^-9$, so $2 - 11 = {}^-9$.

(b) $^-3 - 7 \Rightarrow {}^-3 = 7 + {}^-10$, so $^-3 - 7 = {}^-10$.

(c) $5 - ({}^-8) \Rightarrow 5 = {}^-8 + 13$, so $5 - ({}^-8) = 13$.

(d) $0 - 4 \Rightarrow 0 = 4 + {}^-4$, so $0 - 4 = {}^-4$.

15. (a) $^-2 + (3 - 10) = {}^-2 + ({}^-7) = {}^-2 + {}^-7 = {}^-9$.

(b) $[8 - ({}^-5)] - 10 = [8 + {}^-({}^-5)] - 10 = [8 + 5] - 10 = 13 - 10 = 3$.

(c) $({}^-2 - 7) + 10 = ({}^-2 + {}^-7) + 10 = {}^-9 + 10 = 1$.

(d) $^-2 - (7 + 10) = {}^-2 - (17) = {}^-2 + {}^-17 = {}^-19$.

15. (e) $8 - 11 - 10 = 8 + {}^-11 + {}^-10 = {}^-3 + {}^-10 = {}^-13.$

    (f) ${}^-2 - 7 + 3 = {}^-2 + {}^-7 + 3 = {}^-9 + 3 = {}^-6.$

16. (a) $55 - 60 = T; \; 55 + {}^-60 = T; \; T = {}^-5° \text{ F.}$

    (b) $200 - 220 = B; \; 200 + {}^-220 = B; \; B = {}^-\$20.$

17. (a) We make use of the distributive property of multiplication over addition (Chapter 3); thus:
$3 - (2 - 4x) = 3 + {}^-(2 + {}^-4x) = 3 + {}^-2 - {}^-4x = 3 + {}^-2 + 4x = 1 + 4x.$

    (b) $x - ({}^-x - y) = x + {}^-({}^-x - y) = x + x - {}^-y = x + x + y = 2x + y.$

    (c) $4x - 2 - 3x = (4x - 3x) - 2 = x - 2.$

18. (a) All negative integers.

    (b) All positive integers.

    (c) ${}^-x - 1 > 0 \Rightarrow {}^-x > 1 \Rightarrow x < {}^-1.$

    (d) 2 or ${}^-2.$

    (e) $\emptyset$

    (f) All integers except 0.

    (g) $\emptyset$

19. 784 BC. $1492 - 2275 = {}^-785$, but since there is no year "0", the date is one year after 785 BC.

20. (a) I   (b) W

    (c) I − {0}   (d) $\emptyset$

    (e) $\emptyset$ (f) I⁻

    (g) {0}   (h) W

    (i) I

21. Adding all numbers gives ${}^-9$. Dividing by 3 tells us each row, column, and diagonal must add to ${}^-3$. One possible solution is:

8	${}^-7$	${}^-4$
${}^-13$	${}^-1$	11
2	5	${}^-10$

22. One possible solution is:

	3	5	
7	1	8	2
	4	6	

23. 33 points. Subtract to find out how far off she was: $12 - {}^-21 = 33$. (21 is negative since they lost by 21.)

24. (a) Jack's total was $17 + {}^-8 + {}^-9 + 14 + 45 = 59.$

24.   (b) $^-247 - 11 - 11 = {}^-269°$ C.

     (c) $98 - {}^-94 = 98 + 94 = 192°$ F.

     (d)   Add and subtract 12 to/from 68. Ask a passing truck to call back with the next milepost he sees to determine which of the two is correct.

25. $5 + {}^-10 + 8 + {}^-2 + 3 + {}^-1 + {}^-1 = (5 + 8 + 3) + ({}^-10 + {}^-2 + {}^-1 + {}^-1) = 16 + {}^-14 = 2$. Her stock went up by 2 points.

26. $^-2 + {}^-4 + 3 + 0 + {}^-2 + {}^-3 + 1 + 3 = {}^-4$. Jim lost 4 pounds.

27.   (a)   10W-30 or 10W-40.

     (b)   5W-30.

     (c)   10W-30, or 10W-40.

     (d)   None of the oils shown.

     (e)   10W-30 or 10W-40

28.   (a)   0   (b) $^-101$

     (c)   1   (d) $^-x - 1 = 3$
                                                      $^-x = 4$
                                                      $x = {}^-4$

29.   (a) $f(10) = |1 - 10| = |1 + {}^-10| = |{}^-9| = 9$.

     (b) $f({}^-1) = |1 - {}^-1| = |1 + 1| = |2| = 2$.

     (c)   The result inside the absolute value symbol can be either 1 or $^-1$, so x can be 0 or 2.

     (d)   The range is all the values f(x) can assume. In this case, since we have an absolute value, f(x) can only be positive or zero. Thus the range is the set of all integers equal to or greater than 0.

30.   (a)   All nonnegative integers.

     (b)   (*i*)   5   (*ii*)   5

         (*iii*)   0   (*iv*) $^-7$

31.   For problems such as this, subtract the smaller from the larger, then:
     (*i*)   Add 1 if the ends are to be counted (so as to include the last as well as the first, or vice-versa); or
     (*ii*)   Subtract 1 if neither end is to be counted; e.g., $3 - 2 = 1$, but there are no integers in between, so $1 - 1 = 0$.

     (a)   89. $100 - 10 - 1 = 89$.   (b)   19. $^-10 - {}^-30 - 1 = 19$.

     (c)   19. $10 - {}^-10 - 1 = 19$.   (d) $y - x - 1$

32. Least: $6 - 5 - (4 - {}^-3) = {}^-6$.
    Greatest: $6 - (5 - 4) - {}^-3 = 8$.

33. (a) Subtract 3 from each preceding term; ${}^-12, {}^-15$.

    (b) Subtract 4 from each preceding term; ${}^-9, {}^-13$.

    (c) Subtract y from each preceding term; $x - 2y, x - 3y$.

    (d) Add 2x to each preceding term; $1 + 3x, 1 + 5x$.

34. (a) 0. Rearranging gives ${}^-20 + 20 + {}^-19 + 19 + {}^-18 + 18 + \cdots + 0$.

    (b) 3775. Canceling, as in (a), gives $100 + 99 + \cdots + 51$.
         $(100 + 51) + (99 + 52) + \cdots + (76 + 75) = 25 \cdot 151 = 3775$.

    (c) From Chapter 1, $\frac{54}{2}(100 + {}^-6) = 2538$.

35. (a) ${}^-14$ (b) ${}^-24$

    (c) 2   (d) 5

36. (a) ${}^-18$ (b) ${}^-106$

    (c) ${}^-6$ (d) 22

    (e) ${}^-11$ (f) 2

    (g) ${}^-18$ (h) 23

37. (a) Estimate: $343 + {}^-42 - 402 \doteq 300 - 400 = {}^-100$. Actual: ${}^-101$.

    (b) Estimate: ${}^-1992 + 3005 - 497 \doteq {}^-2000 + 3000 - 500 = 500$. Actual: 516.

    (c) Estimate: $992 - {}^-1003 - 101 \doteq 1000 + 10,000 - 100 = 10,900$. Actual: 10,894.

    (d) Estimate: ${}^-301 - {}^-1303 + 4993 \doteq {}^-300 + 1300 + 5000 = 6000$. Actual: 5995.

38. The signs of both variables are opposites: ${}^-(b - a) = {}^-b - {}^-a = {}^-b + a = a - b$; i.e., the opposite of $b - a$ is $a - b$.

39. (a) $({}^-a + {}^-b) + (a + b) = ({}^-a + a) + ({}^-b + b) = 0 + 0 = 0$.

    (b) ${}^-a + {}^-b$ added to $(a + b)$ gives a sum of zero, so ${}^-a + {}^-b$ is the additive inverse, or opposite, of $(a + b)$; i.e., ${}^-(a + b)$.

40. To add integers with unlike signs, subtract the lesser of the two absolute values of the integers from the greater. The sum has the same sign as the integer with the greater absolute value.

41. (a) True   (b) True

    (c) True   (d) True

    (e) False. If x is negative; e.g., let $x = {}^-2$. Then $\left| \left({}^-2 \right)^3 \right| = |{}^-8| = 8 \neq {}^-8 = ({}^-2^3)$.

    (f) True

1. (3)($^-$1) = $^-$1 + $^-$1 + $^-$1 = $^-$3
   (2)($^-$1) = $^-$1 + $^-$1 = $^-$2
   (1)($^-$1) = $^-$1
   (0)($^-$1) = 0, so continuing the pattern of an answer increasing by 1 each time, we have:
   ($^-$1)($^-$1) = 1.

2.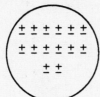

   0 charge   Take away four groups of two negative
   charges; net result is eight positive charges.

3. The car goes back 4 twice, leaving it back 8.

   If you are now at 0 moving west at 4 km/h, you will be at 8 km
   west of 0 two hours from now.

   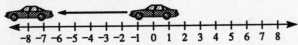

4. (a) 4($^-$20) = $^-$80

   (b) $^-$4($^-$20) = 80

   (c) n($^-$20) = $^-$20n

   (d) $^-$n($^-$20) = 20n

5. (a) For any whole numbers *a* and *b*, ($^-$a)($^-$b) = ab. Thus $^-$3($^-$4) = 12.

   (b) For any whole numbers *a* and *b*, ($^-$a)b = b($^-$a) = $^-$(ab). Thus 3($^-$5) = $^-$15.

   (c) ($^-$5)·3 = $^-$15.

   (d) For any number *n*, n·0 = 0. Thus $^-$5·0 = 0.

   (e) $^-$2($^-$3·5) = $^-$2($^-$15) = 30.

   (f) [$^-$2($^-$5)]($^-$3) = [10]($^-$3) = $^-$30.

   (g) ($^-$4 + 4)($^-$3) = (0)($^-$3) = 0.

   (h) ($^-$5 − $^-$3)($^-$5 − 3) = ($^-$5 + 3)($^-$5 + $^-$3) = ($^-$2)($^-$8) = 16.

6. (a) $^-$40 = 5·($^-$8) ⇒ ($^-$40)÷($^-$8) = 5.

   (b) 143 = ($^-$11)·($^-$13) ⇒ 143÷($^-$11) = $^-$13.

   (c) $^-$143 = 13·($^-$11) ⇒ $^-$143÷13 = $^-$11.

   (d) 0 = ($^-$5)·0 ⇒ 0÷($^-$5) = 0.

   (e) $^-$5 ≠ 0·Any integer ⇒ $^-$5÷0 is not defined.

6.   (f)   By definition, $\frac{0}{0} = c$, where c is a unique integer such that $c \cdot 0 = 0$. c, however, is not unique (i.e., $1 \cdot 0 = 0$, $2 \cdot 0 = 0$, etc.), so $\frac{0}{0}$ is undefined.

7.   (a) $(^-10 \div ^-2)(^-2) = (5)(^-2) = ^-10$.

    (b) $(^-40 \div 8)8 = (^-5)8 = ^-40$.

    (c)   See (b) above. $(a \div b)b = a$ for any integers a and b ($b \neq 0$).

    (d) $(^-10 \cdot 5) \div 5 = (^-50) \div 5 = ^-10$.

    (e)   See (d) above. $(a \cdot b) \div b = a$ for any integrs a and b ($b \neq 0$).

    (f) $(^-8 \div ^-2)(^-8) = (4)(^-8) = ^-32$.

    (g) $(^-6 + ^-14) \div 4 = (^-20) \div 4 = ^-5$.

    (h) $(^-8 + 8) \div 8 = (0) \div 8 = 0$.

    (i) $^-8 \div (^-8 + 8) = ^-8 \div (0) \Rightarrow$ the quotient is undefined.

    (j) $(^-23 - ^-7) \div 4 = (^-23 + 7) \div 4 = (^-16) \div 4 = ^-4$.

    (k) $(^-6 + 6) \div (^-2 + 2) = (0) \div (0) \Rightarrow$ the quotient is undefined.

    (l) $^-13 \div (^-1) = 13$

    (m) $(^-36 \div 12) \div 3 = (^-3) \div 3 = ^-1$.

    (n) $|^-24| \div (3 - 15) = 24 \div (^-12) = ^-2$.

8.   (a) $32 + 30(^-3) = ^-58°$ C.

    (b) $0 + (^-25)(^-4) = 100°$ C.

    (c) $^-20 + (^-30)(^-4) = 100°$ C.

    (d) $25 + (^-20)(3) = ^-35°$ C.

    (e) $0 + (^-m)(^-d) = md°$ C.

    (f) $20 + (^-m)(d) = \ (20 - md)°$ C.

9.   (a) $4(^-11) = ^-44$, or 44 yards lost.

    (b) $^-66 \div 11 = ^-6$, or 66 yards lost over 11 plays means an average of 6 yards lost per play.

10. $(12,000)(14) = 168,000$ acres lost.

11.   The distributive property is that $a(b + c) = ab + ac$.

    (a) $^-1(^-5 + ^-2) = ^-1(^-7) = 7 \Leftrightarrow (^-1)(^-5) + (^-1)(^-2) = 5 + 2 = 7$.

    (b) $^-3(^-3 + 2) = ^-3(^-1) = 3 \Leftrightarrow (^-3)(^-3) + (^-3)(2) = 9 + ^-6 = 3$.

    (c) $^-5(2 + ^-6) = ^-5(^-4) = 20 \Leftrightarrow (^-5)(2) + (^-5)(^-6) = ^-10 + 30 = 20$.

12. (a) $(^-2)^3 = (^-2)(^-2)(^-2) = {}^-8.$

    (b)   16

    (c) $(^-10)^5 \div (^-10)^2 = (^-10)^3 = {}^-1000.$

    (d)   81   (e)   1

    (f) $^-1$ (g)   1

    (h) $^-1$

13. (a) $^-2 + 3\cdot5 - 1 = {}^-2 + 15 + {}^-1 = 13 + {}^-1 = 12.$

    (b) $10 - 3\cdot7 - 4(^-2) + 3 = 10 - 21 - (^-8) + 3 = 10 + {}^-21 + 8 + 3 = {}^-11 + 8 + 3 = 0.$

    (c) $10 - 3 - 12 = 10 + {}^-3 + {}^-12 = 7 + {}^-12 = {}^-5.$

    (d) $10 - (3 - 12) = 10 - (^-9) = 10 + 9 = 19.$

    (e) $(^-3)^2 = (^-3)(^-3) = 9.$

    (f) $^-3^2 = {}^-(3)(3) = {}^-9.$

    (g) $^-5^2 + 3(^-2)^2 = {}^-(5)(5) + 3(^-2)(^-2) = {}^-25 + 3(4) = {}^-25 + 12 = {}^-13.$

    (h) $^-2^3 = {}^-(2)(2)(2) = {}^-8.$

    (i) $(^-2)^5 = (^-2)(^-2)(^-2)(^-2)(^-2) = {}^-32.$

    (j) $^-2^4 = {}^-(2)(2)(2)(2) = {}^-16.$

14. (a) Always negative.   (b) Always positive.

    (c) Always positive.   (d) Positive when $x < 0$; negative when $x > 0$.

    (e) Positive when $x < 0$; negative when $x > 0$.   (f) Always negative.

    (g) Always positive.   (h) Always positive.

    (i) Positive when $x > 0$; negative when $x < 0$.   (j) Positive when $x < 0$; negative when $x > 0$.

15. (b) and (c); (d) and (e); (g) and (h).

16. (a) Commutative property of multiplication.

    (b) Closure property of addition.

    (c) Associative property of multiplication.

    (d) Distributive property of multiplication over addition.

17. (a) Distributive property of multiplication over addition.

    (b) Subtraction is the inverse of addition; i.e., $a - b = a + {}^-b.$

17. (c)   Commutative property of multiplication.

     (d)   Commutative property of addition.

     (e)   Addition as the inverse of subtraction.

18. (a)   xy   (b)   2xy

     (c)   0   (d) $^-$x

     (e)   x + 2y   (f)   b

     (g)   x   (h)   y

19. Use the definition of division backward for problems (a) to (d); forward on (e) to (h).

     (a) $^-3x = 6 \Rightarrow x = 6 \div (^-3) = ^-2$.

     (b) $^-3x = ^-6 \Rightarrow x = ^-6 \div (^-3) = 2$.

     (c) $^-2x = 0 \Rightarrow x = 0 \div (^-2) = 0$.

     (d) $5x = ^-30 \Rightarrow x = ^-30 \div 5 = ^-6$.

     (e) $x \div 3 = ^-12 \Rightarrow x = 3 \cdot (^-12) = ^-36$.

     (f) $x \div (^-3) = ^-2 \Rightarrow x = (^-3) \cdot (^-2) = 6$.

     (g) $x \div (^-x) = ^-1 \Rightarrow x = (^-x)(^-1) = x$. When a trivially true statement such as this (x = x) occurs, it indicates more than one answer. In fact, the only number that will not work here is 0, since division by 0 is undefined.

     (h) $0 \div x = 0 \Rightarrow 0 = (x)(0) = 0$. As in (g), x may represent any number except 0.

     (i)   Since division by 0 is undefined, no value of x will make this true.

     (j) $x^2 = 9 \Rightarrow (^-3)^2 = 9$ or $(3)^2 = 9$. x may equal $^-3$ or 3.

     (k)   Any number to the second power will give a positive result. No value of x will then yield $^-9$.

     (l)   This is similar to (g). Again, x may be any number except 0.

     (m) x^2 is always positive, so $^-x^2$ is always negative (x $\neq$ 0, since 0 is neither positive nor negative). Another way of stating this result is that x may be any non-zero number.

     (n)   All numbers, by the distributive property; i.e., $^-(1 - x) = ^-1 - ^-x = ^-1 + x = x - 1$.

     (o)   All integers. $x - 3x = x + ^-3x = ^-2x$.

20. (a) $^-2(x) - ^-2(1) = ^-2x + 2$.

     (b) $^-2x + 2y$ (c) $x^2 - xy$

     (d) $^-x^2 + xy$ (e) $^-2x - 2y + 2z$

     (f) $^-x^2 + xy + 3x$

20. (g) $^-5(5 + x) + ^-x(5 + x) = ^-25 - 10x - x^2$

    (h) $(x - y - 1)(x + y + 1) = [x - (y + 1)][x + (y + 1)] = x^2 - (y + 1)^2$
           $= x^2 - (y^2 + 2y + 1) = x^2 - y^2 - 2y - 1.$

    (i) $^-x^4 + 3x^2 - 2$

21. The difference-of-squares formula is: $(a + b)(a - b) = a^2 - b^2.$

    (a) $(50 + 2)(50 - 2) = 50^2 - 2^2 = 2500 - 4 = 2496.$

    (b) $(5 - 100)(5 + 100) = 5^2 - 100^2 = 25 - 10{,}000 = ^-9975.$

    (c) $(^-x - y)(^-x + y) = (^-x)^2 - y^2 = x^2 - y^2.$

    (d) $(2 + 3x)(2 - 3x) = 2^2 - (3x)^2 = 4 - 9x^2.$

    (e) $(x - 1)(1 + x) = (x - 1)(x + 1) = x^2 - 1^2 = x^2 - 1.$

    (f) $213^2 - 13^2 = (213 + 13)(213 - 13) = (226)(200) = 45{,}200.$

22. No. The two factors do not fit the pattern $(a - b)(a + b).$ They are of the form $^-(a + b)(a + b).$

23. (a) $3x + 5x = (3)x + (5)x = x(3 + 5) = 8x.$

    (b) $ax + 2x = x(a + 2).$

    (c) $xy + x = (y)x + (1)x = x(y + 1).$

    (d) $ax - 2x = (a)x - (2)x = x(a - 2).$

    (e) $x^2 + xy = (x)x + (y)x = x(x + y).$

    (f) $3x - 4x + 7x = (3 - 4 + 7)x = 6x.$

    (g) $3xy + 2x - xz = (3y)x + (2)x - (z)x = x(3y + 2 - z).$

    (h) $3x^2 + xy - x = (3x)x + (y)x - (1)x = x(3x + y - 1).$

    (i) $abc + ab - a = (bc)a + (b)a - (1)a = a(bc + b - 1) = a[b(c + 1) - 1].$

    (j) $(a + b)(c + 1) - (a + b) = (a + b)[(c + 1) - 1] = (a + b)[c] = c(a + b).$

    (k) $16 - a^2 = 4^2 - a^2 = (4 + a)(4 - a).$

    (l) $x^2 - 9y^2 = x^2 - (3y)^2 = (x + 3y)(x - 3y).$

    (m) $4x^2 - 25y^2 = (2x)^2 - (5y)^2 = (2x + 5y)(2x - 5y).$

    (n) $(x^2 - y^2) + x + y = (x + y)(x - y) + (x + y) = (x + y)[(x - y) + 1] = (x + y)(x - y + 1).$

24. (a) $(a - b)^2 = (a - b)(a - b) = a(a - b) - b(a - b) = a^2 - 2ab + b^2.$

    (b)   (*i*) $98^2 = (100 - 2)^2 = 100^2 - 2(100)(2) + 2^2 = 10{,}000 - 400 + 4 = 9604.$

           (*ii*) $99^2 = (100 - 1)^2 = 100^2 - 2(100)(1) + 1^2 = 9801.$

24. (b) (iii) $997^2 = (1000 - 3)^2 = 1000^2 - 2(1000)(3) + 3^2 = 994{,}009.$

25. The argument is correct. $a^2 + 2a(^-b) + (^-b)^2 = a^2 + (^-2ab) + (^-b)^2 = a^2 - 2ab + (^-b)^2 = a^2 - 2ab + b^2.$

26. (a) False   (b) True

 (c) True   (d) True

27. (a) The sums are always 9 times the middle number.

 (b) The dates in rows 1 and 3 are 7 less than and 7 more than, respectively, their counterparts in row 2. The dates in rows 1 and 2 will then average to the values in row 2. Similarly, the values in columns 1 and 3 average to the values in column 2. Averaging in both directions forces the average to be the middle number. Thus, 9 numbers with an average equal to the middle number m will have a sum of 9 m.

28. (a) The next two terms are 8, 11. The sequence is arithmetic with difference $d = 3$. The nth term is $3n - 13$.

 (b) The next two terms are $^-8$, $^-11$. Arithmetic with $d = ^-3$. nth term is $13 - 3n$.

 (c) The next two terms are $^-128$, $^-256$. Geometric with ratio $r = 2$. nth term is $^-2^n$.

 (d) The next two terms are $^-128$, 256. Geometric with $r = ^-2$. nth term is $(^-2)^n$.

 (e) The next two terms are 2^7, $^-2^8$. Geometric with $r = ^-2$. nth term is $^-(^-2)^n$.

 (f) The next two terms are $^-8 \cdot 2^6$, $9 \cdot 2^7$.

29. Use the expression for sums of arithmetic sequences with n terms, first term a_1, and nth term a_n: $\frac{n}{2}(a_1 + a_n)$

 (a) $a_n = 3n - 13 \Rightarrow a_{100} = 3(100) - 13 = 287.$
   The sume is $\frac{100}{2}(^-10 + 287) = 50(277) = 13{,}850.$

 (b) Since all corresponding terms are the additive inverses of the terms in (a), the sum will be the additive inverse of the sum in (a); i.e., $^-13{,}850.$

30. (a) $^-9, ^-6, ^-1, 6, 15$ (b) $^-2, ^-7, ^-12, ^-17, ^-22$

 (c) $^-3, 3, ^-9, 15, ^-33$ (d) $0, 8, 0, 32, 0$

 (e) $^-1, 4, ^-9, 16, ^-25$ (f) $2, ^-8, 24, ^-64, 160$

 (g) $9, 8, 7, 6, 5$ (h) $0, 8, 0, 32, 0$

31. To solve, we must find the common difference and then work back from $^-8$. Treat $^-8$ as a "first" term, which makes $^-493$ the "98th" term. Using the expression for the nth term $[= a + (n - 1)d]$ gives: $^-493 = ^-8 + (98 - 1)d$, so $^-493 = 97d$ and $d = ^-5$. To obtain a succeeding term, then, we would add $^-5$; thus to obtain a preceding term we would subtract $^-5$, or, equivalently, add $^+5$. Thus if $^-8$ is the 3rd term, $^-8 + 5 = ^-3$ is the 2nd term, and $^-3 + 5 = 2$ is the 1st term.

32. (a) Consider $(^-a)b + ab = (^-a + a)b = 0 \cdot b = 0 \Rightarrow (^-a)b$ is the additive inverse of ab. Since the additive inverse is unique, and the additive inverse of ab is ^-ab, then $(^-a)b$ must equal ^-ab.

 (b) Consider $(^-a)(^-b) + ^-(ab) = (^-a)(^-b) + (^-a)b$ (substituting from (a)) $= ^-a(^-b + b) = ^-a \cdot 0 = 0$. This implies that $(^-a)(^-b)$ is the additive inverse of $^-(ab)$, or that $(^-a)(^-b) = ab$ by uniqueness.

33. The argument is valid, but lacks proof that $(^-1)a + a = 0$. $(^-1)a + a = a(^-1 + 1) = a \cdot 0 = 0$, which implies that $(^-1)a$ is the additive inverse of a. Thus $(^-1)a = {}^-a$, so $(^-1)ab = {}^-(ab)$.

34. Proof should refer to the same property used in 33 [i.e., $(^-1)a = {}^-a$], but is valid.

35. (a) Enter $\boxed{2}\boxed{7}\boxed{+/-}\boxed{\times}\boxed{3}\boxed{=}$ to obtain $^-81$.

    (b) Enter $\boxed{4}\boxed{6}\boxed{+/-}\boxed{\times}\boxed{4}\boxed{+/-}\boxed{=}$ to obtain 184.

    (c) Enter $\boxed{2}\boxed{6}\boxed{+/-}\boxed{\div}\boxed{1}\boxed{3}\boxed{=}$ to obtain $^-2$.

    (d) Enter $\boxed{2}\boxed{6}\boxed{+/-}\boxed{\div}\boxed{1}\boxed{3}\boxed{+/-}\boxed{=}$ to obtain 2.

36. (a) $3 - 6 = 3 + {}^-6 = {}^-3$ (b) $8 + {}^-7 = 1$

    (c) $5 - {}^-8 = 5 + {}^-(^-8) = 5 + 8 = 13$ (d) $^-5 - {}^-8 = {}^-5 + 8 = 3$

    (e) $^-8 + 5 = {}^-3$ (f) $^-8 + {}^-5 = {}^-13$

37. Go back 8, then back 5 more, for a total of 13 back, or $^-13$.

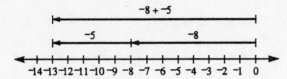

38. (a) 5   (b) $^-7$

    (c) 0

39. (a) 14   (b) $|^-14| + 7 = 14 + 7 = 21$

    (c) $8 - |^-12| = 8 - 12 = 8 + {}^-12 = {}^-4$ (d) $|11| + |^-11| = 11 + 11 = 22$

40. The weight was $(100 + 4) + (100 - 3) + (100 + 5) + (100 - 6) = 400$ pounds.

Problem Set 4-3

1. (a) $^-20, {}^-13, {}^-5, {}^-3, 0, 4$ (b) $^-6, {}^-5, 0\ 5, 6$

   (c) $^-100, {}^-20, {}^-15, {}^-13, 0$ (d) $^-3, {}^-2, 5, 13$

2. (a) $^-3 > {}^-5$ if $^-3 - {}^-5 = 2 > 0$. Since 2 is positive, $^-3 > {}^-5$

   (b) $0 - {}^-6 = 6$, a positive integer. Thus $0 > {}^-6$ and $^-6 < 0$

   (c) $^-8 - {}^-10 = 2$, a positive integer, so $^-8 > {}^-10$

   (d) $4 - {}^-5 = 9$, a positive integer, so $4 > {}^-5$ and $^-5 < 4$.

3. (a) $x + 3 = {}^-15 \Rightarrow x + 3 - 3 = {}^-15 - 3 \Rightarrow x = {}^-15 + {}^-3 \Rightarrow x = {}^-18$.

   (b) $x + 3 > {}^-15 \Rightarrow x + 3 - 3 > {}^-15 - 3 \Rightarrow x > {}^-15 + {}^-3 \Rightarrow x > {}^-18$ and x is an integer.

3. (c) $3 - x = {}^-15 \Rightarrow 3 - 3 - x = {}^-15 - 3 \Rightarrow {}^-x = {}^-18 \Rightarrow x = 18.$

   (d) ${}^-x + 3 > {}^-15 \Rightarrow {}^-x + 3 - 3 > {}^-15 - 3 \Rightarrow {}^-x > {}^-18 \Rightarrow x < 18$ and x is an integer. (Remember that when both sides of an inequality are multiplied by a negative integer, the direction of inequality is reversed.)

   (e) ${}^-x - 3 = 15 \Rightarrow {}^-x - 3 + 3 = 15 + 3 \Rightarrow {}^-x = 18 \Rightarrow x = {}^-18.$

   (f) ${}^-x - 3 \geq 15 \Rightarrow {}^-x - 3 + 3 \geq 15 + 3 \Rightarrow {}^-x \geq 18 \Rightarrow x \leq {}^-18$ and x is an integer.

   (g) $3x + 5 = {}^-16 \Rightarrow 3x + 5 - 5 = {}^-16 - 5 \Rightarrow 3x = {}^-21 \Rightarrow \frac{3}{3}x = \frac{{}^-21}{3} \Rightarrow x = {}^-7.$

   (h) $3x + 5 < {}^-16 \Rightarrow 3x + 5 - 5 < {}^-16 - 5 \Rightarrow 3x < {}^-21 \Rightarrow \frac{3}{3}x < \frac{{}^-21}{3} \Rightarrow x < {}^-7$ and x is an integer.

   (i) ${}^-3x + 5 = 11 \Rightarrow {}^-3x = 6 \Rightarrow x = {}^-2.$

   (j) ${}^-3x + 5 \leq 11 \Rightarrow {}^-3x \leq 6 \Rightarrow x \geq {}^-2$ and x is an integer.

   (k) $5x - 3 = 7x - 1 \Rightarrow 5x - 7x - 3 = 7x - 7x - 1 \Rightarrow {}^-2x - 3 = {}^-1 \Rightarrow {}^-2x - 3 + 3 = {}^-1 + 3$
        $\Rightarrow {}^-2x = 2 \Rightarrow x = {}^-1.$

   (l) $5x - 3 > 7x - 1 \Rightarrow {}^-2x > 2 \Rightarrow x < {}^-1$ and x is an integer.

   (m) $3(x + 5) = {}^-4(x + 5) + 21 \Rightarrow 3x + 15 = {}^-4x + {}^-20 + 21 \Rightarrow 3x + 15 = {}^-4x + 1 \Rightarrow 7x = {}^-14$
        $\Rightarrow x = {}^-2.$

   (n) ${}^-5(x + 3) > 0 \Rightarrow {}^-5x + {}^-15 > 0 \Rightarrow {}^-5x > 15 \Rightarrow x < {}^-3$ and x is an integer.

4. (a) True.   (b) False (except when x = 3).

   (c) True.   (d) True.

   (e) True.   (f) False.

5. (a) $\{1, {}^-2, 0\}$
        (i)   Let x = 1 $\Rightarrow$ Does $(1)^3 + (1)^2 = 2(1)$? $\Rightarrow$ $1 + 1 = 2$ $\Rightarrow$ True.
        (ii)   Let x = ${}^-1$ $\Rightarrow$ Does $({}^-1)^3 + ({}^-1)^2 = 2({}^-1)$? $\Rightarrow$ ${}^-1 + 1 \neq {}^-2$ $\Rightarrow$ False.
        (iii) Let x = ${}^-2$ $\Rightarrow$ Does $({}^-2)^3 + ({}^-2)^2 = 2({}^-2)$? $\Rightarrow$ ${}^-8 + 4 = {}^-4$ $\Rightarrow$ True.
        (iv)   Let x = 0 $\Rightarrow$ Does $(0)^3 + (0)^2 = 2(0)$? $\Rightarrow$ $0 + 0 = 0$ $\Rightarrow$ True.

   (b) $\{9\}$
        (i)   Let x = ${}^-9$ $\Rightarrow$ Does $3({}^-9) - 3 = 24$? $\Rightarrow$ ${}^-21 - 3 \neq 24$ $\Rightarrow$ False.
        (ii)   Let x = 9 $\Rightarrow$ Does $3(9) - 3 = 24$? $\Rightarrow$ $24 = 24$ $\Rightarrow$ True.

   (c) $\{{}^-6, {}^-7\}$
        (i)   Let x = 6 $\Rightarrow$ Is ${}^-(6) \geq 5$? $\Rightarrow$ ${}^-6 \not\geq 5$ $\Rightarrow$ False.
        (ii)   Let x = ${}^-6$ $\Rightarrow$ Is ${}^-({}^-6) \geq 5$? $\Rightarrow$ $6 \geq 5$ $\Rightarrow$ True.
        (iii) Let x = 7 $\Rightarrow$ Is ${}^-(7) \geq 5$? $\Rightarrow$ ${}^-7 \not\geq 5$ $\Rightarrow$ False.
        (iv)   Let x = ${}^-7$ $\Rightarrow$ Is ${}^-({}^-7) \geq 5$? $\Rightarrow$ $7 \geq 5$ $\Rightarrow$ True.

   (d) $\{$All except ${}^-4, 4\}$
        (i)   Let x = ${}^-4$ $\Rightarrow$ Is $({}^-4)^2 < 16$? $\Rightarrow$ $16 \not< 16$ $\Rightarrow$ False.
        (ii)   Let x = ${}^-3$ $\Rightarrow$ Is $({}^-3)^2 < 16$? $\Rightarrow$ $9 < 16$ $\Rightarrow$ True.
        $\vdots$ $\vdots$
        (viii) Let x = 3 $\Rightarrow$ Is $(3)^2 < 16$? $\Rightarrow$ $9 < 16$ $\Rightarrow$ True.
        (ix)   Let x = 4 $\Rightarrow$ Is $(4)^2 < 16$? $\Rightarrow$ $16 \not< 16$ $\Rightarrow$ False.

6. (a) $x = {}^-3$. Checking, ${}^-2({}^-3) + {}^-11 = 3({}^-3) + 4$.

    (b) $x = 0$. Checking, $5(0 + 1) = 5$.

    (c) $y = 1$. Checking, ${}^-3(1) + 4 = (1)$.

    (d) $z = 0$. Checking, ${}^-3(0 - 1) = 8(0) + 3$.

7. (a) "Difference" means to subtract, so the difference of 6 and another number is $n - 6$ or $6 - n$ (the order was not specified).

    (b) $n + 14$ or $14 + n$. "Sum" means addition; the order makes no difference.

    (c) $4n - 7$. Four times n is 4n. "Seven less than" a number means that we subtract 7 from that number.

    (d) $3n + 8$. "Eight greater than" implies adding 8; three times n is 3n.

    (e) $n + 10$. "Increased by" means to add.

    (f) $4n$.

    (g) $13 - n$. "Decreased by" means to subtract. Note the order — thirteen decreased by the number means that we subtract the number from 13, while $n - 13$ would be "the number decreased by 13."

    (h) $n - 4$. "Less four" indicates subtracting 4 from the number.

8. (a) $d = 60t$

    (b) $D = G + Y$, $Y = G + 15$. Then $D + Y + G = [G + (G + 15)] + (G + 15) + G = 4G + 30$.

    (c) $c = \$25x + \$20$

    (d) $N = 3D$, $Q = 2N = 6D$. Then $A = 10D + 5(3D) + 25(6D) = 175D\ \cancel{c}$.

    (e) $S = x + (x + 1) + (x + 2) = 3x + 3$

    (f) $S = x + (x + 2) + (x + 4) = 3x + 6$

    (g) $S = (m - 1) + m + (m + 1) = 3m$

    (h) $P = (m - 1)m(m + 1) = m(m^2 - 1) = m^3 - m$

    (i) $b = q(2^n)$

    (j) $T = 40°\ F - (3°\ F)t$

    (k) $S = 2(s + \$5000) = 2s + \$10,000$

9. The following relationships are stated: (*i*) $A = 2N + 982,800$; (*ii*) $N = S + 1,186,000 \Rightarrow S = N - 1,186,000$; (*iii*) $N = E + 4,383,000 \Rightarrow E = N - 4,383,000$. Now, N is common to all the relationships.
    Thus: $A + N + S + E = 35,692,000$
    $(2N + 982,000) + N + (N - 1,186,000) + (N - 4,383,000) = 35,692,000$
    $(2N + N + N + N) + (982,000 - 1,186,000 - 4,483,000) = 35,692,000$
    $5N - 4,587,000 = 35,692,000$
    $5N = 40,279,000 \Rightarrow N = 8,055,800$ square miles, and:

9. $A = 2(8,055,800) + 982,000 = 17,093,600$ square miles;
        $S = 8,055,800 - 1,186,000 = 6,869,800$ square miles;
        $E = 8,055,800 - 4,383,000 = 3,672,800$ square miles.

10.   If T = Tom's age, then: $3T + 4 > 37 \Rightarrow 3T > 33 \Rightarrow T > 11$. Tom's age is more than 11 years.

11.   Translating: $^-6n + 20 = 50 \Rightarrow ^-6n = 30 \Rightarrow n = ^-5$.

12. $D = 3R \Rightarrow 3R + R = 400 \Rightarrow R = 100$. Rick has $100, and David has three times as much, or $300.

13.   If we let d be the distance from A to B, then 2d is the distance from A to C (from the given relationship).
        B to C is 5 inches. Thus:
        $AB + BC = AC$
        $d + 5 = 2d \Rightarrow d = 5$ (i.e., AB = 5), so AC = 5 + 5 = 10 inches.

14.   Given $A + B + C = 7300$; also that $A = 2B$ and $C = A + 300 = 2B + 300$, then using substitution:
        $2B + B + (2B + 300) = 7300$
        $5B = 7000 \Rightarrow B = 1400$, $A = 2B = 2800$, and $C = 2B + 300 = 3100$.

15.   Let x = the number of pounds of 60¢ tea; then $100 - x$ = the number of pounds of 45¢ tea. The value of
        the tea is the price per pound times the number of pounds, and adding the values of the two teas gives the
        value of the blend:
        $60x + 45(100 - x) = 51(100)$
        $60x + 4500 - 45x = 5100 \Rightarrow 15x = 600$, and $x = 40$.
        Thus there are 40 pounds of 60¢ tea and $(100 - 40) = 60$ pounds of 45¢ tea in the 100-pound blend.

16.   If s = the number of student tickets sold, then $812 - s$ = the number of nonstudent tickets. Adding their
        values gives the total amount taken in:
        $2s + 3(812 - s) = 1912$
        $2s + 2436 - 3s = 1912 \Rightarrow s = 524$ student tickets sold.

17.   The three consecutive integers may be represented by n, n + 1, and n + 2. Then:
        $n + (n + 1) + (n + 2) = 237$
        $3n + 3 = 237 \Rightarrow 3n = 234 \Rightarrow n = 78$.
        The three integers are thus 78, 78 + 1, and 78 + 2, or 78, 79, and 80.

18.   The sum of the three integers is $I + (I + 2) + (I + 4) = 240 \Rightarrow 3I + 6 = 240 \Rightarrow I = 78$. The three
        consecutive even integers are 78, 80, and 82.

19.   If the two integers are represented by x and y: $x + y = 21$ and $x = 2y$. The first equation may be rewritten
        as: $y = 21 - x$, so, substituting, $x = 2y = 2(21 - x)$. Solving:
        $x = 42 - 2x \Rightarrow 3x = 42 \Rightarrow x = 14$.
        The two integers are thus 14 and $21 - 14 = 7$.

20.   We know that $E + M + Y = 64,000$; $E = 3Y$; and $M = Y + 14,000$. Then:
        $(3Y) + (Y + 14,000) + Y = 64,000$
        $5Y + 14,000 = 64,000 \Rightarrow Y = $10,000$ given to the youngest child and:
        $E = 3(10,000) = $30,000$ given to the eldest child;
        $M = 10,000 + 14,000 = $24,000$ given to the middle child.

21.   Three consecutive even integers may be represented by n, n + 2, and n + 4. Then:
        $7n = 5(n + 4)$
        $7n = 5n + 20 \Rightarrow 2n = 20 \Rightarrow n = 10$. The three integers are thus 10, 12, and 14.

22.   We are given: $A = 4S$ and $16A + 6S = 14,000$. Substituting gives:
        $16(4S) + 6S = 14,000 \Rightarrow S = 200$ student tickets and $4(200) = 800$ adult tickets.

23. Ron will overtake Pete when they are the same distance from Albuquerque. First, find how many hours this will take by equating distances (i.e., rates·times). Let P be Pete's time from Albuquerque; then P − 2 will be Ron's time (because he leaves two hours later). Thus, equating:

$$40P = 45(P − 2)$$
$$40P = 45P − 90 \Rightarrow P = 18 \text{ hours from Albuquerque (Ron will have ridden } 18 − 2 = 16 \text{ hours).}$$

The distance from Albuquerque will be 40 kph·18 hours = 720 km.

24. Consider the two cases separately, finding the time until the groups meet. Let t = 2nd troop's time, then t + 2 will be the 1st troop's time.

   (*i*)   If the 2nd troop follows, the distances will be the same when they catch up, or
   $$3(t + 2) = 5t \Rightarrow 3t + 6 = 5t \Rightarrow t = 3 \text{ hours to catch up.}$$

   (*ii*)   If the 2nd troop goes in the opposite direction, the two troops will have covered the 22-mile perimeter, or
   $$3(t + 2) + 5t = 22 \Rightarrow 3t + 6 + 5t = 22 \Rightarrow t = 2 \text{ hours to catch up.}$$

The second troop will get to eat one hour earlier if they travel counterclockwise.

25. Total travel time is 7 hours (not counting the stay at the Grandparent's). Let the time going to Zenith be z; then the time going back to Aurora = 7 − z. The distance (rate·time) is the same each way, so:

$$16z = 12(7 − z)$$
$$16z = 84 − 12z \Rightarrow z = 3 \text{ hours to ride to Zenith.}$$

The distance is then 16 mph·3 hours = 48 miles.

26. (a) $^-4 < x < 4$ (b) $^-3 \leq y \leq 3$

   (c) $0 \leq |x + y| < 7$ and $0 \leq |x − y| < 7$.

27. (a)   Yes. $x^2 + y^2 \geq 2xy$ implies that $x^2 − 2xy + y^2 \geq 0 \Rightarrow (x − y)^2 \geq 0$. Any number squared must be nonnegative (i.e., greater than or equal to 0).

   (b) $x^2 + y^2 = 2xy$ when $x^2 − 2xy + y^2 = 0$, or when $(x − y)^2 = 0$. Only $0^2 = 0$, so $x − y$ must be equal to 0, which occurs when x = y. This then is true for all integers.

28. For $0 < a < b$, consider $(a + b)$, a positive number; and $(a − b)$, a negative number. The product of a positive and a negative is negative, so $(a + b)(a − b) < 0 \Rightarrow a^2 − b^2 < 0 \Rightarrow a^2 < b^2$.

29. No. This is false for any negative integer *a* with a greater absolute value than *b*; for example, let a = $^-5$ and b = 3. Then $(^-5)^2 > 3^2$.

30. $a < b \Rightarrow {}^-a > {}^-b \Rightarrow {}^-a + c > {}^-b + c \Rightarrow c − a > c − b \Rightarrow c − b < c − a$.

31. (a) $x + 1 < 3$ and $^-x + 1 < 5$
          $x < 2$ and $^-x < 4$
          $x < 2$ and $x > {}^-4$
   For these to be true, values of x must be greater than $^-4$ and less than 2, or $\{^-3, {}^-2, {}^-1, 0, 1\}$.

   (b) $2x < {}^-6$ or $1 + x < 0$
          $x < {}^-3$ or $x < {}^-1$
   For these to be true for one or both inequalities, x must be less than $^-1$, or $\{\ldots, {}^-4, {}^-3, {}^-2\}$.
   (Integers satisfying $x < {}^-3$ are a subset of those satisfying $x < {}^-1$)

32. (a)   7   (b) $^-5$

   (c) $^-(^-3) = 3$; additive inverse = $^-3$.

32. (d) $3 - (^-7) = 10$; additive inverse $= ^-10$.

33. (a) $^-3 + ^-7 = ^-10$ (b) $^-3 - ^-7 = ^-3 + 7 = 4$

     (c) $3 + ^-7 = ^-4$ (d) $3 - ^-7 = 3 + 7 = 10$

     (e) $^-3 \cdot 7 = ^-21$ (f) $^-3 \cdot ^-7 = 21$

     (g) $3 - 7 = 3 + ^-7 = ^-4$ (h) $^-21 \div 7 = ^-3$

     (i) $^-21 \div ^-7 = 3$ (j) $7 - 3 - 8 = 7 + ^-3 + ^-8 = ^-4$

     (k) $8 + 2 \cdot 3 - 7 = 8 + 6 + ^-7 = 7$ (l) $^-8 - 7 - 2 \cdot 3 = ^-8 + ^-7 + ^-6 = ^-21$

     (m) $|^-7| \cdot |^-3| = 7 \cdot 3 = 21$ (n) $|^-7| \cdot |^-8| = 7 \cdot 8 = 56$

     (o) $|^-7| + 8 = 7 + 8 = 15$

     (p) $|^-7| - |^-8| = 7 - 8 = 7 + ^-8 = ^-1$

34.

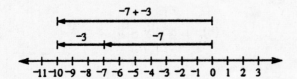

Chapter 4 Test

1. (a) $^-3$ (b) a

    (c) 0   (d) $^-(x + y) = ^-x + ^-y$

    (e) $^-(^-x + y) = x + ^-y$ (f) $^-(^-2^5) = ^-(^-32) = 32$

    (g) $2^5 = 32$

2. (a) $(^-10) + 3 = ^-7$ (b) $^-2 + 5 + 5 = 8$

    (c) $6 + 2 = 8$ (d) $^-3(0) = 0$

    (e) 8   (f) $(^-5)(^-3) = 15$

3. (a) $^-x + 3 = 0 \Rightarrow ^-x = ^-3 \Rightarrow x = 3$

    (b) $^-2x = 10 \Rightarrow x = ^-5$

    (c) All integers except 0.

    (d) $\emptyset$. Division by 0 is undefined.

    (e) $3x - 1 = ^-124 \Rightarrow 3x = ^-123 \Rightarrow x = ^-41$

    (f) True for all integers. $^-2x + 3x = x \Rightarrow x = x$

4. $(^-2) \cdot 3 = ^-6$
    $(^-2) \cdot 2 = ^-4$
    $(^-2) \cdot 1 = ^-2$
    $(^-2) \cdot 0 = 0.$ Continuing the answer sequence gives:
    $(^-2) \cdot (^-1) = 2$
    $(^-2) \cdot (^-2) = 4$
    $(^-2) \cdot (^-3) = 6$

5. (a) $5 - 5 = 0$

    (b) $1 - (^-2) = 3$

6. (a) $(x - y)(x + y) = x(x - y) + y(x - y) = x^2 - xy + xy - y^2 = x^2 - y^2.$

    (b) $(^-2 - x)(^-2 + x) = (^-2)^2 - x^2 = 4 - x^2.$

7. (a) ^-x (b) $^-x - ^-y = ^-x + y$

    (c) $2x - 1 + x = 3x - 1$ (d) $(^-x)^2 + x^2 = 2x^2$

    (e) $(^-x)^3 + x^3 = ^-x^3 + x^3 = 0$

    (f) $(^-3 - x)(3 + x) = ^-3(3 + x) - x(3 + x) = ^-9 + ^-3x - 3x - x^2 = ^-x^2 - 6x - 9.$

8. (a) $(1 - 3)x = ^-2x$ (b) $x(x + 1)$

    (c) $x^2 - 6^2 = (x + 6)(x - 6)$ (d) $(9y^3)^2 - (4x^2)^2 = (9y^3 + 4x^2)(9y^3 - 4x^2)$

    (e) $5(1 + x)$ (f) $(x - y)(x + 1 - 1) = (x - y)x$

9. (a) $^-3x + 7 = ^-x + 11 \Rightarrow ^-2x + 7 = 11 \Rightarrow ^-2x = 4 \Rightarrow x = ^-2.$

    (b)   The only integers a distance of 5 from 0 (definition of absolute value) are 5 or $^-5$.

    (c) $^-2x + 1 < 0 \Rightarrow ^-2x < ^-1 \Rightarrow x > \frac{1}{2}$ (i.e., $\{1, 2, 3, \ldots\}$).

    (d) $^-2(^-3x + 7) < ^-2(^-x + 11) \Rightarrow 6x + ^-14 < 2x + ^-22 \Rightarrow 4x < ^-8 \Rightarrow x < ^-2$ and x an integer.

10. (a)   False. Not positive for $x = 0$.

    (b)   False. Not true when one variable is positive and the other negative.

    (c)   False. Not true when $b < 0$.

    (d)   True.

    (e)   False. $(^-a)(^-b) = ab$, not the additive inverse of ab.

11. (a) $12 \div 6 \neq 6 \div 12.$ (b) $(5 - 4) - 2 \neq 5 - (4 - 2).$

    (c) $6, 12 \in I$, but $6 \div 12 = \frac{1}{2} \notin I.$ (d) $12 \div (6 - 2) \neq 12 \div 6 - 12 \div 2$

12.   (a)
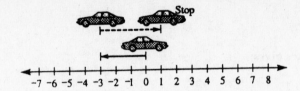

(b)
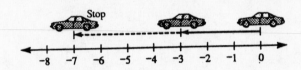

(c)

13.   The new temperature is $^-16 + 9 = {}^-7°$ C.

14.   Let x be the number of 2-kg packages; then $150 - x =$ the number of 1-kg packages. The total weight is given by: $2x + 1(150 - x) = 265 \Rightarrow 2x + 150 - x = 265 \Rightarrow x = 115$. Thus there are 115 2-kg packages and $150 - 115 = 35$ 1-kg packages.

15.   Let d = the number of dimes and n = the number of nickels. Then $d = 2n + 3$. The value of the coins can be represented by: $5n + 10d = 205$ (all in cents) $\Rightarrow 5n + 10(2n + 3) = 205 \Rightarrow 5n + 20n + 30 = 205$ $\Rightarrow 25n = 175 \Rightarrow n = 7$. Thus there are 7 nickels and $2(7) + 3 = 17$ dimes.

16.   Let s = the number of seniors; j = the number of juniors; p = the number of sophomores; and f = the number of freshmen. Then:
$$s + j + p + f = 5715$$
$$s = j + 115$$
$$p = 2s = 2(j + 115) = 2j + 230$$
$f = 2j$. Substituting into the first equation, we have:
$(j + 115) + j + (2j + 230) + 2j = 5715 \Rightarrow 6j + 345 = 5715 \Rightarrow 6j = 5370 \Rightarrow j = 895$.
There are 895 juniors, $(895 + 115) = 1010$ seniors, $[2(895) + 230] = 2020$ sophomores, and $2(895) = 1790$ freshmen.

17.   Let q = quantity originally in each keg. Then $q - 37$ and $q - 7$ remains after the beer has been drawn. The amount $q - 7$ (obviously, the larger quantity) is 7 times the quantity $q - 37$, or:
$$q - 7 = 7(q - 37)$$
Solving, $q - 7 = 7q - 259 \Rightarrow {}^-6q = {}^-252 \Rightarrow q = 42$. 42 gallons were originally in each keg.

18.   Let c = the number of pounds of cashews, p = the number of pounds of pecans, and s = the number of pounds of Spanish peanuts. Then $c + p + s = 10,000$ pounds of nuts. We know that:
$$c = 2p$$
$$3c + 3.2p + 2.2s = 2.72(10,000).$$
Substituting the 2nd equation into the 1st, we have: $2p + p + s = 10,000 \Rightarrow 3p + s = 10,000$, or $s = 10,000 - 3p$. Substituting into the 3rd equation gives:
$$3(2p) + 3.2p + 2.2(10,000 - 3p) = 2.72(10,000)$$
$$6p + 3.2p + 22,000 - 6.6p = 27,200$$
$$2.6p = 5200$$
$$p = 2000.$$
We have 2000 pounds of pecans, $2(2000) = 4000$ pounds of cashews, and $10,000 - 3(2000) = 4000$ pounds of Spanish peanuts.

CHAPTER 5 - NUMBER THEORY

1. (a) True. $30 = 5 \cdot 6$. (b) True. $30 \div 6 = 5$.

   (c) True. $2|30$ and $3|30$, so $6|30$. (d) True. $30 \div 6 = 5$.

   (e) True. $6 \cdot 5 = 30$. (f) False. No integer times 30 equals 6.

2. (a) $7|35$ $(14 + 21 = 35)$. (b) $d|213$ (See Theorem 5-2).

   (c) $d|a$ (See Theorem 5-2). (d) $7|245$

   (e) $d|213$ (f) $d|a$

3. Yes. The question is really, "Does $9|1379$?" Using the divisibility test for 9, $9\nmid(1+3+7+9)$, so $9\nmid1379$. Thus there will be a remainder; i.e., a group of less than 9 players.

4. No. This amounts to, "Does $11|43,682$?" $11\nmid[(4+6+2) - (3+8)]$, so $11\nmid43,682$.

5. (a) Theorem 5-1 with $k = 113$.

   (b) Theorem 5-2(b) with $a = 100$ and $b = 13$.

   (c) None. In fact, $4|1300$.

   (d) Theorem 5-2(b), if $(a + b)$ is thought of as a single integer.

   (e) Theorem 5-1 with $k = a$.

6. (a) No. $17 \cdot 2000 = 34,000$, thus $17|34,000$ and $17\nmid15$ so $17\nmid(34,000 + 15)$.

   (b) Yes. $17|34,000$ and $17|51$.

   (c) No. $19|19,000$ but $19\nmid31$.

   (d) No. $31|31$ but $31\nmid19,000$ (i.e., because $31\nmid19$, $31\nmid1000$, and 31 and 19 are relatively prime).

   (e) No. Even $\nmid$ odd.

   (f) No. All divide $2 \cdot 3 \cdot 5 \cdot 7 \cdot 13 \cdot 17$ and none divide 1, so none divide $2 \cdot 3 \cdot 5 \cdot 7 \cdot 13 \cdot 17 + 1$.

7. (a) 1, 2, 4, 5, 8, 11.

   (b) 1 touchdown and 11 field goals or 4 touchdowns and 4 field goals. (Consider 0 touchdowns - $3\nmid40$, impossible; 2 touchdowns - $3\nmid(40 - 14)$, impossible; etc.)

   (c) An impossible score if an extra point was scored with each touchdown. If not, then there were 5 field goals.

8. (a) (*i*) 1 (*ii*) 2 (*iii*) 3 (*iv*) 7

   (*v*) 3 (*vi*) 6 (*vii*) 6 (*viii*) 0

   (b) The remainder is *a*.

8.   (c)   The remainder is the sum of the digits.

9.   (a)   (*i*)   4   (*ii*)   4   (*iii*)   4

     (b)   (*i*)   8   (*ii*)   8   (*iii*)   8

     (c)   (*i*)   3   (*ii*)   12   (*iii*)   3

     (d)   (*i*)   8   (*ii*)   26   (*iii*)   8

     (e)   (*i*)   2   (*ii*)   20   (*iii*)   2

     (f)   The remainder in the quotient of a given number divided by 9 is the same as the remainder when the sum of the number's digits is divided by 9.

10. (Notation: R1 + R3 = R4 means remainders of 1 + 3 add to a remainder of 4.)

     (a)   R4 + R1 + R2 = R7 (Sum of the individual remainders)
           Sum of numbers = 16,945 → R7

     (b)   R6 + R6 + R8 = R20 → R2
           Sum = 10,208 → R2

     (c)   R8 + R7 + R4 + R2 = R21 → R3
           Sum = 13,458 → R3

     (d)   Yes.   29 + 42 + 3 + 11 = 85
                  R2 + R6 + R3 + R2 → R4; sum = 85 → R4
           (Examples may vary)

     (e)   1003 → R4; 46 → R1. 1003 − 46 = 957 → R3 = R4 − R1.

     (f)   345 → R3; 56 → R2. 345·56 = 19,320 → R6 = R3·R2

     (g)   No. The division may not have an integer quotient, in which case the test fails.

11. (a)   False. Consider d = 7, a = 10, b = 4; 7|(10 + 4) but 7∤10 and 7∤4.

     (b)   False. See above; substitute "or" for "and".

     (c)   True.

     (d)   False. 4|60 but 4∤6 and 4∤10.

     (e)   True.   (f)   True.

     (g)   True.

     (h)   False. If a = 5 and b = ⁻5, then a|b and b|a but a ≠ b.

     (i)   True.   (j)   False. 3∤5 and 3∤7 but 3|(5 + 7).

     (k)   False. $4|10^2$ but 4∤10.

     (l)   False. 4∤6 but $4|6^2$.   (m)   True.

12. (a) True.

(b) False. The <u>sum</u> being divisible does not force every digit to be.

(c) False. E.g., 12.   (d) True.

(e) True.

(f) False. E.g., 20. (The difference between (e) and (f) is that 2 and 3 have no common factors; 2 and 4 do.

(g) True.

13. (a) Always.   (b) Sometimes. E.g., 360.

(c) Never   (d) Always.

(e) Always.   (f) Sometimes. E.g., 24.

(g) Always.

14. (a) $16|n$ if $16|$(last four digits of n). Notice the pattern of divisibility by 2, 4, and 8.

(b) $25|n$ if $25|$(last two digits of n); that is, if n ends in 00, 25, 50, or 75.

15. Yes; equal \$651 installments. The real question is, "Does $12|7812$?"
Checking: $4|7812$ (since $4|12$)
              $3|7812$ [since $3|(7+8+1+2)$]
So $12|7812$ (this is true only because 4 and 3 have no factors in common).

16. 19¢. $209 = 11 \cdot 19$; for whole cent pricing 11¢ and 19¢ are the only possibilities.

17. 85,041. The number must be divisible by 9 and 11. If we write it as 85ab1, then $9|(8+5+a+b+1)$ and $11|[(8+a+1) - (5+b)]$, or $9|(14+a+b)$ and $11|(4+a-b)$. So $a + b = 4$ or 13 and $a - b = {}^-4$ or 7.

Solving, and using trial and error, we find 0 and 4 to be the solutions.

18. The divisors (from the given list) of each number are:

(a) 2, 3, 4, 6, 11   (b) 2, 3, 6, 9

(c) 2, 3, 5, 6, 10   (d) 2, 3, 4, 6

(e) 3, 5   (f) 2, 4

(g) 7, 11   (h) None

(i) 2, 4, 5, 10

19. (a) No. If $5{\not|}n$, then n cannot end in 0, so $10{\not|}n$.

(b) Yes. Any number ending in 5 is divisible by 5, but not by 10.

20. (a) 7   (b) 7

(c) 6

21. The sum of the digits will be of the form $k + k + k + m + m + m + q + q + q = 3k + 3m + 3q$ $= 3(k + m + q)$, which is divisible by 3.

22. $a|b$ implies $a \cdot m = b$ for some integer m. $b|c$ implies $b \cdot n = c$ for some integer n. Substituting $a \cdot m$ for b, we have $(a \cdot m) \cdot n = c$, or $a \cdot (m \cdot n) = c$. Therefore $a|c$.

23. (a) Yes. $4|76$.   (b) No. $4\nmid 86$

(c) Yes. $4|100$ and $400|2000$.   (d) Yes. $4|24$.

24. (a) All are divisible by 11.

(b) Every four-digit palindrome is of the form abba. Since $11|[(a+b) - (b+a)]$, 11 divides all numbers of this form.

(c) No. All are of the form abcba. Using the divisibility test, $(a+c+a) - (b+b)$ is not always divisible by 11.

(d) Yes. Every six-digit palindrome is of the form abccba. Since $11|[(a+c+b) - (b+c+a)]$, 11 divides all numbers of this form.

25. (a) The two numbers with reversed digits will differ by 9.

(b) The numbers will always differ by 18.

(c) Any two-digit number's value may be represented as $10t + u$ (10 times the tens digit plus the units digit). With digits reversed, the value becomes $10u + t$. Taking the difference gives $10t + u - (10u + t) = 9t - 9u = 9(t - u)$, a multiple of 9.

(d) The difference of the two numbers is 9 times the difference of their tens digits.

26. No. This problem is asking for a solution to the problem $6n + 15m = 286$ (see "Diophantine equations" in the text). Since $3|6$ and $3|15$, but $3\nmid 286$, there is no solution. No combinations of 6¢ and 15¢ stamps will make exactly $2.86.

27. For an equation of the form $ax + by = c$ to have integer solutions, the greatest number which divides a and b must divide c.

(a) No solutions. The greatest number which divides both 18 and 27 is 9, and $9\nmid 3111$.

(b) No solutions.   (c) No solutions.

(d) Infinite number of solutions.   (e) No solutions.

(f) Infinite number of solutions.

28. (a) When dividing by 3, the only possible remainders are 0, 1, and 2. Any three consecutive numbers will have these three remainders, in some order. Thus one of the three, and only one, will have remainder 0 and therefore be divisible by 3.

(b) Among a group of n consecutive integers, one and only one of them will always be divisible by n.

29. Prove: If $d|a$ and $d\!\!\not|ab$, then $d\!\!\not|(a+b)$.

   $d|a$ implies $a = md$; $d\!\!\not|b$ implies $b = nd + r$, $0 < r < d$. Then $a + b = md + nd + r = (m+n)d + r$; so $(a+b)\div d = [(m+n)d + r]\div d = m + n + \frac{r}{d}$. Since $0 < r < d$, $\frac{r}{d}$ is not an integer $\Rightarrow m + n + \frac{r}{d}$ is not an integer $\Rightarrow d\!\!\not|(a+b)$.

30. Any five-digit number *abcde* may be written $a\cdot10^4 + b\cdot10^3 + c\cdot10^2 + d\cdot10 + e$, but this is equivalent to $a(9999 + 1) + b(999 + 1) + c(99 + 1) + d(9 + 1) + e$. Distributing and grouping yields $(9999a + 999b + 99c + 9d) + (a + b + c + d + e)$. The first group is divisible by 9, implying that the entire sum (equal to the five-digit number) is divisible by 9 if and only if the second group is divisible by 9; i.e., if the sum of the digits is divisible by 9.

31. Note that $7\cdot11\cdot13 = 1001$. Multiplying any three-digit number by 1001 gives a product with that three-digit number repeated twice. Going the other way, if any "repeated" number of the form *abcabc* is divided by 1001, the quotient is *abc*.

32. This is a matter of solving the Diophantine equation $20t + 50f = 610$ (where t is the number of \$20's and f is the number of \$50's). There are many solutions fitting the conditions of the problem; e.g., $(3\cdot\$20) + (11\cdot\$50)$, or $(8\cdot\$20) + (9\cdot\$50)$, or $(13\cdot\$20) + (7\cdot\$50)$, etc. The solution is not unique.

Problem Set 5-2

1. (a)

$$504 = 2^3 \cdot 3^2 \cdot 7$$

(b)

$$2475 = 3^2 \cdot 5^2 \cdot 11$$

(c)

$$11250 = 2 \cdot 3^2 \cdot 5^4$$

2. (a) Prime. Fails divisibility test for primes to 11; we need not test for primes > 11 because $13^2 > 149$.

   (b) Composite. $13\cdot71 = 923$.

   (c) Prime. Fails divisibility test for primes up to 19 ($23^2 > 433$).

   (d) Prime

   (e) Prime

   (f) Composite. $3|(8+9+7)$ so $3|897$.

3. 73. $73^2 < 5669$, but $79^2 > 5669$. (73 is prime and 79 is the next largest prime.)

4. Multiples of 8, 9, and 10 are multiples of 2 and/or 3, so have been crossed out. All composite numbers ≤ 100 must have a factor ≤ 10; i.e., they will have been crossed out. This leaves only the primes.

5. Use the following procedure:
   (i)   Write the natural numbers from 1 to 200.
   (ii)   Circle 2 because 2 is prime.
   (iii) Cross out multiples of 2; they are not prime.
   (iv)   Circle 3 because 3 is prime.
   (v)   Cross out multiples of 3 that have not already been crossed out.
   (vi)   Circle 5, 7, 11, and 13; cross out their multiples that have not already been crossed out. (We can stop after 13 because 13 is the largest prime whose square is less than 200.)
   (vii) All the numbers remaining in the list and not crossed out are prime. You should end with the following:
          2, 3, 5, 7, 11, 13, 17, 19, 23, 29, 31, 37, 41, 43, 47, 53, 59, 61, 67, 71, 73, 79, 83, 89, 97, 101, 103, 107, 109, 113, 127, 131, 137, 139, 149, 151, 157, 163, 167, 173, 179, 181, 191, 193, 197, 199.

6. 90. If 9 is a factor, then 3 is a factor, as is 1. All possible groupings of these factors yields 12 uniquie factors (1, 2, 3, 5, 9, $2 \cdot 3$, $2 \cdot 5$, $2 \cdot 9$, $3 \cdot 5$, $5 \cdot 9$, $2 \cdot 3 \cdot 5$, $2 \cdot 5 \cdot 9$), so the locker number must in fact be $2 \cdot 5 \cdot 9 = 90$.

7. (a) All pairs of factors of 48 would be possible arrays: 1×48, 2×24, 3×16, or 4×12.

   (b) Since 47 is prime, the only possibility would be 1×47.

8. Yes; 177 flotillas of 1 ship, 1 of 177 ships, 3 of 59 ships, or 59 of 3 ships.

9. (a) Find the prime factorization of 435: $3 \cdot 5 \cdot 29$. Committees can have these numbers of members or products thereof. Thus the possibilities are 3, 5, 15, or 29 members.

   (b) 145 three-member committees ($435 \div 3$)
        87 five-member committees
        29 fifteen-member committees
        15 twenty nine-member committees.

10. This problem is asking for the factors of each number. It is assumed here that a single row is a "degenerate rectangle."

    (a) 1, 2, 3, 4, 6, 9, 12, 18, 36   (b) 1, 2, 4, 7, 14, 28

    (c) 1, 17

    (d) 1, 2, 3, 4, 6, 8, 9, 12, 16, 18, 24, 36, 48, 72, 144

11. 64. Take the smallest prime (2) to one less than the desired number of factors; i.e., $2^6 = 64$. The seven factors are 2^0, 2^1, 2^2, 2^3, 2^4, 2^5, and 2^6 (1, 2, 4, 8, 16, 32, and 64).

12. (a) $2^7 \cdot 41$.

    (b) 16 (2^0, 2^1, ... , 2^7, $2^0 \cdot 41$, $2^1 \cdot 41$, ... , $2^7 \cdot 41$).

    (c) No. (Obvious by the prime factorization, but also since it has an even number of divisors; perfect squares have an odd number of divisors.)

13. (a) Any natural number that is a multiple of 41 (41, 82, 123, ...) will yield a composite number divisible by 41 when substituted into $n^2 - n + 41$. One such number is 6683, where $n = 82$.

13. (b)   Consider a natural number that is a multiple of 41; e.g., 41k. Substituting gives $(41k)^2 - (41k) + 41 = 41(41k^2 - k + 1)$. For each natural number k (an infinite set), there exists such a number divisible by 41.

14.   Each number from 1 to 12 need not be used - we must only have factors of each number, or $\{1, 2, 3, 2^2, 5, 2 \cdot 3, 7, 2^3, 3^2, 2 \cdot 5, 11, 2^2 \cdot 3\}$. The least common multiple is thus $2^3 \cdot 3^2 \cdot 5 \cdot 7 \cdot 11 = 27,720$.

15.   No. Since all pairs of consecutive integers contains one even number, which is divisible by 2 thus making it composite, 2 is the only even prime.

16.   There is no analytic method - one must work through the list of primes. The twin primes are thus: 3 and 5, 5 and 7, 11 and 13, 17 and 19, 29 and 31, 41 and 43, 59 and 61, 71 and 73, 101 and 103, 107 and 109, 137 and 139, 149 and 151, 179 and 181, 191 and 193, and 197 and 199.

17. (a)   6 can be written as a product of primes in only one way; i.e., $2 \cdot 3$. Since $2|n$ and $3|n$ and both are prime, they must be included in the unique factorization. Thus $(2 \cdot 3)(p_1 \cdot p_2 \cdot \ \cdots \ \cdot p_m) = n$, and $6|n$.

   (b) $a|n$ implies $n = ra$. $b|n$ implies $n = sb$. Then $n^2 = (ra)(sb) = (rs)(ab) \Rightarrow ab|(rs)(ab)$ so $ab|n^2$.

18.   No. Using 3 and 4 is correct because they have no common factors. Because 2 and 6 have 2 as a common factor, using them will only ensure divisibility by 6.

19.   Every number would have its "usual" factorization $1 \cdot (p_1 \cdot p_2 \cdot \ \cdots \ \cdot p_n)$, along with infinitely many other such factorizations because $1^n = 1$; n may be any natural number.

20.   All other factors of 42: 1, 2, 3, 6, 7, 14, 21.

21.   No. 5^2 has no factors of either 2 or 3.

22. (a)   0, 4, 6, 8.   All would cause divisibility by 2 at some point; 2 would allow a superprime in the leftmost position only.

   (b)   1, 9. 9 is composite; 1 is not prime by definition.

   (c)   23, 29, 31, 37, 53, 59, 71, 73, 79.

   (d)   Answers may vary. 233, 239, and 373 are three.

23. (a)   49, 121, and 169. They are the squares of numbers in the 2 column.

   (b)   81, 625, and 2401. They are the 4th powers of numbers in the 2 column.

   (c)   38, 39, and 46. Numbers in the 4 column (i.e., numbers with four divisors including 1 and themselves) can be either the cubes of numbers in the 2 column (e.g., divisors of 8 are 2^0, 2^1, 2^2, or 2^3) or products of two primes from the 2 column (e.g., 38 has divisors 1, 2, 19, and 38).

24.   1, by definition, is not a prime number. Thus the prime would have only one (an odd number) divisor; i.e., itself.

25.   9409. Any number with an odd number of factors must be a perfect square. For exactly three factors, the factors must be of the form 1, p, p^2, where p is a prime. Find the largest two-digit prime and square it; i.e., $97^2 = 9409$.

26.   The details of the proof are as follows: If any prime q in the set $\{2, 3, 5, \ldots, p\}$ divides N, then $q|(2 \cdot 3 \cdot 5 \cdot \ \cdots \ \cdot p)$. Because $q \nmid 1$, by Theorem 5-1(b) $q \nmid (2 \cdot 3 \cdot 5 \cdot \ \cdots \ \cdot p + 1)$; that is, $q \nmid N$.

27. In any set of three consecutive integers, exactly one is divisible by (i.e., has a factor of) 3 and either one or two are divisible by 2 (even). The product of these numbers will then contain 2 and 3 as factors, making it divisible by 6.

28. Any such set will contain: 1 number divisible by 4; 1 number divisible by 2 but not 4; and one or two numbers divisible by 3. The product will then have 2, 4, and 3 as distinct and separate factors, making it divisible by $2 \cdot 4 \cdot 3 = 24$.

29. Any number with 3, 6, 9, ... 1's will be divisible by 3 and thus will be composite.

30. All odd terms are composite, since $3(\text{odd}) + 1 = \text{even}$, which implies divisibility by 2.

31. Using $n = 1, 2, \ldots, 15$ gives primes; 16 and 17 yield composite numbers.

32. (a)   False. $11 \nmid (1 + 9) - 8$.

    (b)   True. $13 \cdot 77 = 1001$.

    (c)   True. See Theorem 5-2(b).

    (d)   True. This would be a divisibility test for 77.

33. (a)   Divisors are 2, 3, 6.   (b)   Divisors are 2, 3, 5, 6, 9, 10.

34. If $12|n$ then $n = 12b$ for some integer b. This means that $n = 3 \cdot (4b)$ which implies that $3|n$.

35. Only among eight people; each would get \$422. $8|3376$ but $7 \nmid 3376$.

Problem Set 5-3

1. (a)   (i) $D_{18} = \{1, 2, 3, 6, 9, 18\}$ and $D_{10} = \{1, 2, 5, 10\}$.
                  Thus $\text{GCD}(18, 10) = 2$.

          (ii) $M_{18} = \{18, 36, 54, 72, 90, \ldots\}$ and $M_{10} = \{10, 20, 30, \ldots, 90, \ldots\}$.
                  Thus $\text{LCM}(18, 10) = 90$.

   (b)   (i) $D_{24} = \{1, 2, 4, 6, 8, 12, 24\}$ and $D_{36} = \{1, 2, 3, 4, 6, 9, 12, 18, 36\}$.
                  Thus $\text{GCD}(24, 36) = 12$.

          (ii) $M_{24} = \{24, 48, 72, 96, \ldots\}$ and $M_{36} = \{36, 72, 108, \ldots\}$
                  Thus $\text{LCM}(24, 36) = 72$.

   (c)   (i) $D_8 = \{1, 2, 4, 8\}$, $D_{24} = \{1, 2, 3, 4, 6, 8, 12, 24\}$, and $D_{52} = \{1, 2, 4, 13, 26, 52\}$
                  Thus $\text{GCD}(8, 24, 52) = 4$.

          (ii) $M_8 = \{8, 16, 24, \ldots, 312, \ldots\}$, $M_{24} = \{24, 48, 72, \ldots, 312, \ldots\}$,
                  and $M_{52} = \{52, 104, 156, \ldots, 312, \ldots\}$.
                  Thus $\text{LCM}(8, 24, 52) = 312$.

2. (a) $132 = 2 \cdot 2 \cdot 3 \cdot 11$
          $504 = 2 \cdot 2 \cdot 2 \cdot 3 \cdot 3 \cdot 7$
          Thus $\text{GCD}(132, 504) = 2 \cdot 2 \cdot 3 = 12$ and $\text{LCM}(132, 504) = 2^3 \cdot 3^2 \cdot 7 \cdot 11 = 5544$.

2. (b) $65 = 5 \cdot 13$
           $1690 = 2 \cdot 5 \cdot 13 \cdot 13$
           Thus GCD(65, 1690) $= 5 \cdot 13 = 65$ and LCM(65, 1690) $= 2 \cdot 5 \cdot 13^2 = 1690$ (65 is a factor of 1690).

    (c) $900 = 2 \cdot 2 \cdot 3 \cdot 3 \cdot 5 \cdot 5$
           $96 = 2 \cdot 2 \cdot 2 \cdot 2 \cdot 2 \cdot 3$
           $630 = 2 \cdot 3 \cdot 3 \cdot 5 \cdot 7$
           Thus GCD(900, 96, 630) $= 2 \cdot 3 = 6$ and LCM(900, 96, 630) $= 2^5 \cdot 3^2 \cdot 5^2 \cdot 7 = 50,400$.

    (d) $108 = 2 \cdot 2 \cdot 3 \cdot 3 \cdot 3$
           $360 = 2 \cdot 2 \cdot 2 \cdot 3 \cdot 3 \cdot 5$
           Thus GCD(108, 360) $= 2 \cdot 2 \cdot 3 \cdot 3 = 36$ and LCM(108, 360) $= 2^3 \cdot 3^3 \cdot 5 = 1080$.

    (e) $63 = 3 \cdot 3 \cdot 7$
           $149 = 3 \cdot 7 \cdot 7$
           Thus GCD(63, 149) $= 3 \cdot 7 = 21$ and LCM(63, 149) $= 3^2 \cdot 7^2 = 441$.

    (f) $625 = 5 \cdot 5 \cdot 5 \cdot 5$
           $750 = 2 \cdot 3 \cdot 5 \cdot 5 \cdot 5$
           $1000 = 2 \cdot 2 \cdot 2 \cdot 5 \cdot 5 \cdot 5$
           Thus GCD(625, 750, 1000) $= 5 \cdot 5 \cdot 5 = 125$ and LCM(625, 750, 1000) $= 2^3 \cdot 3 \cdot 5^4 = 15,000$.

3. (a)   GCD(2904, 220) = GCD(220,64) because $2924 \div 220 \rightarrow$ R64
                         = GCD(64, 28) because $220 \div 64 \rightarrow$ R28
                         = GCD(28,8) because $64 \div 28 \rightarrow$ R8
                         = GCD(8,4) because $28 \div 8 \rightarrow$ R4
                         = GCD(4,0) because $8 \div 4 \rightarrow 0$
                         = 4

    (b)   GCD(14595, 10856) = GCD(10856, 3739) because $14595 \div 10856 \rightarrow$ R3739
                            = GCD(3739, 3378) because $10856 \div 3739 \rightarrow$ R3378
                            = GCD(3378, 361) because $3739 \div 3378 \rightarrow$ R361
                            = GCD(361, 129) because $3378 \div 361 \rightarrow$ R129
                            = GCD(129, 103) because $361 \div 129 \rightarrow$ R103
                            = GCD(103, 26) because $129 \div 103 \rightarrow$ R26
                            = GCD(26, 25) because $103 \div 26 \rightarrow$ R25
                            = GCD(25, 1) because $26 \div 25 \rightarrow$ R1
                            = GCD(1, 0) because $25 \div 1 \rightarrow$ R0
                            = 1

    (c)   GCD(123152, 122368) = GCD(122368, 784) because $123152 \div 122368 \rightarrow$ R784
                              = GCD(784, 64) because $122368 \div 784 \rightarrow$ R64
                              = GCD(64, 16) because $784 \div 64 \rightarrow$ R16
                              = GCD(16, 0) because $64 \div 16 \rightarrow$ R0
                              = 16

4. (a)   72   (b)   1440

    (c)   630

5. (a)   GCD(2924, 220) $\cdot$ LCM(2924, 220) $= 2924 \cdot 220$
           $4 \cdot$ LCM(2924, 220) $= 643,280$
           LCM(2924, 220) $= 643,280 \div 4 = 160,820$

5.   (b)   GCD(14595, 10856)·LCM(14595, 10856) = 14595·10856
           1·LCM(14595, 10856) = 158,443,320
           LCM(14595, 10856) = 158,443,320

     (c)   GCD(123152, 122368)·LCM(123152, 122368) = 123,152·122,368
           16·LCM(123152, 122368) = 123,152·122,368
           LCM(123152, 122368) = 123,152·122,368 ÷ 16 = 941,866,496

6.   GCD(6, 10) = 2
     LCM(6, 10) = 30

7.   (a)   The real question is "What is LCM(15, 40, 60)?", since this is when the alarms will coincide.
           LCM(15, 40, 60) = 120, or 120 minutes = 2 hours later, at 8:00 AM.

     (b)   No. This would be equivalent to changing locations of clocks A and B in the room.

8.   5. GCD(9, 12) = 3 and LCM(2, 3) = 6. Since the number is odd, it must be 5.

9.   (a) $60. The smallest number divisible by 1 through 6 is needed; i.e., LCM(1, 2, 3, 4, 5, 6) = 60.

     (b)   60 ÷ 5 = $12.

     (c)   If winners can make change among themselves, 30 bills are needed. If payouts must come exactly
           from the chest, 60 bills ($120) must be in the chest, since four winners of a total of $60 would get $15
           each - not payable in $2 bills.

10. 24. GCD(120, 144) = 24.

11. 24 nights. The question is really "What is the LCM(8, 6)?" LCM(8, 6) = $2^3 \cdot 3$ = 24.

12. 15 cookies. LCM(24, 45) = 360; i.e., $3.60 worth of cookies was sold. $3.60 at 24¢ each is 15 cookies.

13. 2:30 A.M. LCM(90, 75) = 450 minutes = $7\frac{1}{2}$ hours. $7\frac{1}{2}$ hours later than 7:00 P.M. is 2:30 A.M.

14. 36 minutes. LCM(12, 18) = 36.

15. (a)   LCM(a, b) = ab, since a and b have no common factors.

     (b)   GCD(a, a) = a and LCM(a, a) = a. a has all factors in common with a.

     (c)   GCD(a^2, a) = a and LCM(a^2, a) = a^2.

     (d)   GCD(a, b) = a and LCM(a, b) = b.

     (e)   GCD(a, b) = 1 and LCM(a, b) = ab since a and b have no factors in common.

     (f)   a|b. If GCD(a, b) = a, then a must divide both a and b.

     (g)   b|a. If LCM(a, b) = a, then b·n = a (where n can be any integer). Thus a ÷ b = n, or b|a.

16. (a)   True. If both a and b are even, then GCD(a, b) ≥ 2.

     (b)   True. GCD(a, b) = 2 implies that 2|a and 2|b.

     (c)   False. GCD could be any larger multiple of two; e.g., GCD(8, 20) = 4.

16. (d)   False. For a≠b, LCM > GCD.

    (e)   True, by Theorem 5-9.

    (f)   True. If GCD(a, b) were > a, then it could not divide a.

    (g)   True. If LCM(a, b) were < a, then it could not be a multiple.

17. GCD(120, 75) = GCD(75, 45) = GCD(45, 30) = GCD(30, 15) = GCD(15, 0), so GCD(120, 75) = 15.
     Now GCD(105, 15) = GCD(15, 0), so GCD(105, 15) = 15.
     Thus GCD(120, 75, 105) = 15.

18. No. If any pair is relatively prime, then GCD = 1. If any other pair has a common factor, LCM < abc, so
     GCD·LCM < abc. An example is 4, 5, 6: GCD = 1, LCM = 60; 1·60≠4·5·6 = 120.

19. (a)   2 is the only prime factor of 4, and 2∤97,219,988,751.

     (b)   11 is its own only prime factor and 11∤181,345,913 since 11∤(1+1+4+9+3) − (8+3+5+1).

     (c)   3 and 11 are the only prime factors of 33; 11 was ruled out in (b) and 3∤181,345,913 since
            3∤(1+8+1+3+4+5+9+1+3).

20. If GCD(25, x) = 1, then x can have no factors in common with 25, so x cannot have a factor of 5.
     The solution set is thus {1, 2, 3, 4, 6, 7, 8, 9, 11, 12, 13, 14, 16, 17, 18, 19, 21, 22, 23, 24}.

21. (a)   28.   (1 + 2 + 4 + 7 + 14 = 28)

     (b)   Proper divisors of 220 are 1, 2, 4, 5, 10, 11, 20, 22, 44, 55, and 110. Their sum is 284.
            Proper divisors of 284 are 1, 2, 4, 71, and 142. Their sum is 220.

22. Yes. Since GCD(a, b) divides *a* and *b*, any factor, *d*, of GCD(a, b) would also divide *a* and *b*.
     Since d|GCD(a, b), d is a factor.

23. Let x = 64 and y = 15,625. $1,000,000 = 10^6 = 2^6 \cdot 5^6$; if a 2 is paired with a 5 in any factor a 0 results. The
     only way to keep them separate, and thus have no 0's, is to let $x = 2^6 = 64$ and let $y = 5^6 = 15,625$.

24. (a)   Let the number be 83a51. Then 8 + 3 + a + 5 + 1 = 17 + a must be a multiple of 3. If a is a single
            digit, the only possibilities for 17 + a to be a multiple of 3 are 1, 4, or 7.

     (b)   Let the number be 8a691. Then (1+6+8) − (a+9) = 6 − a must be a multiple of 11. The only
            possibility, if a is a single digit, is 6 − a = 0 and a = 6.

     (c)   10306÷23 = 448.09, which implies the number is greater than 23·448. The 2nd factor must end in 2
            to attain the 6 in the units position, which leads to 23·452 = 10396.

25. No. 3|(3+1+1+1) so 3|3111.

26. Answers may vary. 2·3·5·7·11·13 = 30,030 is one.

27. The question is really "What is LCM(1, 2, ... , 11, 12)?"
     Their factors are 1, 2, 3, 2^2, 5, 2·3, 7, 2^3, 3^2, 2·5, 11, and $2^2 \cdot 3$; thus LCM = $2^3 \cdot 3^2 \cdot 5 \cdot 7 \cdot 11$ = 27,720.

28. 43. The next prime squared (47^2) is greater than 2089.

29. The various requirements eliminate numbers one by one:
    "between 62 and 72" eliminates 61;
    "composite" eliminates 67;
    "sum of digits prime" eliminates 63;
    "has more than four factors" eliminates 65 (which has <u>exactly</u> four factors);
    leaves 70 (which has eight factors - 1, 2, 5, 7, 10, 14, 35, 70).

30. (a) 67   (b) 41

    (c) 51, 87, and 93   (d) 91

Problem Set 5-4

1. (a) 3. $(7 + 8 - 12)$ (b) 2. $(4 + 10 - 12)$

    (c) 6. $(3 - 9 + 12)$ (d) 8. $(4 - 8 + 12)$

    (e) 3. $(3 \cdot 9 - 2 \cdot 12)$ (f) 4. $(4 \cdot 4 - 12)$

    (g) Not possible. $1 \oslash 3 = y$ implies $1 = 3 \otimes y$. But $3 \otimes n$ is always $\equiv$ either 0, 3, 6, or 9; so $3 \otimes y \neq 1$.

    (h) 10. $2 \oslash 5 = y$ implies $2 = 5 \otimes y$. Checking numbers 1, 2, 3, ... , 11, 12 finds $y = 10$.

2. (a) 2   (b) 1

    (c) 2   (d) 4

    (e) 2   (f) 1

    (g) 2   (h) 4

3. (a)

$\oplus$	1	2	3	4	5	6	7
1	2	3	4	5	6	7	1
2	3	4	5	6	7	1	2
3	4	5	6	7	1	2	3
4	5	6	7	1	2	3	4
5	6	7	1	2	3	4	5
6	7	1	2	3	4	5	6
7	1	2	3	4	5	6	7

    (b) (i)   Defining subtraction in terms of addition, $5 \ominus 6 = x$ if $5 = 6 \oplus x$. Thus we can follow down the 6 column to find 5 as the answer. This occurs in row 6, so $5 \ominus 6 = 6$.

         (ii) $2 \ominus 5 = x$ if $2 = 5 \oplus x$. Follow down the 5 column to 2, which is on row 4. Thus $2 \ominus 5 = 4$.

    (c) See (b)(i) above.

4. (a)

$\otimes$	1	2	3	4	5	6	7
1	1	2	3	4	5	6	7
2	2	4	6	1	3	5	7
3	3	6	2	5	1	4	7
4	4	1	5	2	6	3	7
5	5	3	1	6	4	2	7
6	6	5	4	3	2	1	7
7	7	7	7	7	7	7	7

(b) (i) Defining division in terms of multiplication, $3 \oslash 5 = x$ (where division is indicated by $\oslash$) if $3 = 5 \otimes x$. Follow down the 5 column to locate the answer of 3. This occurs in row 2, so $3 \oslash 5 = 2$.

(ii) $4 \oslash 6 = x$ if $4 = 6 \otimes x$. Follow down the 6 column to 4, which is on row 3. Thus $4 \oslash 6 = 3$.

(c) Division by numbers other than 7 (1 through 6) is always possible since 1 to 6 is found in all columns (and rows) except the 7th.

5. (a) (i)

$\otimes$	1	2	3
1	1	2	3
2	2	1	3
3	3	3	3

(ii)

$\otimes$	1	2	3	4
1	1	2	3	4
2	2	4	2	4
3	3	2	1	4
4	4	4	4	4

(iii)

$\otimes$	1	2	3	4	5	6
1	1	2	3	4	5	6
2	2	4	6	2	4	6
3	3	6	3	6	3	6
4	4	2	6	4	2	6
5	5	4	3	2	1	6
6	6	6	6	6	6	6

(iv)

$\otimes$	1	2	3	4	5	6	7	8	9	10	11
1	1	2	3	4	5	6	7	8	9	10	11
2	2	4	6	8	10	1	3	5	7	9	11
3	3	6	9	1	4	7	10	2	5	8	11
4	4	8	1	5	9	2	6	10	3	7	11
5	5	10	4	9	3	8	2	7	1	6	11
6	6	1	7	2	8	3	9	4	10	5	11
7	7	3	10	6	2	9	5	1	8	4	11
8	8	5	2	10	7	4	1	9	6	3	11
9	9	7	5	3	1	10	8	6	4	2	11
10	10	9	8	7	6	5	4	3	2	1	11
11	11	11	11	11	11	11	11	11	11	11	11

(b) Division can always be performed by numbers other than the additive identity in the 3 and 11 tables since all numbers occur in each row except the additive identity (i.e., 3 and 11). This is true for all prime number hour clocks.

5. (c)   In those clocks where division cannot always be performed, some rows (and columns) do not contain all numbers (e.g., in the 4-hour clock table in (a), division by 2 is not always possible since 1 and 3 are not in the 2nd row or column. As such, it is not possible to work backwards to find $3 \oslash 2 = x$ by changing to $3 = 2 \otimes x$.

6. (a)   10   (b)   9

    (c)   7   (d)   7. $(^-5 + 12)$

    (e)   1   (f)   6

7. Adding or subtracting multiples of 7 will give dates which fall on the same day of the week.

    (a)   2, 9, 16, 30. $(23 - 21, 23 - 14, 23 - 7, 23 + 7)$

    (b)   3, 10, 17, 24, 31. (Tuesday the 2nd implies Wednesday the 3rd; then add 7's).

    (c)   Wednesday. Since next year is a leap year, it has 366 days. Converting to mod 7, $366 \equiv 52 \cdot 7 + 2 \equiv 2 \pmod 7$. Thus September 3 will be 52 weeks and 2 days later.

8. (a) $29 = 5 \cdot 5 + 4$ so $29 \equiv 4 \pmod 5$

    (b) $3498 \equiv 0 \pmod 3$

    (c) $3498 \equiv 0 \pmod{11}$

    (d)   Adding a multiple of 10 will yield an equivalent number (mod 10); i.e.,
    $^-23 \pmod{10} \equiv (^-22 + 30) \pmod{10} \equiv 7 \pmod{10}$.

9. (a) $81 - 1 = 10 \cdot 8$ (a multiple of 8), so $81 \equiv 1 \pmod 8$. Alternatively:
    $81 = 10 \cdot 8 + 1 = 1 \pmod 8$.

    (b) $81 - 1 = 8 \cdot 10$ (a multiple of 10), so $81 \equiv 1 \pmod{10}$.

    (c) $1000 - {}^-1 = 1001 = 77 \cdot 13$ (a multiple of 13), so $1000 \equiv {}^-1 \pmod{13}$.

    (d)   Just as $10^2 = 99 + 1$, $10^{84} = 9999...99$ (84 nines) $+ 1$. 10^{84} is thus 1 greater than a multiple of 9, so $10^{84} \equiv 1 \pmod 9$.

    (e)   Looking for a pattern, $10^1 \equiv 10 \pmod{11}$, $10^2 \equiv 1 \pmod{11}$, $10^3 \equiv 10 \pmod{11}$, $10^4 \equiv 1 \pmod{11}$, etc. Odd powers of $10 \equiv 10 \pmod{11}$ and even powers of $10 \equiv 1 \pmod{11}$, so $10^{100} = 1 \pmod{11}$.

    (f) $937 - 37 = 900$ (a multiple of 100), so $937 \equiv 37 \pmod{100}$.

10. $a \equiv 0 \pmod m$ implies that $a = km + 0$, which implies $m|a$ since $m|km$. Working the other way, $m|a$ implies $a = km + 0 \equiv 0 \pmod m$.

11. (a)   Since $8|24$, the remainder of $24 \div 8$ is 0. Thus $24 \equiv 0 \pmod 8$.

    (b) $^-90 \equiv 0 \pmod 3$.

    (c) $n|n$ so $n \div n \rightarrow$ remainder of 0, or $n \equiv 0 \pmod n$.

12. (a) $x = 2n$ for n is an integer.   (b) $x = 2n + 1$ for n is an integer.

12. (c) $x = 5n + 3$ for n is an integer.

13. (a) $5^2 = 100 \equiv 1 \pmod 6$
        Then $5^{100} = (5^2)^{50} \equiv (1)^{50} \pmod 6 \equiv 1 \pmod 6$
        So 5^{100} has remainder 1 when divided by 6.

    (b) $5^2 \div 6 \equiv 1 \pmod 6$. Thus $5^{101} = 5^1 \cdot (5^2)^{50} \equiv 5^1 \cdot (1)^{50} \pmod 6 \equiv 5 \pmod 6$.
        The remainder is 5.

    (c) $10^2 = 100 \equiv 1 \pmod{11}$. Thus $10^{99} = 10 \cdot (10^{98}) = 10 \cdot (10^2)^{49} \equiv 10 \cdot (1)^{49} \pmod{11} \equiv 10 \pmod{11}$.
        So the remainder is 10.

    (d) Since $10^2 \equiv 1 \pmod{11}$, then $10^{100} = (10^2)^{50} \equiv (1)^{50} \pmod{11} \equiv 1 \pmod{11}$.
        The remainder is 1.

14. Each indicator is mod 10; e.g., 32 tenths $\equiv$ 2 tenths as far as the tenths wheel is concerned. As a whole, the odometer is mod 100,000 or mod 1,000,000, depending on the make.

15. (a) $^-1$. $10^3 = 76 \cdot 13 + 12 \equiv 12 \pmod{13}$. $12 \pmod{13} \equiv {}^-1 \pmod{13}$ since $12 - 13 = {}^-1$.

    (b) $10^{99} = (10^3)^{33} \equiv ({}^-1)^{33} \pmod{13} \equiv {}^-1 \pmod{13} \equiv 12 \pmod{13}$. The remainder is 12.

16. Since $100 \equiv 0 \pmod 4$, any number with two trailing zeroes $\equiv 0 \pmod 4$. All that must be checked, then, is the number given by the tens and units digits. If this is divisible by 4 $[\equiv 0 \pmod 4]$ then the whole number is $\equiv 0 \pmod 4$; i.e., is divisible by 4.

17. In particular, this fails when $ac \equiv 0 \pmod m$; e.g., $3 \cdot 4 \pmod{12} \equiv 9 \cdot 4 \pmod{12}$ but $3 \not\equiv 9 \pmod{12}$.

Chapter 5 Test

1. (a) False   (b) False

   (c) True   (d) False. This test works only when the two numbers have no common factors.

   (e) False; e.g., 9.

2. (a) False. $7|14$ and $7 \nmid 2$, but $7|14 \cdot 2$.

   (b) False. $3 \nmid (6 + 1)$ but $3|6$.

   (c) True.   (d) True.

   (e) True.   (f) False. $4 \nmid 6$ and $4 \nmid 10$, but $4|6 \cdot 10$.

3. (a) $m = 83,160$

        $2|0$ so $2|m$
        $3|8+3+1+6+0$ so $3|m$
        $4|60$ so $4|m$
        $5|0$ so $5|m$
        $2|m$ and $3|m$ so $6|m$
        Use rule successively:
           $8316 - 2\cdot0 = 8316$
           $831 - 2\cdot6 = 819$
           $81 - 2\cdot9 = 63$
           $7|63$ so $7|m$
        $8|160$ so $8|m$
        $9|8+3+1+6+0$ so $9|m$
        $11|(0+1+8) - (6+3)$ so $11|m$

(b) $n = 83,193$

        $2\nmid3$ so $2\nmid n$
        $3|8+3+1+9+3$ so $3|n$
        $4\nmid93$ so $4\nmid n$
        $5\nmid3$ so $5\nmid n$
        $2\nmid n$ so $6\nmid n$
        Use rule successively:
           $8319 - 2\cdot3 = 8313$
           $831 - 2\cdot3 = 825$
           $82 - 2\cdot5 = 72$
           $7\nmid72$ so $7\nmid n$
        $8\nmid193$ so $8\nmid n$
        $9\nmid8+3+1+9+3$ so $9\nmid n$
        $11|(3+1+8) - (9+3)$ so $11|n$

4. Since $10,007$ is prime, $17\nmid10,007$ and $17|17$. So $17\nmid(10,007+17)$.

5. (a)   Write the number as 87a4.

    $2|4$ so $2|87a4$.

    If $3|87a4$, then $8 + 7 + a + 4 = 19 + a$ must be divisible by 3. Numbers are 21, 24, or 27. Thus $6|87a4$ if $a = 2, 5,$ or 8.

(b)   Write the number as 4a856. To be divisible by 24, it must be divisible by 3 and 8.

    $3|4a856$ if $4 + a + 8 + 5 + 6 = 23 + a$ is divisible by 3; possibilities are 24, 27, and 30, or $a = 1, 4,$ or 7.
    $8|4a856$ if $8|856$; $856 \div 8 = 107$.
    So $24|4a856$ if $a = 1, 4,$ or 7.

(c)   Write the number as 87ab4. Notice that $29|87,000$, so our only concern is that $29|ab4$. The only number to give a 4 in the units position when multiplied by 9 is 6. The only possibilities, then, are $6\cdot29, 16\cdot29$, etc., until the product of $x\cdot29 > 999$. $6\cdot29 = 174, 16\cdot29 = 464, 26\cdot29 = 754,$ and $36\cdot29$ is > 999, so the replacements are 17, 46, or 75.

6. (a)   Composite.   (b)   Prime.

7. The number must be divisible by 3 and 8. $3|4152$ and $8|4152$, so $24|4152$.

8. (a)   4

(b) $GCD(5767, 4453) = GCD(4453, 1314) = GCD(1314, 511) = GCD(511, 292) = GCD(292, 219) = 73$.

9. (a) $LCM = 2^4\cdot5^3\cdot7^4\cdot13\cdot29$.

(b) $GCD(279, 278) = GCD(278, 1) = 1 \Rightarrow$ no common factors.
    Thus $LCD(279, 278)\cdot1 = 279\cdot278 = 77,562$.

10. 16. To obtain k divisors, raise any prime to the $(k - 1)$st power. Here $2^{5-1} = 16$.
    (Divisors are $2^0, 2^1, 2^2, 2^3, 2^4$).

11. 1, 2, 3, 4, 6, 8, 9, 12, 16, 18, 24, 36, 48, 72, 144.

12. (a) $2^2\cdot43$ (b) $2^5\cdot3^2$

(c) $2^2\cdot5\cdot13$ (d) $3\cdot37$

13. This will happen on all common multiples of 3 and 5. The 1st time will be $3\cdot5 = 15$ minutes.

14.   31¢. The price must divide 3193¢; notice that 31|3100 and 31|93.

15.   LCM(45, 30) = 90 minutes. 8:00 A.M. + 90 minutes = 9:30 A.M.

16.   One month of 365 days; five months of 73 days; 365 months of 1 day; 73 months of 5 days.

17.   5 packages. There are 15 children; the candy will come out evenly for LCM(15, 12) = 60.
      60 candies ÷ 12 candies per package = 5 packages.

18.   It does, though; $4235 \cdot 10^0 = 4235$. It can only be written as a multiple of the highest common power (10^0), which makes it appear as though it does not.

19.   n = (99 + 1)a + (9 + 1)b + c = 99a + a + 9b + b + c = 99a + 9b + a + b + c = 9(9a + b)
      + (a + b + c). Since 9 divides 9(9a + b) it divides the entire sum only if it also divides (a + b + c), the sum of the digits. This is in fact the divisibility test for 9.

20.   (a) $7^2 \equiv 1 \pmod{16}$. Thus $7^{100} = (7^2)^{50} \equiv (1)^{50} \pmod{16} \equiv 1 \pmod{16}$
            The remainder is 1.

      (b) $7^2 \equiv 15 \pmod{17}$, so $7^{100} = (7^2)^{50} \equiv (15)^{50} \pmod{17}$.
            $15^2 \equiv 4 \pmod{17}$, so $15^{50} = (15^2)^{25} \equiv 4^{25} \pmod{17}$.
            $4^5 \equiv 4 \pmod{17}$, so $4^{25} = (4^5)^5 \equiv 4^5 \pmod{17} \equiv 4 \pmod{17}$.
            The remainder is 4.

      (c)   First, find a power of 13 for which $13^x \equiv 1 \pmod{10}$.
            $13^4 \equiv 1 \pmod{10}$, so $13^{1937} = 13^{1+1936} = 13^1 \cdot (13^{1936}) = 13 \cdot [(13^4)^{484}] \equiv 13(1)^{484} \pmod{10}$
                $\equiv 13 \pmod{10} \equiv 3 \pmod{10}$.
            The remainder is 3.

21.   Friday. Days of the week here are mod 8. $30 \equiv 6 \pmod 8$, which implies the 30th would be the 6th day of the week, counting Sunday as the 1st day since it begins the month.

22.   Mod 360, since there are 360° in a full circle.

CHAPTER 6 - RATIONAL NUMBERS AS FRACTIONS

Problem Set 6-1

1. (a) The solution to $8x = 7$ is $\frac{7}{8}$.

    (b) Joe ate 7 of the 8 slices of the apple.

    (c) The ratio of boys to girls in this math class is 7 to 8 (also written 7:8).

2. (a) $\frac{1}{6}$ (b) $\frac{1}{4}$

    (c) $\frac{2}{6} = \frac{1}{3}$ (d) $\frac{7}{12}$

    (e) $\frac{5}{16}$ (f) $\frac{2}{16} = \frac{1}{8}$

3. The diagrams illustrate the fundamental law of fractions; i.e., the value of a fraction does not change if its numerator and denominator are multiplied by the same nonzero number.

    (a) Two of the three parts are shaded → $\frac{2}{3}$.

    (b) Four of the six parts are shaded → $\frac{4}{6} = \frac{2}{3}$.

    (c) Six of the nine parts are shaded → $\frac{6}{9} = \frac{2}{3}$.

    (d) Eight of the twelve parts are shaded → $\frac{8}{12} = \frac{2}{3}$.

4. (a)
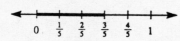

    (b)

    (c)
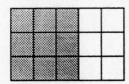

    (d)

    (e)
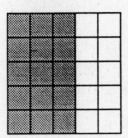

4.   (f)

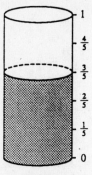

5.   (a) $\dfrac{\text{Dots in circle}}{\text{Total dots}} = \dfrac{9}{24} = \dfrac{3}{8}$

      (b) $\dfrac{\text{Dots in rectangle}}{\text{Total dots}} = \dfrac{12}{24} = \dfrac{1}{2}$

      (c) $\dfrac{\text{Dots in intersection}}{\text{Total dots}} = \dfrac{4}{24} = \dfrac{1}{6}$

      (d) $\dfrac{\text{Dots in rectangle} - \text{circle}}{\text{Total dots}} = \dfrac{8}{24} = \dfrac{1}{3}$

6.   Answers may vary. Some possibilities are:

      (a) $\dfrac{4}{18}, \dfrac{6}{27}, \dfrac{10}{45}$ (b) $\dfrac{^-4}{10}, \dfrac{^-20}{50}, \dfrac{^-24}{60}$

      (c) $\dfrac{0}{6}, \dfrac{0}{9}, \dfrac{0}{12}$ (d) $\dfrac{3a}{6}, \dfrac{5a}{10}, \dfrac{8a}{16}$

7.   (a) $\dfrac{156}{93} = \dfrac{3 \cdot 52}{3 \cdot 31} = \dfrac{52}{31}$ (b) $\dfrac{27}{45} = \dfrac{9 \cdot 3}{9 \cdot 5} = \dfrac{3}{5}$

      (c) $\dfrac{^-65}{91} = \dfrac{^-5 \cdot 13}{7 \cdot 13} = \dfrac{^-5}{7}$ (d) $\dfrac{0}{68} = \dfrac{0}{1}$

      (e) $\dfrac{84^2}{91^2} = \dfrac{(7 \cdot 12)^2}{(7 \cdot 13)^2} = \dfrac{7^2 \cdot 12^2}{7^2 \cdot 13^2} = \dfrac{12^2}{13^2} = \dfrac{144}{169}$

      (f) $\dfrac{662}{703}$ is already in its simplest form because there are no factors common to both the numerator and denominator.

8.   Impossible to determine. Because $\dfrac{20}{25} = \dfrac{24}{30} = \dfrac{4}{5}$, the same fraction of students passed in each class, but the actual scores in one class could have been higher than in the other.

9.   (a)   Undefined. Division by 0 is undefined.

      (b)   Undefined. Division by 0 is undefined.

      (c)   0. $\dfrac{0}{5} = 0$ because $0 \cdot 5 = 0$.

      (d)   Cannot be simplified. Since 2 and a have no common factors other than 1, $\dfrac{2+a}{a}$ cannot be simplified.

      (e)   Cannot be simplified. Note that $\dfrac{15+x}{3x}$ is not the same as $\dfrac{15 \cdot x}{3x} = \dfrac{15x}{3x} = 5$.

      (f) $\dfrac{2}{3}$. $\dfrac{2^6 + 2^5}{2^4 + 2^7} = \dfrac{2^5(2^1 + 1)}{2^4(1 + 2^3)} = \dfrac{2^5(3)}{2^4(9)} = \dfrac{32 \cdot 3}{16 \cdot 9} = \dfrac{2 \cdot 16 \cdot 3}{16 \cdot 3 \cdot 3} = \dfrac{2}{3}$.

      (g) $\dfrac{5}{3}$. $\dfrac{2^{100} + 2^{98}}{2^{100} - 2^{98}} = \dfrac{2^{98}(2^2 + 1)}{2^{98}(2^2 - 1)} = \dfrac{2^{98} \cdot 5}{2^{98} \cdot 3} = \dfrac{5}{3}$.

10. (a) $\frac{x}{x} = 1$

(b) $\frac{14x^2y}{63xy^2} = \frac{7 \cdot 2 \cdot x \cdot x \cdot y}{7 \cdot 9 \cdot x \cdot y \cdot y} = \frac{2x}{9y}$.

(c) $\frac{a^2 + ab}{a + b} = \frac{a(a + b)}{a + b} = \frac{a}{1}$

(d) $\frac{a^3 + 1}{a^3 b}$ cannot be simplified; there are no factors common to both the numerator and denominator.

(e) $\frac{a}{3a + ab} = \frac{a}{a(3 + b)} = \frac{1}{3 + b}$

(f) $\frac{a}{3a + b}$ cannot be simplified.

11. (a) $\frac{375}{1000} = \frac{125 \cdot 3}{125 \cdot 8} = \frac{3}{8}$. The pairs are equal.

(b) $\frac{18}{54} = \frac{18}{3 \cdot 18} = \frac{1}{3}$. $\frac{23}{69} = \frac{23}{3 \cdot 23} = \frac{1}{3}$. The pairs are equal.

(c) $\frac{600}{1000} = \frac{6 \cdot 100}{10 \cdot 100} = \frac{6}{10}$. The pairs are equal.

(d) $\frac{17}{27}$ is in its simplest form. $\frac{25}{45} = \frac{5 \cdot 5}{5 \cdot 9} = \frac{5}{9}$. The pairs are not equal.

12. (a) $16 = 2^4$; $18 = 2 \cdot 3^2$. The LCM $= 2^4 \cdot 3^2 = 144$.
$\frac{10}{16} = \frac{10 \cdot 9}{16 \cdot 9} = \frac{90}{144}$ and $\frac{12}{18} = \frac{12 \cdot 8}{18 \cdot 8} = \frac{96}{144}$. The pairs are not equal.

(b) $12 = 2^2 \cdot 3$; $154 = 2 \cdot 7 \cdot 11$. The LCM $= 2^2 \cdot 3 \cdot 7 \cdot 11 = 924$.
$\frac{3}{12} = \frac{3 \cdot 77}{12 \cdot 77} = \frac{231}{924}$ and $\frac{41}{154} = \frac{41 \cdot 6}{154 \cdot 6} = \frac{246}{924}$. The pairs are not equal.

(c) $\frac{-3}{-12} = \frac{-3}{12} = \frac{-3 \cdot 12}{12 \cdot 12} = \frac{-36}{144}$. The pairs are equal.

(d) $86 = 2 \cdot 43$; $215 = 5 \cdot 43$. The LCM $= 2 \cdot 5 \cdot 43 = 430$.
$\frac{-21}{86} = \frac{-21 \cdot 5}{86 \cdot 5} = \frac{-105}{430}$ and $\frac{-51}{215} = \frac{-51 \cdot 2}{215 \cdot 2} = \frac{-102}{430}$. The pairs are not equal.

13. Yes. $\frac{3}{8} = \frac{3 \cdot 4}{8 \cdot 4} = \frac{12}{32}$, so the board is thick enough. Shaving off $\frac{1}{32}$ will bring it to the required thickness.

14. The shaded area takes in 3 of the 4 columns and 6 of the 8 small rectangles. Since the area in each case is the same, $\frac{3}{4}$ must equal $\frac{6}{8}$. See below.

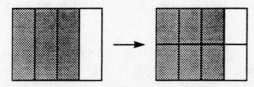

15. To obtain equivalent fractions, multiply numerator and denominator by the same number. All fractions equivalent to $\frac{3}{4}$ will then be of the form $\frac{3x}{4x}$. To satisfy the given requirement, $3x + 4x = 84$, or $x = 12$. The desired fraction is $\frac{3 \cdot 12}{4 \cdot 12} = \frac{36}{48}$.

16. Meter A has $\frac{4}{10}$ of 1 hour left; meter B has $\frac{4}{10}$ of $\frac{1}{2}$ hour $= \frac{2}{10}$ of 1 hour left. Meter A has more time by $\frac{4}{10} - \frac{2}{10} = \frac{2}{10}$ hour $= 12$ minutes.

17. Mr. Gomez had $16 - 6 = 10$ gallons left.
$\frac{10}{16} = \frac{5}{8}$ tank remained; the needle points to the 5th division of 8, as shown to the right.

18. (a) $2\frac{7}{8}$ inch.

(b) $2\frac{3}{8}$ inch.

(c) $1\frac{3}{8}$ inch.

(d) $\frac{7}{8}$ inch.

19. The product is smaller than either. A fraction less than one is multiplied by another fraction less than one; i.e., a part of a part is taken.

20. Yes. Zero has no reciprocal since $\frac{1}{0}$ is undefined.

21. Depending on the application, it may be desireable to leave a fraction unreduced. For example, most will grasp $\frac{65}{100}$ of a dollar (65¢) better than $\frac{13}{20}$ of a dollar.

22. Answers may vary. $\frac{12}{21}$, $\frac{24}{42}$, and $\frac{48}{84}$ also fit the conditions.

23. (a) For equal fractions $\frac{a}{b} = \frac{c}{d}$, ad = bc. With $\frac{2}{3} = \frac{x}{16}$, $2 \cdot 16 = 3 \cdot x \Rightarrow 32 = 3x \Rightarrow x = \frac{32}{3}$.

    (b) $3 \cdot x = 4 \cdot (^-27) \Rightarrow 3x = ^-108 \Rightarrow x = ^-36$.

    (c) $3 \cdot x^2 = x \cdot 3x \Rightarrow 3x^2 = 3x^2$. All nonzero rational numbers are solutions.

24. (a) $ac = bc \Rightarrow a = b \ (c \neq 0)$.

    (b) $b = c \neq 0$, or $a = 0$ and $b \neq 0$ and $c \neq 0$.

25. (a) True. Integers may be made rational with a denominator of 1.

    (b) True. $I \cup W = I$ is a proper subset of Q because there exist elements of Q that are not in I; e.g., $\frac{1}{2}$.

    (c) False. The elements of Q that are not in I are not in W.

    (d) False. $Q \cap I = I$.

    (e) True. The intersection of rational numbers with whole numbers (i.e., numbers that are common to both sets) is the set of whole numbers, since all whole numbers are rational.

26. (a) Unequal.   (b) Unequal.

    (c) Equal.

Problem Set 6-2

1. Since the LCD = 15, we need increments of $\frac{1}{15}$ on the number line. $\frac{1}{5} = \frac{3}{15}$ and $\frac{2}{3} = \frac{10}{15}$, so we have:

2. (a) LCD = 16. $\frac{3}{16} + \frac{^-7}{8} = \frac{3}{16} - \frac{7 \cdot 2}{8 \cdot 2} = \frac{3 - 14}{16} = \frac{^-11}{16}$

    (b) LCD = 12. $\frac{4}{12} - \frac{2}{3} = \frac{4}{12} - \frac{2 \cdot 4}{3 \cdot 4} = \frac{4 - 8}{12} = \frac{^-4}{12} = \frac{^-1}{3}$

    (c) LCD = 18. $\frac{5}{6} + \frac{^-4}{9} + \frac{2}{3} = \frac{5 \cdot 3}{6 \cdot 3} - \frac{4 \cdot 2}{9 \cdot 2} + \frac{2 \cdot 6}{3 \cdot 6} = \frac{15 - 8 + 12}{18} = \frac{19}{18} = 1\frac{1}{18}$

    (d) LCD = 42. $\frac{2}{21} - \frac{3}{14} = \frac{4 - 9}{42} = \frac{^-5}{42}$

3. If $\frac{a}{b}$ and $\frac{c}{d}$ are any two rational numbers, then $\frac{a}{b} + \frac{c}{d} = \frac{ad + bc}{bd}$.

   (a) $\frac{6}{5} + \frac{^-11}{4} = \frac{6}{5} - \frac{11}{4} = \frac{6\cdot4 \; - \; 5\cdot11}{5\cdot4} = \frac{24 \; - \; 55}{20} = \frac{^-31}{20}$

   (b) $\frac{4}{5} + \frac{6}{7} = \frac{4\cdot7 + 5\cdot6}{5\cdot7} = \frac{28 + 30}{35} = \frac{58}{35}$

   (c) $\frac{^-7}{8} + \frac{2}{5} = \frac{^-7\cdot5 + 8\cdot2}{8\cdot5} = \frac{^-35 + 16}{40} = \frac{^-19}{40}$

   (d) $\frac{5}{x} + \frac{^-3}{y} = \frac{5\cdot y \; - \; x\cdot3}{x\cdot y} = \frac{5y \; - \; 3x}{xy}$

4. (a) LCD = 4xy. $\frac{^-3}{2x} + \frac{3}{2y} + \frac{^-1}{4xy} = \frac{^-3\cdot2y}{2x\cdot2y} + \frac{3\cdot2x}{2y\cdot2x} - \frac{1}{4xy} = \frac{^-6y + 6x \; - \; 1}{4xy}$

   (b) LCD = $6x^2y^2$. $\frac{^-3}{2x^2y} + \frac{5}{6xy^2} + \frac{7}{x^2} = \frac{^-3\cdot3y}{2x^2y\cdot3y} + \frac{5\cdot x}{6xy^2\cdot x} + \frac{7\cdot6y^2}{x^2\cdot6y^2} = \frac{^-9y + 5x + 42y^2}{6x^2y^2}$

5. Two methods are shown; either is acceptable.

   (a) $\frac{56}{3} = \frac{3\cdot18 + 2}{3} = \frac{3\cdot18}{3} + \frac{2}{3} = 18 + \frac{2}{3} = 18\frac{2}{3}$

   (b) $14 \div 5 = 2$, remainder $4 \Rightarrow 2\frac{4}{5}$

   (c) $-\frac{293}{100} = -\left(\frac{2\cdot100 + 93}{100}\right) = -2\frac{93}{100}$

   (d) $47 \div 8 = 5$, remainder $7 \Rightarrow -5\frac{7}{8}$

6. (a) $6\frac{3}{4} = \frac{6}{1} + \frac{3}{4} = \frac{6\cdot4 + 1\cdot3}{1\cdot4} = \frac{24 + 3}{4} = \frac{27}{4}$ (b) $\frac{15}{2}$

   (c) $\frac{^-29}{8}$ (d) $\frac{^-14}{3}$

7. (a) $\frac{5}{6} + 2\frac{1}{8} = \frac{5}{6} + \frac{17}{8} = \frac{5\cdot8 + 6\cdot17}{6\cdot8} = \frac{40 + 102}{48} = \frac{142}{48} = \frac{71}{24} = 2\frac{23}{24}$

   (b) $^-4\frac{1}{2} - 3\frac{1}{6} = ^-4\frac{3}{6} - 3\frac{1}{6} = ^-7\frac{4}{6} = ^-7\frac{2}{3} \text{ (or } \frac{^-23}{3})$

   (c) LCD = $2^4\cdot3^4$. $\frac{5}{2^4\cdot3^2} - \frac{1}{2^3\cdot3^4} = \frac{5\cdot3^2}{2^4\cdot3^2\cdot3^2} - \frac{1\cdot2}{2^3\cdot3^4\cdot2} = \frac{45 - 2}{2^4\cdot3^4} = \frac{43}{2^4\cdot3^4}$

   (d) LCD = 45. $11 - \left(\frac{3}{5} + \frac{^-4}{45}\right) = \frac{11\cdot45}{1\cdot45} - \frac{3\cdot9}{5\cdot9} + \frac{4}{45} = \frac{495 - 27 + 4}{45} = \frac{472}{45} = 10\frac{22}{45}$

8. A denominator of 24 eliminates 5; 2 in the denominator would give an answer greater than 1. Trial and error thus yields: $\frac{2}{6} + \frac{5}{8} = \frac{23}{24}$.

9. (a) Round 46 to 45 for ease of computation. $\frac{15}{45} = \frac{1}{3}$. This estimate is too high because the denominator is smaller than actual.

   (b) Change the denominator to 42. $\frac{7}{42} = \frac{1}{6}$. This estimate is too low because the denominator is larger than actual.

   (c) Round 62 to 60. $\frac{60}{80} = \frac{3}{4}$. This estimate is too low because the numerator is smaller than actual.

   (d) Round the numerator to 10 and the denominator to 20. $\frac{10}{20} = \frac{1}{2}$. This estimate is too low because the numerator was increased by a greater percentage than the denominator.

10. (a) Beavers   (b) Ducks

   (c) Bears   (d) Tigers

   (e) Lions   (f) Wildcats and Badgers

11. (a) $\frac{1}{2}$; too high. $\frac{19}{38} = \frac{1}{2}$ so $\frac{19}{39} < \frac{1}{2}$.   (b)   0; too low.

     (c) $\frac{3}{4}$; too high. $\frac{150}{200} = \frac{3}{4}$ so $\frac{150}{201} < \frac{3}{4}$.   (d)   1; too high.

     (e)   1; too low.   (f)   0; too high. $\frac{^{-}2}{117} < 0$.

     (g) $\frac{3}{4}$; too low. $\frac{150}{200} = \frac{3}{4}$ so $\frac{150}{198} > \frac{3}{4}$.   (h) $\frac{1}{2}$; too high. $\frac{1000}{2000} = \frac{1}{2}$ so $\frac{999}{2000} < \frac{1}{2}$.

12. (a)   2. Each of these addends is about $\frac{1}{2}$, so the best approximation would be $4 \cdot \frac{1}{2} = 2$.

     (b) $\frac{3}{4}$. $\frac{30}{41}$ is about $\frac{3}{4}$, and the other two addends are negligible compared to $\frac{3}{4}$.

     (c)   0. The addends are about $\frac{1}{3} + \frac{1}{3} - \frac{2}{3} = 0$.

     (d)   0. Each of the addends is about $\frac{1}{100}$, so we have about $\frac{1 - 1 + 1 - 1}{100} = 0$.

13. (a) $5 + 2 + 3 = 10$ (b) $3 + 5 + 4\frac{1}{2} - 12\frac{1}{2} = 0$

     (c) $5\frac{1}{2} + 3\frac{1}{2} + 4 = 13$ (d) $149 + 2 = 151$

14. (a)   Juan needs a little more than 11 pounds of cereal. He bought about 5 pounds, 3 pounds, and 3 pounds, totalling about 11 pounds. He probably does not have enough (the exact amount he bought was $11\frac{1}{16}$ pounds).

     (b)   Estimating, $1\frac{3}{4} + 3\frac{1}{4} = 5$ hours. The estimate is low since $3\frac{5}{12}$ was rounded down; i.e., Jill did not make the trip in less than 5 hours.

15. Possible thought processes could be:

     (a) $\frac{4}{4} - \frac{3}{4} = \frac{1}{4}$ (b) $(5 + 1) - \frac{7}{8} = 5 + \left(\frac{8}{8} - \frac{7}{8}\right) = 5\frac{1}{8}$

     (c) $\left(3 + 2 + \frac{3}{8} + \frac{2}{8}\right) - 5\frac{5}{8} = 5\frac{5}{8} - 5\frac{5}{8} = 0$

     (d) $\left(2 + 4 + 3 + \frac{6}{10} + \frac{1}{10} + \frac{3}{10}\right) = 9 + \frac{10}{10} = 10$

16. (a) $\frac{20}{8}$ is between 2 and 3; thus region A.

     (b) $\frac{36}{8}$ is between 4 and 5; thus region H.

     (c) $\frac{60}{16}$ is between 3 and 5; thus region T.

     (d) $\frac{18}{4}$ is between 4 and 5; thus region H.

17. (a) $\frac{d}{b} + \frac{a}{bc} = \frac{d \cdot c}{b \cdot c} + \frac{a}{bc} = \frac{dc + a}{bc}$

     (b) $\frac{a}{a - b} + \frac{b}{a + b} = \frac{a(a + b) + b(a - b)}{(a - b)(a + b)} = \frac{a^2 + ab + ab - b^2}{a^2 - b^2} = \frac{a^2 + 2ab - b^2}{a^2 - b^2}$

     (c)   LCD $= (a^2 - b^2) = (a + b)(a - b)$.

           $\frac{a}{a^2 - b^2} - \frac{b}{a - b} = \frac{a}{a^2 - b^2} - \frac{b(a + b)}{(a - b)(a + b)} = \frac{a - ab - b^2}{a^2 - b^2}$

18. (a) $\frac{3 + 3}{3}$ does not equal $\frac{3}{3} + 3$.

     (b) $\frac{4}{2 + 2}$ does not equal $\frac{4}{2} + \frac{4}{2}$.

18.   (c)   There are no factors that are common to both terms of the numerator and to the denominator; thus the a's cannot be canceled.

      (d)   Similar to (c).

      (e)   Similar to (c).

19.   The whole student population is represented by 1. We then subtract to obtain the senior's fraction; i.e., seniors make up $1 - \frac{2}{5} - \frac{1}{4} - \frac{1}{10}$ of the class. Using a LCD of 20: $\frac{20}{20} - \frac{8}{20} - \frac{5}{20} - \frac{2}{20} = \frac{5}{20} = \frac{1}{4}$. Thus seniors make up $\frac{1}{4}$ of the class.

20.   (a) $\frac{1}{5} - \frac{1}{6} = \frac{6}{30} - \frac{5}{30} = \frac{1}{30}$

      (b) $\frac{7}{20} - \frac{1}{4} = \frac{7}{20} - \frac{5}{20} = \frac{1}{10}$

      (c) $\frac{7}{20} - \frac{1}{3} = \frac{21}{60} - \frac{20}{60} = \frac{1}{60}$

      (d)   No. $\frac{1}{10}$ in 1990 is greater than $\frac{1}{20}$ in 1980

21.   Using the completed diagonal, all rows, columns, and diagonals must add to $1 + \frac{11}{12} + \frac{5}{6} = \frac{12}{12} + \frac{11}{12} + \frac{10}{12} = \frac{33}{12}$. Then subtracting to obtain the missing values, we have:

5/3	1/12	1
1/4	11/12	19/12
5/6	7/4	1/6

22. $\frac{1}{3} + 2\frac{3}{4} + 3\frac{1}{2} = \frac{4}{12} + 2\frac{9}{12} + 3\frac{6}{12} = 5\frac{19}{12} = 6\frac{7}{12}$ yards.

23.   It might be easier, but she'd not have a correct solution. Think of the numerator as the number of pieces of pie cut into the denominator's value of slices. Then to add the pieces of pie, we'd add the numerators and have that number of pieces.

24.   No. Since $\frac{4}{5}$ is a proper fraction, there is no equivalent that can be improper.

25.   He should put in $3\frac{1}{2} - \frac{3}{4} - 1 = 3\frac{2}{4} - \frac{3}{4} - \frac{4}{4} = \frac{14}{4} - \frac{3}{4} - \frac{4}{4} = \frac{7}{4}$, or $1\frac{3}{4}$ cups more.

26.   Although they are not whole quantities, they still count and do add up to be whole quantities. A single fractional part may be far from negligible; e.g., $\frac{7}{8}$.

27.   The amount of fabric to be used is $1\frac{7}{8} + 2\frac{3}{8} + 1\frac{2}{3} = 1\frac{21}{24} + 2\frac{9}{24} + 1\frac{16}{24} = 4\frac{46}{24} = 5\frac{22}{24}$ yards. She bought $8\frac{3}{4}$ yards, so there will be $8\frac{18}{24} - 5\frac{22}{24} = 7\frac{42}{24} - 5\frac{22}{24} = 2\frac{20}{24} = 2\frac{5}{6}$ yards left over.

28. $38\frac{1}{4} - 15\frac{3}{4} - \frac{3}{8} = 22\frac{1}{8}$ inches.

29.   (a)   Team 4; they collected $35\frac{3}{16} + 41\frac{1}{2} = 76\frac{11}{16}$ pounds.

      (b)   Collections in April were $28\frac{3}{4} + 32\frac{7}{8} + 28\frac{1}{2} + 35\frac{3}{16} = 125\frac{5}{16}$ pounds.

            Collections in May were $33\frac{1}{3} + 28\frac{5}{12} + 25\frac{3}{4} + 41\frac{1}{2} = 129$ pounds.

            The difference is $129 - 125\frac{5}{16} = 3\frac{11}{16}$ pounds.

30.   (a)   Like digits are being canceled.

      (b)   Numerators and denominators are both being added.

30. (c)   Numerators and denominators of fractional portions are both being subtracted.

     (d)   Multiplication is by $\frac{a}{a}$ rather than by $\frac{a}{1}$.

31. (a)   According to this property, if two rational numbers are added, the sum should also be rational; e.g., $\frac{1}{2} + \frac{3}{4} = \frac{5}{4}$, which is a rational number.

     (b) $\frac{a}{b} + \frac{c}{d}$ should equal $\frac{c}{d} + \frac{a}{b}$; e.g., $\frac{1}{4} + \frac{2}{3} = \frac{11}{12} = \frac{2}{3} + \frac{1}{4}$.

     (c)   The associative property states that $\frac{a}{b} + \left(\frac{c}{d} + \frac{e}{f}\right) = \left(\frac{a}{b} + \frac{c}{d}\right) + \frac{e}{f}$. E.g., $\frac{1}{2} + \left(\frac{2}{3} + \frac{3}{4}\right) = \frac{23}{12} = \left(\frac{1}{2} + \frac{2}{3}\right) + \frac{3}{4}$.

32. (a)   Yes. Closure is inherited from addition, since subtraction is equivalent to addition of an opposite.

     (b)   No. Switching order results in opposites (additive inverses).

     (c)   No. $\frac{a}{b} - \left(\frac{c}{d} - \frac{e}{f}\right) = \frac{a}{b} - \frac{c}{d} + \frac{e}{f} \neq \left(\frac{a}{b} - \frac{c}{d}\right) - \frac{e}{f} = \frac{a}{b} - \frac{c}{d} - \frac{e}{f}$.

     (d)   No. If there is an identity for subtraction it must be 0, since only for 0 does $\frac{a}{b} - 0 = \frac{a}{b}$. However, in general $0 - \frac{a}{b} \neq \frac{a}{b} - 0$, and thus there is no identity.

     (e)   No. Since there is no identity, an inverse cannot be defined.

33. (a) $\frac{3}{2}, \frac{7}{4}, 2$. Arithmetic; difference is $\frac{1}{4}$.

     (b) $\frac{6}{7}, \frac{7}{8}, \frac{8}{9}$. Each term is $\frac{n}{n+1}$; it is not arithmetic because there is no constant difference.

     (c) $\frac{17}{3}, \frac{20}{3}, \frac{23}{3}$. Arithmetic; difference is $\frac{3}{3}$.

     (d) $\frac{^-5}{4}, \frac{^-7}{4}, \frac{^-9}{4}$. Arithmetic; difference is $\frac{^-1}{2}$.

34. (a) $\frac{1}{4}n$ (b) $\frac{n}{n+1}$

     (c) $n - \frac{1}{3}$, or $\frac{3n-1}{3}$ (d) $\frac{7}{4} - \frac{1}{2}n$, or $\frac{7-2n}{4}$

35. Use the methodology for arithmetic sequences from Chapter 1 [i.e., $a_n = a_1 + (n-1)d$].
     Our sequence is: 1, a_2, a_3, a_4, a_5, a_6, 2. Thus $a_1 = 1$ and $a_7 = 2$, so $2 = 1 + (7-1)d$.
     Solving for d, we have $d = \frac{1}{6}$. Then $a_2 = 1 + \frac{1}{6} = \frac{7}{6}$; $a_3 = \frac{7}{6} + \frac{1}{6} = \frac{8}{6}$; etc.

     Our sequence is 1, $\frac{7}{6}$, $\frac{8}{6}$, $\frac{9}{6}$, $\frac{10}{6}$, 2.

36. (a)   (i) $\frac{3}{4}$ (ii) $2\frac{1}{12}$

            (iii)   0

     (b)   (i) $\frac{1}{4}$ (ii) $\frac{^-7}{4}$

            (iii) $\frac{^-1}{4}$

37. (a) $f(0) = \frac{0+2}{0-1} = \frac{2}{^-1} = {}^-2$ (b) $f(^-2) = \frac{^-2+2}{^-2-1} = \frac{0}{^-3} = 0$

     (c) $f(^-5) = \frac{^-5+2}{^-5-1} = \frac{^-3}{^-6} = \frac{1}{2}$ (d) $f(5) = \frac{5+2}{5-1} = \frac{7}{4}$

38. (a)   (i) $\frac{1}{4} + \frac{1}{3 \cdot 4} = \frac{3 \cdot 1}{3 \cdot 4} + \frac{1}{3 \cdot 4} = \frac{3}{12} + \frac{1}{12} = \frac{4}{12} = \frac{1}{3}$

            (ii) $\frac{1}{5} + \frac{1}{4 \cdot 5} = \frac{4}{20} + \frac{1}{20} = \frac{1}{4}$

38. (a) *(iii)* $\frac{1}{6} + \frac{1}{5\cdot6} = \frac{5}{30} + \frac{1}{30} = \frac{1}{5}$

    (b) $\frac{1}{n} = \frac{1}{n+1} + \frac{1}{n(n+1)}$

    (c) $\frac{1}{n+1} + \frac{1}{n(n+1)} = \frac{n\cdot1}{n(n+1)} + \frac{1}{n(n+1)} = \frac{n+1}{n(n+1)} = \frac{1}{n}$

39. (a) $\frac{14}{21} = \frac{2\cdot7}{3\cdot7} = \frac{2}{3}$ (b) $\frac{117}{153} = \frac{3\cdot3\cdot13}{3\cdot3\cdot17} = \frac{13}{17}$

    (c) $\frac{5^2}{7^2} = \frac{25}{49}$ (d) $\frac{a^2 + a}{1 + a} = \frac{a(a+1)}{a+1} = \frac{a}{1}$

    (e) $\frac{a^2 + 1}{a + 1}$ is already in simplest form.

40. (a) Equal. (b) Unequal.

    (c) Equal. (d) Unequal.

Problem Set 6-3

1. (a) The shaded vertical region represents $\frac{1}{3}$ of the total area. The shaded horizontal region represents $\frac{1}{4}$ of the total area. The cross-hatched region represents $\frac{1}{4}$ of $\frac{1}{3}$, or the product of the two fractions. Since one of the twelve blocks is cross-hatched, then, the product of $\frac{1}{4}$ and $\frac{1}{3}$ is $\frac{1}{12}$.

    (b) The shaded vertical region represents $\frac{3}{5}$ of the total area. The shaded horizontal region represents $\frac{2}{4}$ of the total area. The cross-hatched region represents $\frac{2}{4}$ of $\frac{3}{5}$, or the product of the two fractions. Since six of the twenty blocks are cross-hatched, then, the product of $\frac{2}{4}$ and $\frac{3}{5}$ is $\frac{6}{20}$.

2. (a)

    (b)

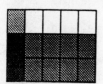

    (c)

3. B. The product of C and D can be neither greater than C or D nor negative.

4. (a) $\frac{1}{5}$ (b) $\frac{b}{a}$

    (c) $\frac{az}{x^2y}$ (d) $\frac{35}{4}$ or $8\frac{3}{4}$

    (e) $\frac{44}{3}$ or $14\frac{2}{3}$ (f) $\frac{^-25}{4}$ or $^-6\frac{1}{4}$

5. (a) $4\frac{1}{2}\cdot 2\frac{1}{3} = (4 + \frac{1}{2})\cdot(2 + \frac{1}{3}) = 4(2 + \frac{1}{3}) + \frac{1}{2}(2 + \frac{1}{3}) = 8 + \frac{4}{3} + 1 + \frac{1}{6} = 9 + \frac{8}{6} + \frac{1}{6} = 10\frac{1}{2}$

(b) $3\frac{1}{3}\cdot 2\frac{1}{2} = (3 + \frac{1}{3})\cdot(2 + \frac{1}{2}) = 3(2 + \frac{1}{2}) + \frac{1}{3}(2 + \frac{1}{2}) = 6 + \frac{3}{2} + \frac{2}{3} + \frac{1}{6} = 6 + \frac{9}{6} + \frac{4}{6} + \frac{1}{6} = 8\frac{1}{3}$

(c) $248\frac{2}{5}\cdot 100\frac{1}{8} = 248(100 + \frac{1}{8}) + \frac{2}{5}(100 + \frac{1}{8}) = 24{,}800 + 31 + 40 + \frac{1}{20} = 24{,}871\frac{1}{20}$

6. (a) $\frac{3}{-1} = {}^{-}3$ (b) $\frac{3}{10}$

(c) $\frac{y}{x}$ (d) $\frac{1}{-7} = \frac{^{-}1}{7}$

7. The plumber needs $5\cdot 2\frac{1}{8} = 10\frac{5}{8}$ feet of pipe. Assuming no waste in cutting, there will be $12 - 10\frac{5}{8} = 1\frac{3}{8}$ feet of pipe left over.

8. (a) $\frac{11}{5}$ or $2\frac{1}{5}$ (b) $\frac{77}{12}$ or $6\frac{5}{12}$

(c) $4\frac{2}{5}\cdot 1\frac{2}{3} = 7\frac{1}{3}$ (d) $2\frac{1}{2}$

(e) $\frac{5}{6}\div\frac{1}{6} = 5$ (f) $\frac{7}{4}\div(\frac{^{-}1}{24}) = {}^{-}42$

(g) $(\frac{^{-}5}{4})\div(\frac{^{-}5}{8}) = 2$ (h) $\frac{z}{y}$

(i) z (j) $\frac{5}{x}$

(k) $\frac{xy}{z}$

9. (a) 20. $3\frac{11}{12}\cdot 5\frac{3}{100}$ is approximately $4\cdot 5$.

(b) 16. $2\frac{1}{10}\cdot 7\frac{7}{8}$ is approximately $2\cdot 8$.

(c) 2. $20\frac{2}{3}\div 9\frac{7}{8}$ is approximately $20\div 10$.

(d) 1. $\frac{1}{101}$ and $\frac{1}{103}$ are approximately equal.

10. (a) $6\cdot 3 = 18$ (b) $5\cdot 5 = 25$

(c) $21\div 3 = 7$ (d) $12\div 2 = 6$

11. (a) Less than 1. $\frac{13}{14}\cdot\frac{17}{19}$ is the product of two proper fractions, thus each less than 1. Their product is therefore less than 1, or a fraction of a fraction is less than 1.

(b) Less than 1. $3\frac{2}{7}\div 5\frac{1}{9}$ is a number divided by a larger number, so the quotient would be less than 1.

(c) Greater than 2. $4\frac{1}{3}\div 2\frac{3}{100}$ is a number larger than 4 divided by a number <u>very</u> slightly more than 2.

(d) Less than 4. $16\div 4\frac{3}{18}$ is 16 divided by more than 4.

(e) Greater than 4. $16\div 3\frac{8}{9}$ is 16 divided by less than 4.

12. (c), between $6 and $8. Estimation gives a cost of $6\cdot 60\text{¢} + 3\cdot 80\text{¢} = \$6.00$. All rounding was down, so the estimate is low.

13. Possible thought processes are described.

(a) $3\cdot 8 = 24$, $\frac{1}{4}\cdot 8 = 2$, and $24 + 2 = 26$.

(b) $7\cdot 4 = 28$, $\frac{1}{4}\cdot 4 = 1$, and $28 + 1 = 29$.

13. (c) $9 \cdot 10 = 90$, $\frac{1}{5} \cdot 10 = 2$, and $90 + 2 = 92$.

    (d) $8 \cdot 2 = 16$, $8 \cdot \frac{1}{4} = 2$, and $16 + 2 = 18$.

    (e) $3 \div \frac{1}{2} = 3 \cdot \frac{2}{1} = 6$.

    (f) $3\frac{1}{2} \div \frac{1}{2} = 3\frac{1}{2} \cdot 2 = 7$.

    (g) $3 \div \frac{1}{3} = 3 \cdot 3 = 9$.

    (h) $4\frac{1}{2} \div 2 = 4\frac{1}{2} \cdot \frac{1}{2}$. Then $4 \cdot \frac{1}{2} = 2$, $\frac{1}{2} \cdot \frac{1}{2} = \frac{1}{4}$, and $2 + \frac{1}{4} = 2\frac{1}{4}$.

14. The second number is the reciprocal of the first number. For example, if the first number is 4 (greater than 1), then the second number must be $\frac{1}{4}$ (less than 1), and their product is 1.

15. (a)   Use the multiplicative indenty property:
$\frac{1}{3}x = \frac{7}{8} \Rightarrow \frac{3}{1} \cdot \frac{1}{3}x = \frac{3}{1} \cdot \frac{7}{8} \Rightarrow x = \frac{21}{8}$.

    (b) $\frac{1}{5} = \frac{7}{3}x \Rightarrow \frac{3}{7} \cdot \frac{1}{5} = \frac{3}{7} \cdot \frac{7}{3}x \Rightarrow \frac{3}{35} = x$.

    (c) $\frac{1}{2}x - 7 = \frac{3}{4}x \Rightarrow \frac{1}{2}x - \frac{1}{2}x - 7 = \frac{3}{4}x - \frac{1}{2}x \Rightarrow {}^-7 = \frac{1}{4}x \Rightarrow \frac{4}{1}({}^-7) = \frac{4}{1} \cdot \frac{1}{4}x \Rightarrow {}^-28 = x$.

    (d) $\frac{2}{3}(\frac{1}{2}x - 7) = \frac{3}{4}x \Rightarrow \frac{1}{3}x - \frac{14}{3} = \frac{3}{4}x \Rightarrow \frac{1}{3}x - \frac{1}{3}x - \frac{14}{3} = \frac{3}{4}x - \frac{1}{3}x \Rightarrow \frac{{}^-14}{3} = \frac{5}{12}x$

         $\Rightarrow \frac{12}{5} \cdot (\frac{{}^-14}{3}) = \frac{12}{5} \cdot \frac{5}{12}x \Rightarrow \frac{{}^-56}{5} = x$.

    (e) $\frac{2}{5} \cdot \frac{3}{6} = x \Rightarrow \frac{1}{5} = x$.

    (f) $x \div \frac{3}{4} = \frac{5}{8} \Rightarrow x \cdot \frac{4}{3} = \frac{5}{8} \Rightarrow \frac{3}{4} \cdot \frac{4}{3}x = \frac{3}{4} \cdot \frac{5}{8} \Rightarrow x = \frac{15}{32}$.

    (g) $2\frac{1}{3}x + 7 = 3\frac{1}{4} \Rightarrow \frac{7}{3}x + 7 - 7 = \frac{13}{4} - 7 \Rightarrow \frac{7}{3}x = \frac{{}^-15}{4} \Rightarrow \frac{3}{7} \cdot \frac{7}{3}x = \frac{3}{7} \cdot (\frac{{}^-15}{4}) \Rightarrow x = \frac{{}^-45}{28}$.

    (h) $\frac{{}^-2}{5}(10x + 1) = 1 - x \Rightarrow {}^-4x + \frac{{}^-2}{5} = 1 - x \Rightarrow {}^-4x + x - \frac{2}{5} + \frac{2}{5} = 1 + \frac{2}{5} - x + x$

         $\Rightarrow {}^-3x = \frac{7}{5} \Rightarrow (\frac{{}^-1}{3}) \cdot ({}^-3)x = (\frac{{}^-1}{3}) \cdot \frac{7}{5} \Rightarrow x = \frac{{}^-7}{15}$.

16. (i) $5\frac{1}{2}$. $\frac{1}{7}$ of $35 = 5$; $\frac{1}{7}$ of $4 = \frac{4}{7} \div \frac{1}{2}$.   (ii)   6. $\frac{1}{7} = \frac{2}{14} \div \frac{2}{13}$; $\frac{1}{13}$ of $39 = 3$ so $\frac{2}{13}$ of $39 = 6$

17. If F is the number of faculty members originally, then $F - \frac{1}{5}F = 320 \Rightarrow \frac{4}{5}F = 320 \Rightarrow F = \frac{5}{4} \cdot 320$ $\Rightarrow F = 400$ members originally.

18. Alberto has $\frac{5}{9}$; Renatta has $\frac{1}{2} \cdot \frac{5}{9} = \frac{5}{18}$. Then $1 - \frac{5}{9} - \frac{5}{18} = \frac{1}{6}$ of the stock not owned by them.

19. (a)   If U is the number of uniforms to be made, then (assuming no waste) $U = 29\frac{1}{2} \div \frac{3}{4} \Rightarrow U = \frac{59}{2} \cdot \frac{4}{3}$ $\Rightarrow U = \frac{118}{3} = 39\frac{1}{3}$. Thus 39 uniforms can be made.

    (b)   Enough material for $\frac{1}{3}$ of a uniform will be left over. Each uniform requires $\frac{3}{4}$ yard of material; there will be $\frac{1}{3} \cdot \frac{3}{4} = \frac{1}{4}$ yard of material remaining.

20. Never less than *n*. Division by a positive rational number less than 1 (i.e., a proper fraction) is equivalent to multiplying by its reciprocal, a rational number greater than 1 (i.e., an improper fraction). This product will always be greater than *n*.

21. (a) $\frac{1}{2} \div \frac{2}{3} \neq \frac{2}{3} \div \frac{1}{2}$. $\frac{1}{2} \div \frac{2}{3} = \frac{3}{4}$; $\frac{2}{3} \div \frac{1}{2} = \frac{4}{3}$.

    (b) $(\frac{1}{2} \div \frac{2}{3}) \div \frac{3}{4} = 1$, but $\frac{1}{2} \div (\frac{2}{3} \div \frac{3}{4}) = \frac{9}{16}$.

21. (c)   The identity property for division would require that for the identity I, $\frac{a}{b} \div I = \frac{a}{b} = I \div \frac{a}{b}$. The left half of this relationship is true, but the right half fails because of non-commutivity.

(d)   The inverse of $\frac{a}{b}$ would be the number which would divide $\frac{a}{b}$ to give the identity as a quotient. Since there is no identity, this is impossible.

22.   If n is the number for which we are looking, then $3n - \frac{7}{18} = 2n + \frac{5}{12}$. Solving for n, we find the number to be $\frac{29}{36}$.

23.   The 6000 students living in dorms are $\frac{5}{8}$ of the student population, P; i.e., $6000 = \frac{5}{8}P$. Then $\frac{8}{5} \cdot 6000 = \frac{8}{5} \cdot \frac{5}{8}P \Rightarrow 9600 = P$.

24. $P - \frac{1}{4}P = 180 \Rightarrow \frac{3}{4}P = 180 \Rightarrow P = \$240$ original price.

25. (a)   Increasing a salary by $\frac{1}{10}$ means the salary will be $1\frac{1}{10}$, or $\frac{11}{10}$, of its previous value. With two such raises, Martha will make $(100,000 \cdot \frac{11}{10}) \cdot \frac{11}{10} = \$121,000$.

(b) $\$99,000$ is $\frac{11}{10}$ of what Aaron made last year; i.e., $99,000 = \frac{11}{10}S$ (where S is Aaron's salary one year ago). Then, solving for S, $\frac{10}{11} \cdot 99,000 = \frac{10}{11} \cdot \frac{11}{10}S \Rightarrow S = \$90,000$.

(c)   Let S be Juanita's salary two years ago. Then $363,000 = \frac{11}{10}(\frac{11}{10}S)$, since two raises brought her to that value. Solving, $\frac{100}{121} \cdot 363,000 = \frac{100}{121} \cdot \frac{121}{100}S \Rightarrow S = \$300,000$.

26.   Let W be the number of women who apply. Then 3W is the number of men who apply and $W + 3W = 4W$ is the total number who apply.
    So $\frac{1}{10} \cdot 4W = \frac{2}{5}W$ is the total number hired; $\frac{1}{20} \cdot 3W = \frac{3}{20}W$ is the number of men hired.
    Thus the number of women hired is $\frac{2}{5}W - \frac{3}{20}W = \frac{1}{4}W$.
    Or, $\frac{1}{4}$ of the women who apply are hired.

27.   Jasmine has read $\frac{3}{4}$ of the book so she has $1 - \frac{3}{4} = \frac{1}{4}$ yet to read; i.e., 82 pages $= \frac{1}{4}$. Then $\frac{3}{4} = 3 \cdot 82 = 246$ pages read so far.

28.   Let A be the amount of money in the account. After spending \$50 there was $A - 50$ left. He spent $\frac{3}{5}$ of that, or $\frac{3}{5}(A - 50)$, leaving him $\frac{2}{5}(A - 50)$. Half goes back into the bank, or $\frac{1}{2} \cdot \frac{2}{5}(A - 50) = \frac{1}{5}(A - 50)$. The other half was \$35, or $\frac{1}{5}(A - 50) = 35$. Solving, A = \$225.

29. (a)   Peter: $\frac{1}{2} \cdot 60$ min. = 30 min.   Paul: $\frac{5}{12} \cdot 60$ min. = 25 min.   Mary: $\frac{1}{3} \cdot 60$ min. = 20 min.

(b)   Each will be back at the starting line in multiples of the time it takes for one lap; i.e., the LCM of 30, 25, and 20 = 300 minutes, or 5 hours. Thus: Peter, 10 times; Paul, 12 times; Mary, 15 times.

30. $20 \div 2\frac{1}{3} = 8\frac{4}{7} \Rightarrow$ 8 full receipes.

31. (a) $F = \frac{9}{5} \cdot 32 + 32 = \frac{288}{5} + \frac{32 \cdot 5}{5} = \frac{448}{5} = 89\frac{3}{5}° $ F.

(b) $^-40 = \frac{9}{5}C + 32 \Rightarrow {}^-72 = \frac{9}{5}C \Rightarrow \frac{5}{9}(^-72) = \frac{5}{9} \cdot \frac{9}{5}C \Rightarrow C = {}^-40°$ C. (This is the only temperature where Celsius and Fahrenheit are numerically the same.

32.   Glen lost $48\frac{1}{4} - 35\frac{3}{8} = 12\frac{7}{8}$ on each share, or a total loss of $175 \cdot 12\frac{7}{8} = \$2253\frac{1}{8}$.

33.   Al's marbles are halved three times in the process of Dani receiving 4 marbles; i.e., $\frac{1}{2} \cdot \frac{1}{2} \cdot \frac{1}{2} \cdot A = 4$, or $\frac{1}{8}A = 4$. Solving, A = 32 marbles (where A is the number of marbles Al had originally).

34.   The first factor in each product is reciprocated before multiplication.

35.   Use commutivity and associativity: $\frac{1}{4} \cdot 15 \cdot 12 = (\frac{1}{4} \cdot 12) \cdot 15 = 3 \cdot 15 = 45$.

36. Let B be the weight of the unpeeled banana. Then $\frac{1}{8}$B is the weight of the peel and $B - \frac{1}{8}B = \frac{7}{8}B$ is the weight of the banana fruit. So $B = \frac{7}{8}B + \frac{7}{8}$; solving, B = 7 ounces.

37. (*i*)   Multiply by $\frac{1}{2}$. $\frac{1}{32}, \frac{1}{64}$. Geometric (common ratio).

  (*ii*)   Multiply by $\frac{^-1}{2}$. $\frac{^-1}{32}, \frac{1}{64}$. Geometric.

  (*iii*)   Multiply by $\frac{3}{4}$. $\frac{81}{256}, \frac{243}{1024}$. Geometric.

  (*iv*) $\frac{n}{3^n}$. $\frac{5}{3^5}, \frac{6}{3^6}$. Not geometric (no common ratio).

38. (a)   The square would be $n \cdot (n + 1) + (\frac{1}{2})^2$.

  (b) $(n + \frac{1}{2})^2 = n^2 + n + \frac{1}{4} = (n^2 + n) + \frac{1}{4} = n(n + 1) + (\frac{1}{2})^2$.

39. (a)   (*i*) $f(0) = \frac{3 \cdot 0 + 4}{3 \cdot 0 - 5} = \frac{^-4}{5}$

  (*ii*) $f\left(\frac{2}{5}\right) = \frac{3 \cdot \frac{2}{5} + 4}{4 \cdot \frac{2}{5} - 5} = \frac{\frac{6}{5} + \frac{20}{5}}{\frac{8}{5} - \frac{25}{5}} = \frac{26}{5} \cdot (\frac{^-5}{17}) = \frac{^-26}{17}$

  (*iii*) $f\left(\frac{^-2}{5}\right) = \frac{3 \cdot \frac{^-2}{5} + 4}{2 \cdot \frac{^-2}{5} - 5} = \frac{\frac{^-6}{5} + \frac{20}{5}}{\frac{^-8}{5} - \frac{25}{5}} = \frac{14}{5} \cdot (\frac{^-5}{33}) = \frac{^-14}{33}$

  (b)   (*i*) $\frac{3x + 4}{4x - 5} = 0$ only if $3x + 4 = 0 \Rightarrow 3x = {}^-4 \Rightarrow x = \frac{^-4}{3}$

  (*ii*) $\frac{3x + 4}{4x - 5} = \frac{2}{5} \Rightarrow 5(3x + 4) = 2(4x - 5) \Rightarrow 15x + 20 = 8x - 10 \Rightarrow 7x = {}^-30$

    $\Rightarrow x = \frac{^-30}{7}$

  (*iii*) $\frac{3x + 4}{4x - 5} = \frac{^-1}{2} \Rightarrow 2(3x + 4) = {}^-1(4x - 5) \Rightarrow 6x + 8 = {}^-4x + 5 \Rightarrow 10x = {}^-3$

    $\Rightarrow x = \frac{^-3}{10}$

  (c)   The value of x that makes the denominator equal 0 is not in the domain. Thus if $4x - 5 = 0$ $\Rightarrow 4x = 5 \Rightarrow x = \frac{5}{4}$ makes the denominator 0, so $\frac{5}{4}$ is not in the domain.

40. (a)   (*i*) $2(\frac{3}{2}) = 3$ (*ii*) $2(\frac{3}{2})(\frac{4}{3}) = 4$

  (*iii*) $2(\frac{3}{2})(\frac{4}{3})(\frac{5}{4}) = 5$ (*iv*) $5(\frac{6}{5}) = 6$

  (b)   102   (c)   n + 2

41. This equality has the restriction $b \neq 0$ and is true only if:
  (*i*) c = 0. Then $\frac{a}{b} = \frac{a + 0}{b + 0} = \frac{a}{b}$, or (*ii*) a = b. Then $\frac{a}{b} = \frac{a}{a} = \frac{a + c}{a + c}$.

42. (a) $2S = 2\left(\frac{1}{2} + \frac{1}{2^2} + \frac{1}{2^3} + \cdots + \frac{1}{2^{64}}\right) = 1 + \frac{1}{2} + \frac{1}{2^2} + \cdots + \frac{1}{2^{63}}$

  (b) $2S - S = \left(1 + \frac{1}{2} + \frac{1}{2^2} + \cdots + \frac{1}{2^{63}}\right) - (\frac{1}{2} + \frac{1}{2^2} + \cdots + \frac{1}{2^{64}}) = 1 - \frac{1}{2^{64}}$

  (c) $1 - \frac{1}{2^n}$

43. (a) From the general form of an arithmetic sequence: $a_n = a_1 + (n - 1)d$, where a_n is the nth term of the sequence, a_1 is the first term, n is the number of terms, and d is the common difference, we have: $2 = 1 + (100 - 1)d \Rightarrow 1 = 99d \Rightarrow d = \frac{1}{99}$. Then $a_{50} = 1 + (50 - 1)\frac{1}{99} = 1\frac{49}{99}$.

(b) The sum of the first 50 terms is $1 + 1\frac{1}{99} + 1\frac{2}{99} + \cdots + 1\frac{48}{99} + 1\frac{49}{99}$. Rearranging gives: $(1 + 1\frac{49}{99}) + (1\frac{1}{99} + 1\frac{48}{99}) + \cdots + (1\frac{24}{99} + 1\frac{25}{99})$, or 25 pairs, each adding to $2\frac{49}{99}$. The sum is then $25 \cdot 2\frac{49}{99} = 62\frac{37}{99}$.

44. (a) $\frac{25}{16} = 1\frac{9}{16}$ (b) $\frac{25}{18} = 1\frac{7}{18}$

(c) $\frac{5}{216}$ (d) $\frac{259}{30} = 8\frac{19}{30}$

(e) $\frac{37}{24} = 1\frac{13}{24}$ (f) $\frac{^-39}{24} = {}^-9\frac{3}{4}$

45. The portion of students that take one of the three foreign languages is $\frac{2}{3} + \frac{1}{9} + \frac{1}{18} = \frac{5}{6}$. The portion of students not taking one of the three is then $1 - \frac{5}{6} = \frac{1}{6}$. That number of students is then $\frac{1}{6} \cdot 720 = 120$ students.

Problem Set 6-4

1. (a) $>$. LCD = 24, so $\frac{7}{8} = \frac{21}{24}$ and $\frac{5}{6} = \frac{20}{24}$.

(b) $>$. LCD = 30, so $2\frac{4}{5} = 2\frac{24}{30}$ and $2\frac{3}{6} = 2\frac{15}{30}$.

(c) $<$. LCD = 40, so $\frac{^-7}{8} = \frac{^-35}{40}$ and $\frac{^-4}{5} = \frac{^-24}{40}$. (Note that $^-35 < {}^-24$.)

(d) $<$. LCD = 56, so $\frac{^-1}{7} = \frac{^-1}{7} = \frac{^-8}{56}$ and $\frac{1}{8} = \frac{^-7}{56}$.

(e) $=$. $\frac{2}{5} = \frac{2 \cdot 2}{2 \cdot 5} = \frac{4}{10}$.

(f) $=$. $\frac{0}{7} = 0 = \frac{0}{17}$.

2.

3. (a) $\frac{11}{13}, \frac{11}{16}, \frac{11}{22}$. When fractions have the same numerators, those with larger denominators have lesser value.

(b) $3, \frac{33}{16}, \frac{23}{16}$. $(3 = \frac{48}{16}.)$

(c) $\frac{^-1}{5}, \frac{^-19}{36}, \frac{^-17}{30}$. LCD = 180, so $\frac{^-1}{5} = \frac{^-36}{180}, \frac{^-19}{36} = \frac{^-95}{180}$, and $\frac{^-17}{30} = \frac{^-102}{180}$. Then $^-36 > {}^-95 > {}^-102$.

4. (a) LCD = 24. Thus $24(\frac{2}{3}x - \frac{7}{8}) \le 24(\frac{1}{4}) \Rightarrow 16x - 21 \le 6 \Rightarrow 16x \le 27 \Rightarrow x \le \frac{27}{16}$.

(b) LCD = 15. Thus $15(x - \frac{1}{3}) < 15(\frac{2}{3}x + \frac{4}{5}) \Rightarrow 15x - 5 < 10x + 12 \Rightarrow 5x < 17 \Rightarrow x < \frac{17}{5}$.

(c) LCD = 15. Thus $15(\frac{1}{5}x - 7) \ge 15(\frac{2}{3}) \Rightarrow 3x - 105 \ge 10 \Rightarrow 3x \ge 115 \Rightarrow x \ge \frac{115}{3}$.

(d) LCD = 24. Thus $120 - 16x \le 6x - 21 \Rightarrow 141 \le 22x \Rightarrow x \ge \frac{141}{22}$.

5. (a) No. $\frac{a}{b} > \frac{c}{d}$ if and only if $ad < bc$. To arrive at the second inequality both sides must be multiplied by bd (a negative number), thus reversing the direction of the inequality.

5.   (b)   Yes. Multiplying both sides by bd (a positive number) maintains the direction of the inequality.

6.   (a)   Estimate: The product is about $20 \cdot 20 = 400$.
             Actual: $19\frac{8}{9} \cdot 20\frac{1}{9} = 399\frac{80}{81}$.

      (b)   Estimate: The product is about $20 \cdot 9 = 180$.
             Actual: The product is $180\frac{89}{90}$.

      (c)   Estimate: The product is about $4 \cdot 1 = 4$.
             Actual: The product is $3\frac{699}{820}$.

7.   (a)   Over 7. $\frac{5}{8}$ and $\frac{5}{9}$ are both greater than $\frac{1}{2}$, so their sum is greater than 1. Added to $4 + 2$, the sum is greater than 7.

      (b)   Under 13. $7\frac{1}{10} + 5\frac{6}{11} < 7\frac{1}{10} + 5\frac{6}{10} = 12\frac{7}{10} < 13$.

      (c)   Under 1. Any number divided by a larger number results in a quotient of less than 1.

      (d)   Over 6. $6\frac{1}{10} \div \frac{11}{12} = 6\frac{1}{10} \cdot \frac{12}{11}$; i.e., a product of more than 6 and more than 1.

      (e)   Over 6. 10 reduced by less than 4 yields more than 6.

8.   Bren's class. $\frac{5}{23} > \frac{6}{31}$ since $5 \cdot 31 > 6 \cdot 23$.

9.   (a) $19\frac{8}{9} \cdot 9\frac{1}{10} \doteq 20 \cdot 9 = 180$.   (b) $80\frac{3}{4} \cdot 9\frac{1}{8} \doteq 81 \cdot 9 = 729$.

      (c) $77\frac{3}{5} \cdot 6\frac{1}{4} \doteq 78 \cdot 6 = 468$.   (d) $48\frac{2}{3} \div 8\frac{4}{9} \doteq 49 \div 8 \doteq 6$.

      (e) $5\frac{2}{3} \div 2\frac{1}{17} \doteq 6 \div 2 = 3$.

10. $21 \cdot 16 \div 12 = 28$; i.e., about 28 packages may be produced.

11.   (a)   The square of a positive proper fraction is less than the original fraction.

      (b)   For a positive proper fraction $\frac{a}{b}$, $b > a > 0$ and $b^2 > a^2 > 0$. Then $\frac{a^2}{b^2} < \frac{a}{b}$ since $a^2 b < a b^2$.

      (c)   The square is greater.

      (d)   Similar to (b), but now $a > b > 0$, so $a^2 > b^2 > 0$. Thus $a^2 b > a b^2$ and $\frac{a^2}{b^2} > \frac{a}{b}$.

12. $\frac{a}{b} < 1$ and $\frac{c}{d} > 0$ imply $\frac{a}{b} \cdot \frac{c}{d} < 1 \cdot \frac{c}{d}$, or $\frac{a}{b} \cdot \frac{c}{d} < \frac{c}{d}$.

13.   xy is greater. $x > 1$ and $y > 0$ implies $x \cdot y > 1 \cdot y$, or $xy > y$.

14.   Any two consecutive terms are of the form $\frac{n}{n+1}$, $\frac{n+1}{n+2}$. Comparison by cross-multiplication gives

      $n(n + 2) < (n + 1)(n + 1)$ or $n^2 + 2n < n^2 + 2n + 1$ or $0 < 1$.

15.   Answers may vary. One example is $\frac{3}{2}, \frac{4}{3}, \frac{5}{4}, \ldots$.

16.   (a) and (b)   Both whole numbers and integers have a set increment (1) between consecutive numbers. As such, two given consecutive whole numbers or integers cannot have another between them; i.e., they do not exhibit the denseness property.

17. Answers may vary. One method is to convert the given fractions to equivalent fractions having larger common denominators, thus creating spaces between the two.

(a) $\frac{3}{7} = \frac{9}{21}$; $\frac{4}{7} = \frac{12}{21}$. Two rational numbers between them are $\frac{10}{21}$ and $\frac{11}{21}$.

(b) $\frac{^-7}{9} = \frac{^-28}{36}$; $\frac{^-8}{9} = \frac{^-32}{36}$. Numbers between them are $\frac{^-30}{36}$ and $\frac{^-31}{36}$.

(c) $\frac{5}{6} = \frac{1000}{1200}$; $\frac{83}{100} = \frac{996}{1200}$. Numbers between them are $\frac{997}{1200}$ and $\frac{998}{1200}$.

(d)   There are many values between a negative fraction and a positive fraction. Two are 0 and $\frac{1}{2}$ in this case.

18. (a)   33   (b)   133

(c)   0

(d)   None. Solving gives x $> 6\frac{11}{16}$, but 7 is the <u>least</u> possible.

19. (a)   Answers may vary. Perhaps begin by pointing out the relevance of the denominator, and then illustrate with examples.

(b)   Again, answers may vary. Point out the relevance, this time, of the numerator. Illustrate.

20. (a) $\frac{94}{94} = 1$ (b) $\frac{86}{86} = 1$

(c)   The numerators and denominators are equal. Each of the interior numbers satisfies exactly one of the following relationships as compared to a unique circled number: ten less; ten greater; one less; one greater. As such, the sum of these interior numbers is the same as that of the circled exterior numbers.

21. (a) $\frac{1}{3}$, $\frac{1}{3}$, $\frac{1}{3}$, and $\frac{1}{3}$.

(b) $\frac{1+3+5+7+\cdots+201}{203+205+207+\cdots+403} = \frac{1}{3}$. The numerator of the nth term follows the pattern $1 + 3 + 5 + \cdots$ for $n + 1$ numbers (up to the number $2n + 1$; e.g., in the 3rd term, up to $2(3) + 1 = 7$). The denominator picks up at this point with its 1st term $2n + 3$ (e.g., $2(3) + 3 = 9$ in the 3rd term) and last being $4n + 3$ (e.g., $4(3) + 3 = 15$).

(c)   The sum of the first n terms of $1 + 3 + 5 + 7 + \cdots$ is given by n^2. The sum of the first $n + 1$ terms, as in each numerator, is $(n + 1)^2$. Thinking of the numerator and denominator as one sequence run together gives the first $2n + 2$ terms of the series, having a sum of $(2n + 2)^2 = 4(n + 1)^2$. To get the sum of the denominator alone, subtract the numerator; i.e., $4(n + 1)^2 - (n + 1)^2 = 3(n + 1)^2$. All terms of the sequence are then of the form:

$$\frac{(n + 1)^2}{3(n + 1)^2} = \frac{1}{3}.$$

22. Getting a common denominator and eliminating fractions from $\frac{a}{b} < \frac{1}{2}\left(\frac{a}{b} + \frac{c}{d}\right) < \frac{c}{d}$ gives $\frac{2ad}{bd} < \frac{ad+bc}{bd} < \frac{2bc}{bd}$. To show that this is true, we must show $2ad < ad + bc < 2bc$. Since $0 < \frac{a}{b} < \frac{c}{d}$, we know $ad < bc$. Adding ad and bc to each side (in separate inequalities) gives $2ad < ad + bc$ and $ad + bc < 2bc$; or, combined, $2ad < ad + bc < 2bc$, our desired result.

23. Less than. Consider $\frac{a}{b}$ and $\frac{a+n}{b+n}$, where a $<$ b (because $\frac{a}{b}$ is a proper fraction) and n can be any positive number. Then, because ab $+$ an $<$ ab $+$ bn, $\frac{a}{b} < \frac{a+n}{b+n}$.

24. (a) $3\frac{5}{8}$ (b) $1\frac{19}{68}$

(c) $\frac{25}{144}$ (d)   1 (if $|x| \neq |y|$)

25. Distance is rate times time, so time is distance divided by rate. Thus t $= 28\frac{3}{4} \div 4\frac{1}{2} = 6\frac{7}{18}$ hours.

26. (a) $x = \frac{^-4}{3}$ (b) $x = {}^-1\frac{3}{8}$

    (c) $x = 1\frac{7}{17}$ (d) $x = {}^-3$

27. Altogether there were $3 \cdot 5 = 15$ practices lasting a total of $15 \cdot 1\frac{3}{4} = 26\frac{1}{4}$ hours.

28. (a) $\frac{1}{2} + 1\frac{1}{2} + 1 = 3 < \frac{8}{9} + 1\frac{19}{20} + \frac{14}{13} < 1 + 2 + 1 = 4$. The sum is between 3 and 4.

    (b) $16\frac{2}{10} - 6\frac{1}{10} = 10\frac{1}{10} < 16\frac{2}{9} - 6\frac{1}{10} < 16\frac{2}{9} - 6\frac{1}{9} = 10\frac{1}{9}$, so $\frac{7}{15}(10\frac{1}{10}) < \frac{7}{15}(16\frac{2}{9} - 6\frac{1}{10}) < \frac{7}{15}(10\frac{1}{9})$

    If $\frac{7}{15}(\frac{101}{10}) < \frac{7}{15}(\frac{91}{9})$, then $\frac{5}{15}(\frac{105}{10}) < \frac{8}{15}(\frac{90}{8})$, or $\frac{7}{2} < 6$, or $3 < \frac{7}{15}(16\frac{2}{9} - 6\frac{1}{10}) < 6$. The product is between

    3 and 6.

Problem Set 6-5

1. (a) $\dfrac{\text{Poodles}}{\text{Cockers}} = \frac{18}{12} = \frac{3}{2}$ (b) $\dfrac{\text{Cockers}}{\text{Poodles}} = \frac{12}{18} = \frac{2}{3}$

2. (a) $\frac{5}{21}$

    (b)   Answers may vary. Break is one.

3. (a)   We know that $\frac{a}{b} = \frac{c}{d}$ only if ad = bc. Thus if $\frac{12}{x} = \frac{18}{45}$, then:
          $18 \cdot x = 12 \cdot 45 \Rightarrow x = \frac{540}{18} = 30$.

    (b) $21 \cdot x = {}^-10 \cdot 7 \Rightarrow x = \frac{^-70}{21} = \frac{^-10}{3}$.

    (c) $7 \cdot 3x = 5 \cdot 98 \Rightarrow x = \frac{490}{21} = 23\frac{1}{3}$.

    (d) $\dfrac{3\frac{1}{2}}{5} = \dfrac{x}{15} \Rightarrow 5 \cdot x = 3\frac{1}{2} \cdot 15 \Rightarrow 5x = \frac{105}{2} \Rightarrow x = \frac{105}{10} = \frac{21}{2}$.

4. $\frac{2}{5} = \frac{x}{90} \Rightarrow x = 36$ pounds.

5. $\dfrac{5 \text{ adults}}{1 \text{ teen}} = \dfrac{12{,}345 \text{ adults}}{x \text{ teens}} \Rightarrow 5x = 12{,}345 \Rightarrow x = \frac{12345}{5} = 2469$ teenage drivers.

6. $\frac{4}{79} = \frac{6}{x} \Rightarrow 4x = 474 \Rightarrow x = 118\frac{1}{2}\cancel{c}$, or, rounding, \$1.19.

7. $\dfrac{1 \backslash 3 \text{ inch}}{5 \text{ miles}} = \dfrac{18 \text{ inches}}{x \text{ miles}} \Rightarrow \frac{1}{3}x = 90 \Rightarrow x = 90 \div \frac{1}{3} \Rightarrow x = 270$ miles.

8. $\frac{40}{50} = \frac{x}{80} \Rightarrow 50x = 3200 \Rightarrow x = 64$ pages.

9. The candle has burned 5 inches in 12 minutes; thus $\dfrac{5 \text{ inches}}{12 \text{ minutes}} = \dfrac{30 \text{ inches}}{x \text{ minutes}} \Rightarrow 5x = 360 \Rightarrow x = 72$ minutes for 30 inches.

10. (a) $3x + 4x = 98 \Rightarrow x = 14$. Thus x = 14; 3x = 42 and 4x = 56. The numbers are 42 and 56.

    (b) $3x \cdot 4x = 768 \Rightarrow x = 8$. Thus the numbers are 24 and 32 (or $^-24$ and $^-32$).

11. Let the width be represented by 5x and the length by 9x. Then the ratio of width to length will be 5x to 9x, or 5:9. We also know that the perimeter of a rectangle is twice the width plus twice the length. Thus: $2(5x) + 2(9x) = 2800 \Rightarrow 28x = 2800 \Rightarrow x = 100$. Then the width is 5x = 500 feet and the length is 9x = 900 feet.

12. $\frac{2}{11} = \frac{\text{Gary}}{\$82,000}$, $\frac{4}{11} = \frac{\text{Bill}}{\$82,000}$, and $\frac{5}{11} = \frac{\text{Carmella}}{\$82,000}$. Thus $11 \cdot \text{Gary} = 164,000 \Rightarrow \text{Gary} = \$14,909.09$.

Similarly, Bill = \$29,818.18 and Carmella = \$37,272.73.

13. If the amount Sheila earned is $3\frac{1}{2}x$ and the amount Dora earned is $4\frac{1}{2}x$, then the ratio of Sheila's hours to Dora's hours is $3\frac{1}{2}x{:}4\frac{1}{2}x$. Thus:
$3\frac{1}{2}x + 4\frac{1}{2}x = 176 \Rightarrow 8x = 176 \Rightarrow x = 22$. Then Sheila's earnings were $3\frac{1}{2} \cdot 22 = \$77$ and Dora's earnings were $4\frac{1}{2} \cdot 22 = \$99$.

14. Success:Failure = 5:9 $\Rightarrow \frac{5}{9} = \frac{75}{A}$, and A = 135 attempts.

15. (a) $\frac{\text{Rise}}{\text{Half-Span}} = \frac{10}{14}$. The pitch is $\frac{5}{7}$, or 5:7.

    (b) $\frac{\text{Rise}}{\text{Half-Span}} = \frac{\text{Rise}}{8} = \frac{3}{4}$. Thus $4 \cdot \text{Rise} = 24$, or the Rise is 6 feet.

16. $6 \cdot 20 = 120$ feet.

17. $\frac{9 \text{ months}}{6 \text{ vacation days}} = \frac{12 \text{ months}}{x \text{ vacation days}} \Rightarrow 9x = 72 \Rightarrow x = 8$ days per year.

18. (a) $\frac{4}{6} = \frac{18}{t} \Rightarrow 4t = 108 \Rightarrow 27$ teeth on the large gear.

    (b) $\frac{200}{600} = \frac{t}{60} \Rightarrow t = 20$ teeth on the small gear.

19. $\frac{\text{length}}{\text{wingspan}} = \frac{230 \text{ feet}}{195 \text{ feet}} = \frac{40 \text{ cm}}{W \text{ cm}}$. Thus $230W = 7800$ and $W = \frac{7800}{230} = 33\frac{21}{23}$ cm, or about 34 cm.

20. $\frac{160}{416} = \frac{120}{W}$ and W = 312 pounds on Jupiter.

21. (a) $\frac{\text{footprint length}}{\text{body length}} = \frac{40 \text{ cm}}{700 \text{ cm}} = \frac{2}{35}$, or 2:35.

    (b) $\frac{\text{footprint length}}{\text{body length}} = \frac{2}{35} = \frac{30}{x} \Rightarrow 2x = 1050$, or x = 525 cm long.

    (c) For the first set, $\frac{\text{footprint length}}{\text{thighbone length}} = \frac{40}{100} = \frac{20}{50}$; i.e., a 50 cm thighbone would correspond to a 20 cm

    footprint. Thus it is not likely that the 50 cm thighbone is from the animal which left the 30 cm footprint.

22. If 3 painters can paint 4 houses in 5 days, then 3 painters can paint $\frac{4}{5}$ houses in 1 day. One painter can paint $\frac{1}{3} \cdot \frac{4}{5} = \frac{4}{15}$ houses in 1 day. Then 7 painters can paint $7 \cdot \frac{4}{15} = \frac{28}{15}$ in 1 day. Thus:
$\frac{\frac{28}{15} \text{ houses}}{1 \text{ day}} = \frac{18 \text{ houses}}{x \text{ days}} \Rightarrow \frac{28}{15}x = 18$ and $x = 9\frac{9}{14}$ days.

23. No. The price would be based on the area of pizza, which is not proportional to its diameter as is suggested by the given proportion. (Area is proportional to the square of the diameter.)

24. (a) 2:5. In an average group of 5 students, there are 2 boys (and 3 girls).

    (b) $\frac{m}{m+n}$ or m:(m + n)

25. Sherwin can paint $\frac{1}{2}$ house per day; William $\frac{1}{4}$ house per day. Together they should paint $\frac{1}{2} + \frac{1}{4} = \frac{3}{4}$ house

    per day, so $\frac{\frac{3}{4} \text{ house}}{1 \text{ day}} = \frac{1 \text{ house}}{x \text{ days}} \Rightarrow \frac{3}{4}x = 1 \Rightarrow x = \frac{4}{3}$ days for the two together to paint the house.

26. Let C be the number of hours for Carter to do the job alone. Then in 1 hour Mary can do $\frac{1}{8}$ of the job and Carter can do $\frac{1}{C}$ of the job. Working together, they can do $\frac{1}{8} + \frac{1}{C} = \frac{1}{5}$ of the job. Solving:
$5C + 40 = 8C \Rightarrow C = 13\frac{1}{3}$ hours for Carter alone.

27. $\frac{a}{b} = \frac{c}{d}$ implies that $ad = bc$, or $a = \frac{bc}{d}$. Then $\frac{b}{a} = \frac{b}{\left(\frac{bc}{d}\right)} = \frac{b}{1} \cdot \frac{d}{bc} = \frac{d}{c}$.

28.   For two such fractions, $\frac{a}{b}$ and $\frac{c}{d}$, $a < b$ and $c < d$ $\Rightarrow$ $ac < bc$ and $ac < ad$. Then $\frac{ac}{bd} < \frac{bc}{bd}$ and $\frac{ac}{bd} < \frac{ad}{bd}$, or $\frac{ac}{bd} < \frac{c}{d}$ and $\frac{ac}{bd} < \frac{a}{b}$; i.e., the product — $\frac{ac}{bd}$ — is less than either of the original fractions.

29.   (a)   The total number of men in all three rooms is $1 + 2 + 5 = 8$. The total number of women in all three rooms is $2 + 4 + 10 = 16$. Thus the ratio of men to women is $\frac{8}{16} = \frac{1}{2}$.

      (b)   If $\frac{a}{b} = \frac{c}{d} = \frac{e}{f}$, then $\frac{c}{d} = \frac{a \cdot m}{b \cdot m}$ and $\frac{e}{f} = \frac{a \cdot n}{b \cdot n}$. So $\frac{a+c+e}{b+d+f} = \frac{a+am+an}{b+bm+bn} = \frac{a(1+m+n)}{b(1+m+n)} = \frac{a}{b}$.

30.   (a) $\frac{a}{b} = \frac{c}{d}$ $\Rightarrow$ $\frac{a}{b} + 1 = \frac{c}{d} + 1$ $\Rightarrow$ $\frac{a}{b} + \frac{b}{b} = \frac{c}{d} + \frac{d}{d}$ $\Rightarrow$ $\frac{a+b}{b} = \frac{c+d}{d}$.

      (b) $\frac{a}{b} = \frac{c}{d}$ $\Rightarrow$ $ad = bc$ $\Rightarrow$ $ac + ad = ac + bc$ $\Rightarrow$ $a(c + d) = c(a + b)$ $\Rightarrow$ $\frac{a}{a+b} = \frac{c}{c+d}$.

      (c) $\frac{a}{b} = \frac{c}{d}$ $\Rightarrow$ $\frac{a}{a+b} = \frac{c}{c+d}$ $\Rightarrow$ $\frac{2a}{a+b} = \frac{2c}{c+d}$ $\Rightarrow$ $\frac{2a}{a+b} - 1 = \frac{2c}{c+d} - 1$ $\Rightarrow$

           $\frac{2a-(a+b)}{a+b} = \frac{2c-(c+d)}{c+d}$ $\Rightarrow$ $\frac{a-b}{a+b} = \frac{c-d}{c+d}$.

31.   Dick can run $4\frac{9}{10} \div 5 = \frac{49}{50}$ as far as Tom. Harry can run $4\frac{4}{5} \div 5 = \frac{24}{25}$ as far as Dick. Thus Harry can run $\frac{24}{25} \cdot \frac{49}{50} = \frac{1176}{1250}$ as far as Tom, or, in a 5-mile race, $\frac{1176}{1250} \cdot 5 = \frac{588}{125}$ miles. The difference is $5 - \frac{588}{125} = \frac{37}{125}$ miles.

32.   (a) $\frac{^-3}{5}, \frac{^-2}{5}, 0, \frac{1}{5}, \frac{2}{5}$ (b) $\frac{13}{24}, \frac{7}{12}, \frac{13}{18}$

33.   (a) $\frac{3}{4}x - \frac{5}{8} \geq \frac{1}{2}$ $\Rightarrow$ $6x - 5 \geq 4$ $\Rightarrow$ $6x \geq 9$ $\Rightarrow$ $x \geq \frac{9}{6} = \frac{3}{2}$

      (b) $\frac{^-x}{5} + \frac{1}{10} < \frac{^-1}{2}$ $\Rightarrow$ $^-2x + 1 < ^-5$ $\Rightarrow$ $^-2x < ^-6$ $\Rightarrow$ $x > 3$

      (c) $\frac{^-2}{5}(10x + 1) < 1 - x$ $\Rightarrow$ $^-4x - \frac{2}{5} < 1 - x$ $\Rightarrow$ $^-20x - 2 < 5 - 5x$ $\Rightarrow$ $^-15x < 7$ $\Rightarrow$ $x > \frac{^-7}{15}$

      (d) $\frac{2}{3}(\frac{1}{2}x - 7) \geq \frac{3}{4}x$ $\Rightarrow$ $\frac{1}{3}x - \frac{14}{3} \geq \frac{3}{4}x$ $\Rightarrow$ $4x - 56 \geq 9x$ $\Rightarrow$ $^-56 \geq 5x$ $\Rightarrow$ $x \leq \frac{^-56}{5}$

34.   Answers may vary.

      (a) $\frac{6}{15}, \frac{7}{15}$, and $\frac{8}{15}$ are between $\frac{1}{3}$ and $\frac{2}{3}$ (b) $\frac{^-3}{36}, \frac{^-4}{36}$, and $\frac{^-14}{36}$ are between $\frac{^-5}{12}$ and $\frac{^-1}{18}$

Problem Set 6-6

1.   (a) $3^{^-7} \cdot 3^{^-6} = 3^{^-7 + ^-6} = 3^{^-13} = \frac{1}{3^{13}}$ (b) $3^7 \cdot 3^6 = 3^{7+6} = 3^{13}$

      (c) $5^{15} \div 5^4 = 5^{15-4} = 5^{11}$ (d) $5^{15} \div 5^{^-4} = 5^{15 - ^-4} = 5^{15+4} = 5^{19}$

      (e) $(^-5)^{^-2} = \frac{1}{(^-5)^2} = \frac{1}{5^2} = \frac{1}{25}$ (f) $\frac{a^2}{a^{^-3}} = a^{2 - ^-3} = a^{2+3} = a^5$

      (g) $\frac{a}{a^{^-1}} = a^{1 - ^-1} = a^{1+1} = a^2$ (h) $\frac{a^{^-3}}{a^{^-2}} = a^{^-3 - ^-2} = a^{^-1} = \frac{1}{a}$

2.   (a) $\frac{1}{2^{10}} = \left(\frac{1}{2}\right)^{10}$ (b) $\frac{1}{2^3} = \left(\frac{1}{2}\right)^3$

      (c) $\left(\frac{2}{3}\right)^9$ (d) 1

      (e) $\left(\frac{3}{5}\right)^3$ (f) $\left(\frac{5}{6}\right)^{21}$

3.   (a)   False. $2^3 \cdot 3^2 = 2^5 = 32 \neq (2 \cdot 3)^5 = 6^5 = 7776$ (The bases must be equal; they are not multiplied)

3. (b) False. The bases are not the same; when multiplying numbers with exponents the exponents are added and not multiplied.

(c) False. The bases must be the same for the exponents to be added. $a^m \cdot b^m = (ab)^m$.

(d) False. By definition, any number to the zero power is 1.

(e) False. $(a + b)^2 = (a + b)(a + b) = a^2 + 2ab + b^2 \neq a^2 + b^2$.

(f) False. $(a + b)^{-m} = \dfrac{1}{(a + b)^m}$.

(g) False. $a^m \cdot a^n = a^{m+n}$; $a^{mn} = (a^m)^n$.

(h) True. $\left(\frac{a}{b}\right)^{-1} = \dfrac{1}{\left(\frac{a}{b}\right)} = \dfrac{b}{a}$

4. (a) Since $32 = 2^5$, $2^n = 2^5$, so $n = 5$.

(b) Since $6^2 = 36$ and $(^-6)^2 = 36$, $n = 6$ or $^-6$.

(c) $2^{n+7} = 2^5$, so $n + 7 = 5$ and $n = {}^-2$.

(d) Since $8 = 2^3$, $2^n \cdot 2^7 = 2^3$, or $2^{n+7} = 2^3$. Thus $n + 7 = 3$, or $n = {}^-4$.

(e) $(2 + n)(2 + n) = 2^2 + n^2 \Rightarrow 2^2 + 4n + n^2 = 2^2 + n^2 \Rightarrow 4n = 0$, so $n = 0$.

(f) $3^n = (3^3)^5 \Rightarrow 3^n = 3^{15} \Rightarrow n = 15$.

5. (a) Each cell has a "length" equal to twice its radius. The length of the line, then, would be twice the radius times the number of cells, or:
$2(4 \cdot 10^{-3})(25 \cdot 10^{12}) = (2 \cdot 4 \cdot 25) \cdot (10^{-3} \cdot 10^{12}) = 200 \cdot 10^9 = (2 \cdot 10^2) \cdot 10^9 = 2 \cdot 10^{11}$ mm.

(b) $2 \cdot 10^{11} \div 10^6 = 2 \cdot (10^{11-6}) = 2 \cdot 10^5$ km. There are 1.6 km per mile; thus the line of red blood cells would be $1.2 \cdot 10^5 = 120{,}000$ miles long.

6. (a) $3^x \leq 3^4 \Rightarrow x \leq 4$

(b) $(2^2)^x < 2^3 \Rightarrow 2x < 3 \Rightarrow x < \frac{3}{2}$. Since x must be an integer, however, $x \leq 1$.

(c) $3^{2x} > 3^3 \Rightarrow 2x > 3 \Rightarrow x > \frac{3}{2}$. Since x must be an integer, $x \geq 2$.

(d) $2^x > 2^0 \Rightarrow x > 0$.

7. (a) $x^{-1} - x = \frac{1}{x} - x = \frac{1}{x} - \frac{x^2}{x} = \frac{1 - x^2}{x}$.

(b) $x^2 - y^{-2} = x^2 - \frac{1}{y^2} = \frac{x^2 y^2}{y^2} - \frac{1}{y^2} = \frac{x^2 y^2 - 1}{y^2}$.

(c) $2x^2 + (2x)^2 + 2^2 x = 2x^2 + 4x^2 + 4x = 6x^2 + 4x$.

(d) $y^{-3} + y^3 = \frac{1}{y^3} + y^3 = \frac{1}{y^3} + \frac{y^6}{y^3} = \frac{1 + y^6}{y^3}$.

(e) $\dfrac{3a - b}{(3a - b)^{-1}} = (3a - b)(3a - b) = (3a - b)^2$.

(f) $\dfrac{a^{-1}}{a^{-1} + b^{-1}} = \dfrac{\frac{1}{a}}{\frac{1}{a} + \frac{1}{b}} = \dfrac{\frac{1}{a}}{\left(\frac{a + b}{ab}\right)} = \frac{1}{a} \cdot \frac{ab}{a + b} = \frac{b}{a + b}$

8. (a) $\left(\frac{1}{2}\right)^3$ (b) $\left(\frac{3}{4}\right)^8$

    (c) $\left(\frac{4}{3}\right)^{10}$ (d) $\left(\frac{4}{5}\right)^{10}$

    (e) $\left(\frac{4}{3}\right)^{10}$ (f) $\left(\frac{3}{4}\right)^{100}$

9. (a) $Q(0) = 10^{10}\left(\frac{6}{5}\right)^0 = 10^{10}\cdot 1 = 10^{10}$ bacteria when t = 0.

    (b) $Q(2) = 10^{10}\left(\frac{6}{5}\right)^2 = 10^{10}\cdot\frac{36}{25}$ bacteria when t = 2 seconds.

10. (a) $\frac{3}{2}, \frac{3}{4}, \frac{3}{8}, \frac{3}{16}, \frac{3}{32}$ (b) There is a common ratio of $\frac{1}{2}$.   (c) $\frac{3}{1024}$

11. (a) $f(0) = \frac{3}{4}\cdot 2^0 = \frac{3}{4}\cdot 1 = \frac{3}{4}$

    (b) $f(5) = \frac{3}{4}\cdot 2^5 = \frac{3}{4}\cdot 32 = 24$

    (c) $f(^-5) = \frac{3}{4}\cdot 2^{-5} = \frac{3}{4}\cdot\frac{1}{2^5} = \frac{3}{4}\cdot\frac{1}{32} = \frac{3}{128}$.

    (d) We are looking for the greatest integer *n* for which $\frac{3}{4}\cdot 2^n < \frac{3}{400}$, or simplifying, $\frac{3}{4}\cdot 2^n = \frac{3}{2^2}\cdot\frac{1}{2^{-n}} = \frac{3}{2^{2-n}}$.

    For $\frac{3}{2^{2-n}} < \frac{3}{400}$, $2^{2-n} > 400$. $2^9 = 512$ is the first power of 2 greater than 400, so $2 - n \geq 9$ or

    $^-n \geq 7$ or $n \leq {}^-7$. Thus $^-7$ is the greatest integer for which the statement is true.

12. (a) 3^{400}

    (b) $4^{300} = (4^3)^{100} = 64^{100}$, while $3^{400} = (3^4)^{100} = 81^{100}$, and $81^{100} > 64^{100}$.

    (c) "ERROR". The number is too large to fit into the calculator's logic.

13. (a) $32^{50} = (2^5)^{50} = 2^{250}$, while $4^{100} = (2^2)^{100} = 2^{200}$. $2^{250} > 2^{200}$, so $32^{50} > 4^{100}$.

    (b) $(^-27)^{-15} = [(^-3)^3]^{-15} = (^-3)^{-45} = \frac{1}{(^-3)^{45}} = {}^-\left[\frac{1}{3^{45}}\right]$. $(^-3)^{-75} = \frac{1}{(^-3)^{75}} = {}^-\left[\frac{1}{3^{75}}\right]$.

    $\frac{1}{3^{45}} > \frac{1}{3^{75}}$; their negatives reverse the direction of the inequality; thus $(^-3)^{-75}$ is the greater.

14. No. Any integral power of 3 ends in either 1, 3, 7, or 9.

15. Look for a pattern:
$$5^1 = 5$$
$$5^2 = 25$$
$$5^3 = 125$$
$$5^4 = 625$$
$$5^5 = 3125$$
$$5^6 = 15{,}625$$
For n > 2, all powers have the last two digits equal to 25, preceded by 1 for odd powers and 6 for even powers. Since 127 is odd, the last three digits of 5^{127} are 125.

16. $\frac{6 \text{ items}}{5 \text{ seconds}} = \frac{x \text{ items}}{180 \text{ seconds}} \Rightarrow 5x = 1080 \Rightarrow x = 216$ items.

17. $\frac{3}{80} = \frac{d}{720} \Rightarrow 80d = 2160 \Rightarrow d = 27$ items defective.

18. (a) $\frac{2}{7}$ (b) $\frac{40}{3}$

    (c) $\frac{1}{3^4} = \frac{1}{81}$ (d) $\frac{1}{100}$

18.   (e) $\frac{9}{4}$ (f) $\frac{7^2}{10^2} = \frac{49}{100}$

      (g) $\frac{9}{16}$ (h) $\frac{x}{x + y}$

19.   (a) $\frac{^-3}{4}x = 1 \Rightarrow \frac{^-4}{3} \cdot \frac{^-3}{4}x = \frac{^-4}{3} \cdot 1 \Rightarrow x = \frac{^-4}{3}$

      (b) $\frac{2}{3}x = \frac{^-3}{5} \Rightarrow \frac{3}{2} \cdot \frac{2}{3}x = \frac{3}{2} \cdot \frac{^-3}{5} \Rightarrow x = \frac{^-9}{10}$

      (c) $\frac{1}{3}x - 5 = \frac{^-3}{4}x \Rightarrow 4x - 60 = {^-9}x \Rightarrow 13x = 60 \Rightarrow x = \frac{60}{13}$

      (d) $\frac{x}{3} = \frac{^-3}{4} \Rightarrow 4x = {^-9} \Rightarrow x = \frac{^-9}{4}$

      (e) $\frac{x}{3} = \frac{27}{x} \Rightarrow x^2 = 81.$ Since $9^2 = 81$ and $(^-9)^2 = 81$, $x = 9$ or $x = {^-9}$

      (f) $\frac{x + 1}{3} = \frac{3}{4}x \Rightarrow 4(x + 1) = 9x \Rightarrow 4x + 4 = 9x \Rightarrow 4 = 5x \Rightarrow x = \frac{4}{5}$

20. $\frac{\frac{5}{6} \text{ house}}{1 \text{ day}} = \frac{1 \text{ house}}{x \text{ days}} \Rightarrow \frac{5}{6}x = 1 \Rightarrow x = \frac{6}{5}$ days.

21.   The ratios will change since the additional students do not fit the ratio of existing students; e.g., if there were originally 6 boys and 16 girls (6 to 16 ratio), the new ratio would be a $6 + 2$ to $16 + 2$, or 8 to 18. In other words, $\frac{3x}{8x} < \frac{3x + 2}{8x + 2}$.

22. $\frac{^-6}{7}, \frac{^-3}{4}, \frac{^-2}{3}, \frac{^-1}{2}, 0, \frac{7}{9}, \frac{4}{5}, \frac{6}{7}, \frac{9}{7}$

Chapter 6 Test

1.   (a)   3 of 4 blocks shaded:

      (b)   2 of 3 bars shaded:

      (c)   Three of four vertical bars are shaded, meshed with two of three horizontal bars. Thus six of the twelve blocks are cross-hatched $(\frac{3}{4} \cdot \frac{2}{3} = \frac{6}{12})$.

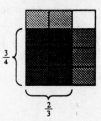

2.   Answers may vary. Three are $\frac{10}{12}$, $\frac{15}{18}$, and $\frac{50}{60}$.

3.   (a) $\frac{24}{28} = \frac{6 \cdot 4}{7 \cdot 4} = \frac{6}{7}$ (b) $\frac{ax^2}{bx} = \frac{(ax)x}{(b)x} = \frac{ax}{b}$

      (c) $\frac{0}{1}$ (d) $\frac{5}{9}$

      (e) $\frac{b^2 + bx}{b + x} = \frac{b(b + x)}{b + x} = \frac{b}{1}$ (f) $\frac{2}{27}$

4.   (a) $=$ (b) $>$

      (c) $>$ (d) $<$

5.   (a) $\frac{5}{6} + \frac{4}{15} = \frac{25}{30} + \frac{8}{30} = \frac{33}{30} = \frac{11}{10}$ (b) $\frac{4}{25} - \frac{3}{35} = \frac{28}{175} - \frac{15}{175} = \frac{13}{175}$

      (c) $\frac{5}{6} \cdot \frac{12}{13} = \frac{5}{1} \cdot \frac{2}{13} = \frac{10}{13}$ (d) $\frac{5}{6} \div \frac{12}{15} = \frac{5}{6} \div \frac{4}{5} = \frac{5}{6} \cdot \frac{5}{4} = \frac{25}{24}$

      (e) $(5\frac{1}{6} + 7\frac{1}{3}) \div 2\frac{1}{4} = (12 + \frac{1}{6} + \frac{2}{6}) \div 2\frac{1}{4} = 12\frac{1}{2} \div 2\frac{1}{4} = \frac{25}{2} \div \frac{9}{4} = \frac{25}{2} \cdot \frac{4}{9} = \frac{25}{1} \cdot \frac{2}{9} = \frac{50}{9}$

      (f) $(^-5\frac{1}{6} + 7\frac{1}{3}) \div \frac{^-9}{4} = 2\frac{1}{6} \div \frac{^-9}{4} = \frac{13}{6} \cdot \frac{^-4}{9} = \frac{13}{3} \cdot \frac{^-2}{9} = \frac{^-26}{27}$

6.   <u>Additive</u>   <u>Multiplicative</u>

      (a) $^-3$ $\frac{1}{3}$

      (b) $^-3\frac{1}{7}$ $\frac{7}{22}$

      (c) $\frac{^-5}{6}$ $\frac{6}{5}$

      (d) $\frac{3}{4}$ $\frac{^-4}{3}$

7. $^-2\frac{1}{3}$, $^-1\frac{7}{8}$, 0, $(\frac{71}{140})^{300}$, $\frac{69}{140}$, $\frac{1}{2}$, $\frac{71}{140}$, $(\frac{74}{73})^{300}$

8.   (a) $\frac{\frac{^-1}{4}}{\frac{^-1}{24}} = \frac{6}{1} = 6$ (b) $\frac{\frac{5}{8}}{\frac{1}{2}} = \frac{5}{4}$

      (c) $\frac{(\frac{1}{2} + \frac{3}{4})(\frac{1}{2} - \frac{3}{4})}{\frac{1}{2} + \frac{3}{4}} = \frac{1}{2} - \frac{3}{4} = \frac{^-1}{4}$

9.   (a) $\frac{1}{4}x - \frac{3}{5} \leq \frac{1}{2}(3 - 2x) \Rightarrow 5x - 12 \leq 10(3 - 2x) \Rightarrow 5x - 12 \leq 30 - 20x \Rightarrow 25x \leq 42$
            $\Rightarrow x \leq \frac{42}{25}$

      (b) $\frac{x}{3} - \frac{x}{2} \geq \frac{^-1}{4} \Rightarrow 4x - 6x \geq ^-3 \Rightarrow ^-2x \geq ^-3 \Rightarrow x \leq \frac{3}{2}$

      (c) $\frac{2}{3}(\frac{3}{4}x - 1) = \frac{2}{3} - x \Rightarrow \frac{1}{2}x - \frac{2}{3} = \frac{2}{3} - x \Rightarrow 3x - 4 = 4 - 6x \Rightarrow 9x = 8 \Rightarrow x = \frac{8}{9}$

      (d) $\frac{5}{6} = \frac{4 - x}{3} \Rightarrow 6(4 - x) = 15 \Rightarrow 24 - 6x = 15 \Rightarrow ^-6x = ^-9 \Rightarrow x = \frac{3}{2}$

10.   The definition of division is that $a \div b = c$ if and only if $b \cdot c = a$. Translating to rational numbers, $\frac{a}{b} \div \frac{c}{d} = \frac{e}{f}$ if and only if $\frac{c}{d} \cdot \frac{e}{f} = \frac{a}{b}$. Solving for the quotient $\frac{e}{f}$, we have $\frac{d}{c}(\frac{c}{d} \cdot \frac{e}{f}) = \frac{d}{c} \cdot \frac{a}{b}$, or $\frac{e}{f} = \frac{a}{b} \cdot \frac{d}{c}$; i.e., the quotient is equal to the product of the dividend and the multiplicative inverse of the divisor — the invert-and-multiply algorithm.

11. $\frac{\text{Boys}}{\text{Girls}} = \frac{3}{5} = \frac{B}{15}$, so $5B = 45 \Rightarrow$ 9 boys are in Ms. Garcia's class.

12.   (a) $(\frac{1}{2})^{11}$ (b) $\frac{1}{5^{20}}$

      (c) $(\frac{2}{3})^{^-28} = (\frac{3}{2})^{28}$ (d) 3^{18}

13.   Assuming no waste, $54\frac{1}{4} \div 3\frac{1}{12} = 17\frac{22}{37}$ pieces can be cut; i.e., 17 pieces with $\frac{22}{37}$ piece $= \frac{22}{37} \cdot 3\frac{1}{12} = \frac{11}{6}$ yards left over.

14.   (a)   15, or approximately $\frac{30}{4} \cdot \frac{8}{4} = \frac{15}{2} \cdot 2$.

      (b)   15, or approximately $\frac{15}{6} \cdot 6$.

      (c)   4, or approximately $\frac{1}{400} \div \frac{1}{1000}$.

15. Answers may vary. $\frac{61}{80}$ and $\frac{62}{80}$ are two.

16. $\frac{3}{4}\left[\frac{2}{5}(S - 10)\right] = 18$ $\Rightarrow$ S = \$70 in savings originally.

17. Let H be the number of hamburgers, D the number of hot dogs, and T the number of tacos. Then $H = 4\frac{1}{2}$ D

and $T = \frac{3}{4}D$. Thus $\frac{H}{T} = \frac{4\frac{1}{2}D}{\frac{3}{4}D} = \frac{9}{2} \div \frac{3}{4} = 6$, or a 6:1 ratio of hamburgers to tacos.

18. Think of $504792 \div 23$ as $504792 \cdot \frac{1}{23}$ and enter: [5] [0] [4] [7] [9] [2] [x] [2] [3] [$\frac{1}{x}$] [=]

19. Jim ate $\frac{1}{3} \cdot \frac{1}{2}$ the pizza, or $\frac{1}{6} \cdot 2000 = 333\frac{1}{3}$ calories.

20. $\frac{1500}{20} = \frac{1200}{m}$ $\Rightarrow$ m = 16 minutes.

21. Let C be the total of Joyce's credits. Then $\frac{1}{4}C + \frac{1}{3}C + 25 = C$. Solving, C = 60, and Joyce has 60 credits in all.

CHAPTER 7 - DECIMALS AND DECIMAL OPERATIONS

<u>Problem</u> <u>Set</u> <u>7-1</u>

1. (a) $0.023 = 0 \cdot \frac{1}{10^1} + 2 \cdot \frac{1}{10^2} + 3 \cdot \frac{1}{10^3} = 0 \cdot 10^{-1} + 2 \cdot 10^{-2} + 3 \cdot 10^{-3} = 2 \cdot 10^{-2} + 3 \cdot 10^{-3}$

   (b) $206.06 = 2 \cdot 10^2 + 0 \cdot 10^1 + 6 \cdot 10^0 + 0 \cdot 10^{-1} + 6 \cdot 10^{-2} = 2 \cdot 10^2 + 6 \cdot 1 + 6 \cdot 10^{-2}$

   (c) $312.0103 = 3 \cdot 10^2 + 1 \cdot 10^1 + 2 \cdot 10^0 + 1 \cdot 10^{-2} + 3 \cdot 10^{-4} = 3 \cdot 10^2 + 1 \cdot 10 + 2 \cdot 1 + 1 \cdot 10^{-2} + 3 \cdot 10^{-4}$

   (d) $0.000132 = 1 \cdot 10^{-4} + 3 \cdot 10^{-5} + 2 \cdot 10^{-6}$

2. (a) $4000 + 300 + 50 + 6 + 0.7 + 0.08 = 4356.78$

   (b) $4000 + 0.6 + 0.008 = 4000.608$

   (c) $40,000 + 0.03 = 40,000.03$

   (d) $0.2 + 0.0004 + 0.0000007 = 0.2004007$

3. (a) 536.0076

   (b) 3.008

   (c) 0.000436

   (d) $5,000,000.2$

4. (a) $0.436 = \frac{436}{1000} = \frac{109}{250}$

   (b) $25.16 = 25\frac{16}{100} = \frac{2516}{100} = \frac{629}{250}$

   (c) $^-316.027 = {}^-316\frac{27}{1000} = \frac{^-316027}{1000}$

   (d) $28.1902 = 28\frac{1902}{10000} = \frac{281902}{10000} = \frac{140951}{5000}$

   (e) $^-4.3 = {}^-4\frac{3}{10} = \frac{^-43}{10}$

   (f) $^-62.01 = {}^-62\frac{1}{100} = \frac{^-6201}{100}$

5. (a) Terminating decimal; the denominator contains only 5 as a prime factor.

   (b) Terminating decimal; the denominator contains no prime factors other than 2 and 5.

   (c) Terminating decimal; the reduced denominator contains only 2 as a prime factor.

   (d) Terminating decimal; the denominator contains only 2 as a prime factor.

   (e) Terminating decimal; the denominator contains only 5 as a prime factor.

   (f) Terminating decimal; the denominator contains only 5 as a prime factor.

   (g) Nonterminating decimal; the denominator contains 3 as a prime factor.

   (h) Terminating decimal; the denominator contains only 5 as a prime factor.

5. (i) Nonterminating decimal; the denominator contains 13 as a prime factor.

6. (a) 0.8   (b) 3.05

    (c) 0.5   (d) 0.03125

    (e) 0.01152   (f) 0.2128

    (g) Nonterminating decimal   (h) 0.08

    (i) Nonterminating decimal

7. (a)
$$\begin{array}{r} 36.812 \\ 0.43 \\ +\ 1.96 \\ \hline 39.202 \end{array}$$
(Note that we line up the decimal points)

    (b)
$$\begin{array}{r} 200.010 \\ -\ 32.007 \\ \hline 168.003 \end{array}$$
(We add a zero to the end of 200.01)

    (c)
$$\begin{array}{r} ^-4.6120 \\ -\ 386.0193 \\ \hline ^-390.6313 \end{array}$$

    (d)
$$\begin{array}{r} 3.6\ 1 \\ \times\ 0.4\ 1\ 3 \\ \hline 1\ 0\ 8\ 3 \\ 3\ 6\ 1\ \ \\ 1\ 4\ 4\ 4\ \ \ \\ \hline 1.4\ 9\ 0\ 9\ 3 \end{array}$$
3.6 1 (Two digits after the decimal point)
× 0.4 1 3 (Three digits after the decimal point)
1.4 9 0 9 3 (2 + 3 = 5 digits after the decimal point)

    (e)
$$\begin{array}{r} ^-2.6 \\ \times\ \ 4 \\ \hline ^-1\ 0.4 \end{array}$$

    (f)
$$\begin{array}{r} 4.6\ 8\ 1 \\ 2.3\overline{)1\ 0.7\ 6\ 6\ 3} \\ \underline{9\ 2\ \ } \\ 1\ 5\ 6 \\ \underline{1\ 3\ 8} \\ 1\ 8\ 6 \\ \underline{1\ 8\ 4} \\ 2\ 3 \\ \underline{2\ 3} \\ 0 \end{array}$$
(Multiply divisor and dividend by 10)

8. (a) $13.62 = 13\frac{62}{100} = \frac{1362}{100}$; $4.082 = 4\frac{82}{1000} = \frac{4082}{1000}$

$\frac{1362}{100} + \frac{4082}{1000} = \frac{13620}{1000} + \frac{4082}{1000} = \frac{17702}{1000} = 17.702$

    (b) $12.62 = 12\frac{62}{100} = \frac{1262}{100}$; $4.082 = 4\frac{82}{1000} = \frac{4082}{1000}$

$\frac{1262}{100} - \frac{4082}{1000} = \frac{12620}{1000} - \frac{4082}{1000} = \frac{8538}{1000} = 8.538$

8.   (c) $1.36 = 1\frac{36}{100} = \frac{136}{100}$; $0.02 = \frac{2}{100}$

$$\frac{136}{100} \cdot \frac{2}{100} = \frac{272}{10000} = 0.0272$$

     (d) $1.36 = \frac{136}{100}$; $0.02 = \frac{2}{100}$

$$\frac{136}{100} \div \frac{2}{100} = \frac{136}{100} \cdot \frac{100}{2} = \frac{13600}{200} = \frac{136}{2} = 68$$

9.   Maura bought a total of:
$$\begin{array}{r} \$17.95 \\ 13.59 \\ 14.86 \\ 179.98 \\ 2.43 \\ \underline{2.43} \\ \$231.24 \end{array}$$
in her shopping.

10. Subtraction can be accomplished by grouping integers, tenths, hundredths, ... , and subtracting. Consequently, subtraction of decimals can be accomplished by lining up the decimal points and subtracting as with whole numbers. In other words, lining up the decimal points aligns place value.

11. (a) $4.63 \cdot 10^8 = 4.63 \cdot 100,000,000 = 463,000,000.0$ (multiplying by 10^8 has the effect of moving the decimal point 8 places to the right)

     (b) $0.04 \cdot 10^8 = 0.04 \cdot 100,000,000 = 4,000,000.0$

     (c) $46.3 \cdot 10^8 = 46.3 \cdot 100,000,000 = 4,630,000,000.0$

     (d) $463.0 \cdot 10^8 = 463.0 \cdot 100,000,000 = 46,300,000,000.0$

     (e) $0.00463 \cdot 10^8 = 0.00463 \cdot 100,000,000 = 463,000.0$

     (f) $0.0000000463 \cdot 10^8 = 0.0000000463 \cdot 100,000,000 = 4.63$

     (g) $4.63 \cdot 10^{-4} = 4.63 \cdot \frac{1}{10^4} = 4.63 \cdot 0.0001 = 0.000463$ (multiplying by 10^{-4} has the effect of moving the decimal point 4 places to the left.

     (h) $0.04 \cdot 10^{-4} = 0.04 \cdot 0.0001 = 0.000004$

     (i) $46.3 \cdot 10^{-4} = 46.3 \cdot 0.0001 = 0.00463$

     (j) $0.0000463 \cdot 10^{-4} = 0.0000463 \cdot 0.0001 = 0.00000000463$

     (k) $4.63 \div 10^{-4} = 4.63 \div \frac{1}{10^4} = 4.63 \cdot \frac{10^4}{1} = 4.63 \cdot 10^4 = 4.63 \cdot 10,000 = 46,300.0$ (dividing by 10^{-4} has the effect of moving the decimal point 4 places to the right)

     (l) $0.04 \div 10^{-4} = 0.04 \cdot 10^4 = 0.04 \cdot 10,000 = 400.0$

     (m) $46.3 \div 10^{-4} = 46.3 \cdot 10^4 = 46.3 \cdot 10,000 = 463,000.0$

     (n) $0.0000463 \div 10^{-4} = 0.0000463 \cdot 10^4 = 0.0000463 \cdot 10,000 = 0.463$

12. (a) $20\overline{|180} = 2\overline{|18}$ so it is equivalent.

(b) $0.2\overline{|0.18} = 2\overline{|1.8}$ so it is not equivalent.

(c) $0.002\overline{|0.018} = 2\overline{|18}$ so it is equivalent.

(d) $20\overline{|1800} = 2\overline{|180}$ so it is not equivalent.

(e) $0.0002\overline{|0.00018} = 2\overline{|1.8}$ so it is not equivalent.

(f) $0.2\overline{|1.8} = 2\overline{|18}$ so it is equivalent.

13. (a) $(0.22)(0.35)$ on the calculator is 0.077. Multiplying by the rule in this section results in a product of 0.0770, but the calculator deletes the last zero because it is not a significant digit (i.e., it does not change the value of the number).

(b) $0.2436 \div 0.0006$ on the calculator is 406, with no decimal point. Dividing by the rule in this section results in a quotient of $406.\overline{0}$, but the calculator deletes the decimal point and all following zeros.

14. Answers (a) to (f) may vary.

(a) Add 23.35 and 62.69.

(b) Add: $27.89 + 142.06 + 82.14 + 111.67$.

(c) Subtract 42.89 from 139.61.

(d) Multiply 0.92 by 0.015.

(e) Subtract 4.7 from 4.82.

(f) Divide 29.841 by 14.7.

15. (2.082 lbs per quart)(29.922 quarts per cubic foot) = 62.297604. Rounding to the nearest thousandth, we have 62.298 pounds.

16. We sum along the diagonal, obtaining 16.5. In rows and columns with two figures, we subtract their sum from 16.5 to obtain the missing element. We thus obtain:

8.2	1.9	6.4
3.7	5.5	7.3
4.6	9.1	2.8

17. There would be a total of $30 + 20 + 10 = 60$ pounds of nuts. At an average price per pound of $4.50, Keith would pay $(4.50)(60) = \$270.00$ for the 60 pounds.

He has already paid $(3.00)(30) + (5.00)(20) = 90.00 + 100.00 = \$190.00$ for nuts, so he has $270.00 - 190.00 = \$80.00$ left to pay for the additional 10 pounds.

$80.00 \div 10 = \$8.00$ per pound for the additional nuts.

18. (a) (3 heaters)(1200 watts per hour each)(24 hours per day) = 86,400 watt hours = 86.4 kilowatt hours. (86.4 kilowatt hours)($0.03715 per kilowatt hour) = $3.20976, which rounds to $3.21 per day.

(b) 75 watts is 0.075 kilowatts. Then (0.075 kw)(1 hour)($0.03715 per kw hour) = $0.0278625 to operate one bulb for one hour. $1.00 \div \$0.03715$, rounded, is 359 hours.

19. (a)   If there are 2.54 cm per inch, there are $(2.54)^3 = 16.387064$ cm^3 per cubic inch.
           $(16.387064$ cm^3 per in$^3)(390$ cubic inches$) = 6391$ cm^3 (rounded to the nearest cm^3) in the engine.

    (b) $(3000$ cm$^3)\div(16.387064$ cm^3 per in$^3) = 183$ in^3 (rounded to the nearest in^3) in the engine.

20. $(39.37$ in per m$)(100$ m$) = 3937$ inches traveled. $(3937$ in$)\div(63360$ in per mi$) = 0.062137$ miles traveled.
    $(10.49$ sec$)\div(3600$ sec per hr$) = 0.002914$ hours spent.
    $(0.062137$ miles$)\div(0.002914$ hour$) = 21.3$ (rounded to the nearest tenth) miles per hour.

21. $(\$61.48$ per share$)(18$ shares$) - (\$964$ cost$) = \$142.64$ profit in the first group.
    $(\$85.35$ per share$)(350$ shares$) - (\$27,422.50$ cost$) = \$2450.00$ profit in the second group.
    $[(\$142.64 + \$2450.00)$ profit$] - (\$495.00$ commission$) = \$2097.64$ profit, or $2098 rounded.

22. (a) $(235)(1.56) = 366.60$ francs for \$235 cash.

    (b) $(452.85$ francs $+ 284.65$ francs$)\div(1.56$ francs per \$ cash$) = 472.76$, or a minimum of \$473.

    (c) $(687.75$ francs$)\div(1.59$ francs per \$ in traveler's checks$) = \$432.55$. She will need to cash \$400 plus \$40, or four \$100 checks and two \$20 checks.

23. (a)   There is a difference of 0.9 between each element of the sequence, so it is arithmetic.
           Then $4.5 + 0.9 = 5.4$; $5.4 + 0.9 = 6.3$; $6.3 + 0.9 = 7.2$; ... .

    (b)   There is a difference of 0.2 between each element of the sequence, so it is arithmetic.
           Then $1.1 + 0.2 = 1.3$; $1.3 + 0.2 = 1.5$; $1.5 + 0.2 = 1.7$; ... .

    (c)   Each element of the sequence is 0.5 times the previous element, so it is geometric.
           Then $0.125\cdot0.5 = 0.0625$; $0.0625\cdot0.5 = 0.03125$; $0.0315\cdot0.5 = 0.015625$; ... .

    (d)   There is a difference of 1.3 between each element of the sequence, so it is arithmetic.
           Then $5.4 + 1.3 = 6.7$; $6.7 + 1.3 = 8.0$; $8.0 + 1.3 = 9.3$; ... .

24. 42095 is 1000 times 42.095, so the error could be corrected by dividing by 1000.

25. We would divide 93,000,000 by 1565, or 93000000÷1565=. (It would take 59,425 hours, or about $6\frac{3}{4}$ years.)

26. (a)   91,000,000.1106

    (b)   ⁻90,753,086.5318

    (c)   154,815,802.09496

    (d)   102,880,657,928.6

27. (a)   System A: $(12$ checks$)(\$0.10$ per check$) = \$1.20$.
           System B: $(12$ checks$)(\$0.07$ per check$) + \$0.75 = \$1.59$.
           System A is more economical for an average of 12 checks per month.

    (b)   System A: $(52$ checks$)(\$0.10) = \$5.20$.
           System B: $(52$ checks$)(\$0.07) + \$0.75 = \$4.39$.
           System B is more economical for an average of 52 checks per month.

27. (c)   If we let n = the number of checks averaged per month, then we want 0.10n to equal 0.07n + 0.75:
          0.10n = 0.07n + 0.75
          0.03n = 0.75
          n = 25, so the break-even point is 25 checks per month.

          This problem could also be solved by making a table of cost for each system versus the number of checks written.

28.   The total of outstanding checks is $54.19. Adding the total of outstanding checks to the checkbook balance, we have $75.88, which differs from the bank statement. The bank is not correct.

29.   The alternate plan is a geometric sequence, with 1st term $0.01 and ratio 2. From Chapter 1 we learned the nth term of a geometric sequence with first term a and ratio r is given by ar^{n-1}. In this case, we have: $0.01 \cdot 2^{30-1} = 0.01 \cdot 536,870,912 = \$5,368,709$. The second option is more profitable by $\$5,368,709 - \$1,000,000 = \$4,368,709$.

30.   The number of digits in the terminating decimal will be the greater of m or n.

Problem Set 7-2

1. (a) $4 \div 9 = 0.444\ldots = 0.\overline{4}$

   (b) $2 \div 7 = 0.285714285714\ldots = 0.\overline{285714}$

   (c) $3 \div 11 = 0.2727\ldots = 0.\overline{27}$

   (d) $1 \div 15 = 0.0666\ldots = 0.0\overline{6}$

   (e) $2 \div 75 = 0.2666\ldots = 0.2\overline{6}$

   (f) $1 \div 99 = 0.010101\ldots = 0.\overline{01}$

   (g) $5 \div 6 = 0.8333\ldots = 0.8\overline{3}$

   (h) $1 \div 13 = 0.076923076923\ldots = 0.\overline{076923}$

2. (a)   (i) $0.\overline{142857}$

         (ii) $0.\overline{285714}$

         (iii) $0.\overline{428571}$

         (iv) $0.\overline{571428}$

         (v) $0.\overline{714285}$

         (vi) $0.\overline{857142}$

   (b)   Six

   (c)   The sum of the digits in each case is 27, so each repetend is divisible by 3. The ratio between each, starting with $\frac{2}{7} \div \frac{1}{7}$, is $\frac{2}{1}, \frac{3}{2}, \frac{4}{3}, \frac{5}{4}$, and $\frac{6}{5}$. Additionally, the answers all contain the same digits: 1, 2, 4, 5, 7, and 8. The digits always repeat in the same sequence.

3. (a)   All the sums obtained in this manner are 999.

    (b) $\frac{5}{13} = 0.\overline{384615}$. $384 + 615 = 999$, so the same result is obtained.

    (c)   If there are an even number of digits in the repetend, the sums of the halves will always be a series of numbers divisible by 3, or a power of 10 less 1.

    (d)   No. The repetend does not have an even number of digits.

4. (a) $0.\overline{076923}$

    (b) $0.\overline{047619}$

    (c) $0.\ \overline{157894736842105263}$

5. (a) $n = 2.4\overline{5}$; $10n = 24.\overline{5}$. We now have a one-digit repetend, so:

    $$10(10n) = 245.\overline{5}$$
    $$\underline{-10n = -24.\overline{5}}$$
    $$90n = 221 \qquad \text{and } n = \tfrac{221}{90}$$

    (b) $n = 2.\overline{45}$; we have a two-digit repetend, so:

    $$100n = 245.\overline{45}$$
    $$\underline{-n = -2.\overline{45}}$$
    $$99n = 243 \qquad \text{and } n = \tfrac{243}{99} = \tfrac{27}{11}$$

    (c) $n = 2.4\overline{54}$; $10n = 24.\overline{54}$. We now have a two-digit repetend, so:

    $$100(10n) = 2454.\overline{54}$$
    $$\underline{-10n = -24.\overline{54}}$$
    $$990n = 2430 \qquad \text{and } n = \tfrac{2430}{990} = \tfrac{27}{11}$$

    (d) $n = 0.2\overline{45}$; $10\,n = 2.\overline{45}$. We now have a two-digit repetend, so:

    $$100(10n) = 245.\overline{45}$$
    $$\underline{-10n = -2.\overline{45}}$$
    $$990n = 243 \qquad \text{and } n = \tfrac{243}{990} = \tfrac{27}{110}$$

    (e) $n = 0.02\overline{45}$; $100n = 2.\overline{45}$. We now have a two-digit repetend, so:

    $$100(100n) = 245.\overline{45}$$
    $$\underline{-100n = -2.\overline{45}}$$
    $$9900n = 243 \qquad \text{and } n = \tfrac{243}{9900} = \tfrac{27}{1100}$$

    (f) $n = {}^{-}24.\overline{54}$; we have a two-digit repetend, so:

    $$100n = {}^{-}2454.\overline{54}$$
    $$\underline{-n = +24.\overline{54}}$$
    $$99n = {}^{-}2430 \qquad \text{and } n = \tfrac{{}^{-}2430}{99} = \tfrac{{}^{-}270}{11}$$

    (g) $n = 0.\overline{4}$; we have a one-digit repetend, so:

    $$10n = 4.\overline{4}$$
    $$\underline{-n = -.\overline{4}}$$
    $$9n = 4 \qquad \text{and } n = \tfrac{4}{9}$$

    (h) $n = 0.\overline{6}$; we have a one-digit repetend, so:

    $$10n = 6.\overline{6}$$
    $$\underline{-n = -.\overline{6}}$$
    $$9n = 6 \qquad \text{and } n = \tfrac{6}{9} = \tfrac{2}{3}$$

5. (i) n = 0.5$\bar{5}$; 10n = 5.$\bar{5}$. We have a one-digit repetend, so:

$$10(10n) = 55.\bar{5}$$
$$\underline{-10n = -5.\bar{5}}$$
$$90n = 50 \qquad \text{and } n = \tfrac{50}{90} = \tfrac{5}{9}$$

(Note that 0.5$\bar{5}$ is the same as 0.$\bar{5}$)

(j) n = 0.$\overline{34}$; we have a two-digit repetend, so:

$$100n = 34.\overline{34}$$
$$\underline{-n = -.\overline{34}}$$
$$99n = 34 \qquad \text{and } n = \tfrac{34}{99}$$

(k) n = $^-$2.$\overline{34}$; we have a two-digit repetend, so:

$$100n = {}^-234.\overline{34}$$
$$\underline{-n = +2.\overline{34}}$$
$$99n = {}^-232 \qquad \text{and } n = {}^-\tfrac{232}{99}$$

(l) n = $^-$0.$\overline{02}$; we have a two-digit repetend, so:

$$100n = {}^-2.\overline{02}$$
$$\underline{-n = +.\overline{02}}$$
$$99n = {}^-2 \qquad \text{and } n = {}^-\tfrac{2}{99}$$

6. (a) Lining up the decimal points, we have:

3.2000
3.2222...
3.2323...
3.2333...
3.2300

Thus, ordering yields {3.2$\bar{3}$, 3.$\overline{23}$, 3.23, 2.$\overline{22}$, 3.2}

(b) Lining up the decimal points, we have:

$^-$1.454000
$^-$1.454444...
$^-$1.450000
$^-$1.454545...
$^-$1.454454...

Thus, ordering yields {$^-$1.45, $^-$1.454, $^-$1.45$\bar{4}$, $^-$1.4$\overline{54}$, $^-$1.4$\overline{54}$}

7. Answers to (a) through (d) may vary.

(a) 3.25 is between 3.2 and 3.3.

(b) 462.245 is between 462.24 and 462.25.

(c) 462.24$\bar{3}$ is between 462.2$\bar{4}$ and 462.$\overline{24}$.

(d) 0.02 is between 0.003 and 0.03.

8. (a) 3.25   (b) 462.245

(c) 0.01515   (d) 462.24$\overline{34}$

9. (a) 4⑨⑦36.⑤②8①   (b) 4①②3⑤.⑥⑦8⑨

10. (a) 200   (b) 200

10. (c)   204   (d)   203.7

     (e)   203.65

11. (224 miles) ÷ (12 gallons) = 18.$\bar{6}$ = 19 mpg rounded to the nearest mile.

12. (a)   Rounding to the nearest dime:
                2 gums at about 20¢ each → 40¢
                3 lollipops at 10¢ each → 30¢
                1 licorice at about 10¢ → 10¢
                1 drink at about 80¢ → 80¢
                1 floss at about 100¢ → 100¢
     For a total of about 260¢, or $2.60. We should have enough money.

     (b)   Rounding to the nearest dollar:
                7 gallons at about $1 each → $7
                2 quarts at about $1 each → $2
                1 wash at about $2 → $2
                Batteries at about $3 → $3
                Freshener at about $1 → $1
                Fluid at about $1 → $1
                Ticket at $1 → $1
                Wiper at about $2 → $2
                Drink for about $1 → $1
     For a total of about $20. To avoid embarrassment, it might be best to return one of the $1 items
     (the exact cost is $20.42).

13. Camera — about $25
     Film — about $4
     Case — about $8
     For a total estimated cost of about $37.

14. (a)   (i)   65.84 →   66
                     24.29 →   24
                     12.18 →   12
                   + 19.75 →   + 20
                                 122

     (ii)   66 might be rounded to 65.5 or 66.4
             24 might be rounded to 23.5 or 24.4
             12 might be rounded to 11.5 or 12.4
             20 might be rounded to 19.5 or 20.4
             So the total could be between 120.0 and 123.6.

     (iii)   The actual sum is 122.06

     (b)   (i)   89.47 →   89
                    -32.16 → - 32
                                57

     (ii)   89 might be rounded to 88.5 or 89.4
             32 might be rounded to 31.5 or 32.4
             So the difference could be between 56.1 and 57.9.

     (iii)   The actual difference is 57.31

14. (c) (*i*) $5.85 \rightarrow 6$
                    $6.13 \rightarrow 6$
                    $9.10 \rightarrow 9$
                   $+\ 4.32 \rightarrow +\ 4$
                   $\overline{\qquad\qquad\ \ 25}$

     (*ii*)   6 might be rounded to 5.5 or 6.4
              6 might be rounded to 5.5 or 6.4
              9 might be rounded to 8.5 or 9.4
              4 might be rounded to 3.5 or 4.4
              So the sum could be between 23.0 and 26.6.

     (*iii*) The actual sum is 25.4

     (d) (*i*) $223.75 \rightarrow 224$
                  $\dfrac{-87.60 \rightarrow -\ 88}{\ 136}$

     (*ii*)   224 might be rounded to 223.5 or 224.4
              88 might be rounded to 87.5 or 88.4
              So the difference could be between 135.0 and 136.9.

     (*iii*) The actual difference is 136.15

15. (a) $3.325 \cdot 10^3$ (b) $4.632 \cdot 10^1$

     (c) $1.3 \cdot 10^{-4}$ (d) $9.30146 \cdot 10^5$

16. (a) 0.0000000032   (b) 3,200,000,000

     (c) 0.42   (d) 620,000

17. (a) The diameter of the earth is about $1.27 \cdot 10^7$ km.

     (b) The distance from Pluto to the sun is $5.797 \cdot 10^6$ km.

     (c) Each year, about $5 \cdot 10^7$ cans are discarded in the United States.

18. (a) A computer requires 0.0000044 sec to do an addition problem.

     (b) There are about 19,900 km of coastline in the United States.

     (c) The earth has existed for approximately 3,000,000,000 years.

19. (a) $(8 \cdot 10^{12}) \cdot (6 \cdot 10^{15}) = 8 \cdot 6 \cdot 10^{12} \cdot 10^{15} = 48 \cdot 10^{27} = 4.8 \cdot 10^{28}$.

     (b) $(16 \cdot 10^{12}) \div (4 \cdot 10^5) = \frac{16}{4} \cdot 10^{12} \cdot 10^{-5} = 4 \cdot 10^7$.

     (c) $(5 \cdot 10^8) \cdot (6 \cdot 10^9) \div (15 \cdot 10^{15}) = \frac{5 \cdot 6}{15} \cdot 10^8 \cdot 10^9 \cdot 10^{-15} = 2 \cdot 10^2$

20. $100,000^3 = (10^5)^3 = 10^{15}$; $1000^5 = 10^{15}$; $100,000^2 = 10^{12}$.
     Thus $100,000^3$ and 1000^5 are equal and larger than $100,000^2$.

21. Light travels $(1.86 \cdot 10^5$ miles per sec$) \cdot (3.1536 \cdot 10^7$ secs per year$) \doteq 5.87 \cdot 10^{12}$ miles per year.
     $(5.87 \cdot 10^{12}$ miles per year$) \cdot (4$ years$) \doteq 2.35 \cdot 10^{13}$ miles that Alpha Centauri is away from the earth.

22.   (i) $\frac{26}{99} = 0.\overline{26}$ and $\frac{78}{99} = 0.\overline{78}$.

    (ii) $\frac{51}{99}$ should be $0.\overline{51}$.

    (iii)   Not always.

    (iv) $\frac{1}{99} = 0.\overline{01}$, so $\frac{51}{99} = 51 \cdot \frac{1}{99} = 0.5151\ldots = 0.\overline{51}$. The technique will not work, however, if the numerator is greater than 99.

23.   (a)   We add $0.\overline{3}$ to each term to obtain the next term, so the continuing pattern is $1.\overline{6}$, 2, $2.\overline{3}$, ...

    (b)   If we convert each of these terms to fractions, we have 0, $\frac{1}{2}$, $\frac{2}{3}$, $\frac{3}{4}$, $\frac{4}{5}$, and $\frac{5}{6}$; it can be seen that each term is arrived at by adding 1 to the numerator and denominator of the previous term. Thus, the next terms are $\frac{6}{7}$, $\frac{7}{8}$, $\frac{8}{9}$, ... Converting back to decimals, the next terms are $0.\overline{857142}$, 0.875, $0.\overline{8}$, ...

24.   (a) $a + b = 0.32323232\ldots + 0.123123123\ldots = 0.446355446355\ldots$. There are six digits in the repetend.

    (b) $a + b = 1.3\overline{5775}$. Since the sum is a repeating decimal, it is a rational number $\left(\frac{67981}{49995} \right.$, specifically$\left. \right)$. There are four digits in the repetend.

25.   (a) $(0.18 \text{ of body weight}) \cdot (120 \text{ lbs}) = 21.6$ pounds of bones.

    (b) $(0.4 \text{ of body weight}) \cdot (120 \text{ lbs}) = 48$ pounds of muscle.

26.   Total deductions were $1520.63 + 723.30 + 2843.62 = \$5087.55$.
Gross pay less deductions was $27849.50 - 5057.55 = \$22,761.95$.

27.   If the denominator of a fraction in its simplest form has no prime factors other than 2 or 5, it represents a terminating decimal.

28.   (a) $\frac{418}{25}$ (b) $\frac{3}{1000}$

    (c) $\frac{^-507}{100}$ (d) $\frac{123}{1000}$

Problem Set 7-3

1.   (a) $7.89 = (100 \cdot 7.89)\% = 789\%$.

    (b) $0.032 = (100 \cdot 0.032)\% = 3.2\%$.

    (c) $193.1 = (100 \cdot 193.1)\% = 19,310\%$.

    (d) $0.2 = (100 \cdot 0.2)\% = 20\%$.

    (e) $\frac{5}{6} = \left(100 \cdot \frac{5}{6}\right)\% = (100 \cdot 0.8\overline{3})\% = 83.\overline{3}\%$ or $83\frac{1}{3}\%$.

    (f) $\frac{3}{20} = \left(100 \cdot \frac{3}{20}\right)\% = (100 \cdot 0.15)\% = 15\%$.

    (g) $\frac{1}{8} = \left(100 \cdot \frac{1}{8}\right)\% = (100 \cdot 0.125)\% = 12.5\%$.

    (h) $\frac{3}{8} = \left(100 \cdot \frac{3}{8}\right)\% = (100 \cdot 0.375)\% = 37.5\%$ (or 3 times $12.5\% = 37.5\%$).

    (i) $\frac{5}{8} = \left(100 \cdot \frac{5}{8}\right)\% = (100 \cdot 0.625)\% = 62.5\%$ (or 5 times $12.5\% = 62.5\%$).

1. (j) $\frac{1}{6} = \left(100 \cdot \frac{1}{6}\right)\% = (100 \cdot 0.1\overline{6})\% = 16.\overline{6}\%$ or $16\frac{2}{3}\%$.

   (k) $\frac{4}{5} = \left(100 \cdot \frac{4}{5}\right)\% = (100 \cdot 0.8)\% = 80\%$.

   (l) $\frac{1}{40} = \left(100 \cdot \frac{1}{40}\right)\% = (100 \cdot 0.025)\% = 2.5\%$.

2. (a) 0.16

   (b) 0.045

   (c) 0.002

   (d) $0.00\overline{285714}$

   (e) $0.13\overline{6}$

   (f) 1.25

   (g) $0.00\overline{3}$

   (h) 0.0025

3. (a) <u>Four</u>

   (b) <u>Two</u>

   (c) <u>25</u>

   (d) <u>200</u>

   (e) <u>12.5</u>

4. Depending on the calculator:

   (a) Yes

   (b) Yes

5. (a) 6% of 34 = $0.06 \cdot 34$ = 2.04.

   (b) $17 = n\% \cdot 34$
   $n\% = \frac{17}{34}$
   $n\% = \left(100 \cdot \frac{17}{34}\right)\% = (100 \cdot 0.5)\% = 50\%$

   (c) $18 = 0.3 \cdot n$
   $n = \frac{18}{0.3} = 60$

   (d) 7% of 49 = $0.07 \cdot 49$ = 3.43.

   (e) $61.5 = n\% \cdot 20.5$
   $n\% = \frac{61.5}{20.5}$
   $n\% = \left(100 \cdot \frac{61.5}{20.5}\right)\% = 300\%$

   (f) $16 = 0.40 \cdot n$
   $n = \frac{16}{0.40} = 40$

6. $(75\%) \cdot (84 \text{ boxes}) = 63$ boxes sold.

7. 6% of \$16,000 is $0.06 \cdot 16,000 = \$960$, which is the amount of the raise.
   She now makes $16,000 + 960 = \$16,960$.

8. (7% of last salary) + (100% of last salary) = \$15,515, so 107% of last salary is \$15,515; or
   $1.07 \cdot (\text{Last salary}) = 15,515$
   Last salary $= \frac{15,515}{1.07} = \$14,500$.

9. If C is the original cost, then 80% of C is \$350, or $0.80 \cdot C = 350$.
   $C = \frac{350}{0.80} = \$437.50$ original cost.

10. (a)   Joe sold 180 newspapers.
          Bill sold $(0.85) \cdot (260) = 221$ newspapers.
          Ron sold 212 newspapers.
          So Bill sold the most newspapers.

    (b)   Joe sold $\frac{180}{200} = 90\%$ of his newspapers.
          Bill sold 85% of his newspapers.
          Ron sold 80% of his newspapers.
          So Joe sold the greatest percentage of his newspapers.

    (c)   Joe started with 200 newspapers.
          Bill started with 260 newspapers.
          Ron started with $\frac{212}{0.80} = 265$ newspapers.
          So Ron started with the greatest number of newspapers.

11. The amount of the discount is $35 - 28 = \$7$. We want to find out how much \$7 is as a percentage of \$35, or $\frac{7}{35} = 0.2 = 20\%$ discount.

12. The amount of depreciation was $8000 - 6800 = \$1200$.
     Depreciation as a percentage of cost was $\frac{1200}{8000} = 15\%$.

13. The number of eagles by which the population decreased was $728 - 594 = 134$.
     The decrease as a percentage of the original population is $\frac{134}{728} \doteq 0.184 = 18.4\%$.

14. The amount of increase was $55,000 - 29,000 = \$26,000$.
     The increase as a percentage of the original cost was $\frac{26,000}{29,000} \doteq 89.7\%$.

15. The amount of Xuan's weight increase was $18 - 9 = 9$ pounds.
     The increase as a percentage of his weight at birth is $\frac{9}{9} = 1.00 = 100\%$.

16. Regular price $-$ 20% of regular price $=$ Sale price.
     $28.00 - (0.20) \cdot (28.00) = 28.00 - 5.60 = \$22.40$ sale price.

17. The amount of the discount is 25% of \$6.80, or $0.25 \cdot 6.80 = \$1.70$.
     The sale price is $6.80 - 1.70 = \$5.10$.

18. As a proportion, we have $\frac{1/4 \ cup}{x \ cups} = \frac{0.5\%}{100\%}$
     $0.005x = \frac{1}{4} \cdot 1$
     $x = \frac{1}{4} \div 0.005 = 50$ cups.

19. The amount of the tax is 5% of \$320, or $0.05 \cdot 320 = \$16$.
     Then the total cost is $320 + 16 = \$336$.

20. Bill answered $\frac{80 - 52}{80} = 35\%$ of the answers incorrectly.

21. 4% of \$80,000 is $0.04 \cdot 80,000 = \$3200$ received.

22. $66\frac{2}{3}\%$ of 1800 is $\frac{2}{3} \cdot 1800 = 1200$ employees.

23. The house payment as a percentage of total income is $\frac{400}{2400} = 0.1\bar{6} = 16.\bar{6}\%$ or $16\frac{2}{3}\%$.

24. 110% of the previous wage $= \$19.80$. Thus the previous wage was $\frac{19.80}{1.1} = \$18.00$. There was a \$1.80 per hour increase.

25. Let S be the salary of the previous year; then S + 10% of S = new salary.
    S + 0.10S = 100,000 (this year); or 1.1S = 100,000; so S = $\frac{100,000}{1.1} \doteq$ $90,909.09 (last year).
    Last year, 1.1S = 90,909.09, so S = $\frac{90,909.09}{1.1} \doteq$ $82,644.63 two years ago.

26. 6 cans at 45¢ each is $2.70. The savings would be 2.70 − 2.40 = $0.30.
    Then savings as a percent of 6-can cost is $\frac{0.30}{2.70} \doteq$ 11%.

27. The amount of John's 20% profit is 0.20·330 = $66, so the net price of the bike after a 10% discount must
    be 330 + 66 = $396.
    Now let L be the list price; then L − 10% of L = Net (or selling) price.
    Thus L − 0.10L = 396; or 0.90L = 396; and L = $\frac{396}{0.90}$ = $440. If John then prices the bike at $440, he can
    offer a 10% discount of $44 and still realize his $66 profit.

28. 25% of $100 = $25, so the sale price was 100 − 25 = $75.
    Then increasing the price by $25 a is $\frac{25}{75}$ = $33\frac{1}{3}$% increase.

29. Let M be the amount of money with which Howard enters the first store. If the owner then gives him as
    much money as he has with him, he will have M + M = 2M. He will spend 80% of that total,
    leaving him with 20%, or 0.20·2M = 0.4M.
    In the second store, he will have left 20% of 2·0.4M, or 0.20·2·0.4M = 0.16M.
    In the third store, he will have left 0.20·2·0.16M = 0.064M.
    If 0.064M = $12, then M = $\frac{12}{0.064}$ = $187.50 in the beginning.

30. 12.13% of price = $1116.88. Price = $\frac{1116.88}{0.1213} \doteq$ $9207.58 purchase price.

31. (a) 10% of 22 = $2.20. 5% of 22 is half 10%, or $1.10. Adding, we have 2.20 + 1.10 = $3.30.

    (b) 10% of 120 is $12. 20% of 120 is twice 10%, or $24.

    (c) 10% of 38 is $3.80. 5% of 38 is half 10%, or $1.90.

    (d) 25% is $\frac{1}{4}$, and 98·$\frac{1}{4}$ = 98÷4 = $24.50.

32. (a) Only the four corner blocks will have four faces painted; thus there are $\frac{4}{100}$ = 4% painted.

    (b) The blocks along each edge, exclusive of the corner blocks, will have three faces painted. There are 8
         of these along each edge, or 4·8 = 32 blocks; thus there are $\frac{32}{100}$ = 32% painted.

    (c) Each of the interior blocks will have two faces painted. There are 100 − 4 − 32 = 64 of these; thus
         there are $\frac{64}{100}$ = 64% painted.

33. (a) (i)   Only the four corner blocks will have four faces painted; thus there are $\frac{4}{81} \doteq$ 0.049 = 4.9%
               painted.

         (ii) The blocks along each edge, exclusive of the corner blocks, will have three faces painted. There
               are 7 of these along each edge, or 4·7 = 28 blocks; thus there are $\frac{28}{81} \doteq$ 0.346 = 34.6% painted.

         (iii) Each of the interior blocks will have two faces painted. There are 81 − 4 − 28 = 49 of these;
               thus there are $\frac{49}{81} \doteq$ 0.605 = 60.5% painted.

    (b) (i) $\frac{4}{64}$ = 6.25% painted.

         (ii) $\frac{24}{64}$ = 37.5% painted.

         (iii) $\frac{36}{64}$ = 56.25% painted.

33. (c) (i) $\frac{4}{49} \doteq 8.2\%$ painted.

      (ii) $\frac{20}{49} \doteq 40.8\%$ painted.

      (iii) $\frac{25}{49} \doteq 51.0\%$ painted.

    (d) (i) $\frac{4}{144} = 2.\overline{7}\%$ painted.

      (ii) $\frac{40}{144} = 27.\overline{7}\%$ painted.

      (iii) $\frac{100}{144} = 69.\overline{4}$ painted.

34. (a) False. The increase was 110% of the original price, but the 10% decrease was on a different value; or 110% − 10% of 110% = 99% of the original price.

    (b) False. The increase was on 90% of the original value; or 90% + 10% of 90% = 99% of the original price.

35. (a) Answers may vary. If you are 20 years old, your range would be a rate of 60% of 220 − 20 = 120 to 80% of 220 − 20 = 160.

    (b) (i) $\frac{15\ seconds}{41\ beats} = 0.\overline{36585}$ seconds between beats.

      (ii) $\frac{1/4\ minute}{41\ beats} = 0.00\overline{60975}$ minutes between beats.

36. (a) 50 is larger than 40 by $\frac{10}{40} = 25\%$.

    (b) 40 is smaller than 50 by $\frac{10}{50} = 20\%$.

    (c) 20% increase.

    (d) You can now buy $\frac{100\%}{80\%} = 125\%$ of the previous amount of goods, so your purchasing power has increased by 25%.

37. A journeyman makes 200% of an apprentice's pay.
    A master makes 150% of a journeyman's pay = 150%·200% = 1.5·2 = 3 = 300% of an apprentice's pay.
    Thus the $4200 needs 1 + 2 + 3 = 6 shares, or $700 per share.
    The apprentice earns $700; the journeyman earns 200% of $700 = $1400; the master earns 150% of $1400 = $2100.

38. (a) $\frac{20}{500} = 4\%$.

    (b) (i)   5% of 480 = 24 students. 20 + 24 = 44 math majors.

      (ii) $\frac{44}{500} = 8.8\%$.

39. Dinner + 15% of dinner = $35; or 115% of dinner = $35. Dinner may thus be a maximum of $\frac{35}{1.15} \doteq \$30.43$.

40. (a) 84 + 6 = 90%   (b) $\frac{6}{90} = 0.0\overline{6} = 6.\overline{6}\%$ or $6\frac{2}{3}\%$.

    (c) 48%   (d) About 60.42%

    (e) (Children's Svcs + Corrections + Other) or (Mental Health + Adult & Family Svcs + Senior Svcs)

    (f) Yes

41. (a)   Marie owed $310 + 9% of ($16,250 − $5,000) = 310 + 0.09(11,250) = 310 + 1012.50 = $1322.50.

     (b)   (*i*)   Filing separately: Peter owed 310 + 0.09(12,321 − 5000) = $968.89.
                               Holly owed 310 + 0.09(6532 − 5000) = $447.88.
                         Together they owed 968.89 + 447.88 = $1416.77.

            (*ii*)   Filing jointly: Total income was 12,321 + 6352 = $18,853.
                               Tax owed was 620 + 0.09(18,853 − 10,000) = $1416.77.

            Peter and Holly would pay the same tax either way.

42. $6137.19 \div 63.27 = 97$ days overdue.

43. $33.21 = 33\frac{21}{100} = \frac{3321}{100}$

44. $\frac{2}{9} = 0.\bar{2}$

45. If $n = 31.0\bar{5}$, then $10n = 310.\bar{5}$ and we have a 1-digit repetend.
                $10(10n) = 3105.\bar{5}$
                $\underline{- 10n = -310.\bar{5}}$
                $90n = 2795$, and $n = \frac{2795}{90} = \frac{559}{18}$

46. (a) $3.25 \cdot 10^{6}$

     (b) $1.2 \cdot 10^{-4}$

47. (a) $32.015 \doteq 32.0$

     (b) $32.015 \doteq 32$

Problem Set 7-4

1.   (a)   6% annually $= \frac{6}{2} = 3\%$ per semiannual period.
            2 years compounded semiannually = 4 periods.
            $A = 1000(1 + 0.03)^{4} = 1000(1.03)^{4} \doteq 1000(1.12551) = \$1125.51.$
            Interest = 1125.51 − 1000 = $125.51.

     (b)   8% annually $= \frac{8}{4} = 2\%$ per quarterly period.
            3 years compounded quarterly = 12 periods.
            $A = 1000(1 + 0.02)^{12} \doteq \$1268.24.$
            Interest = 1268.24 − 1000 = $268.24.

     (c)   10% annually $= \frac{10}{12} = 0.8\bar{3}\%$ per monthly period.
            5 years compounded monthly = 60 periods.
            $A = 1000(1 + 0.008\bar{3})^{60} \doteq \$1645.31.$
            Interest = 1645.31 − 1000 = $645.31.

     (d)   12% annually $= \frac{12}{365}\%$ per daily period.
            4 years compounded daily = 1460 periods.
            $A = 1000(1 + \frac{0.12}{365})^{1460} \doteq 1615.95.$
            Interest = 1615.95 − 1000 = $615.95.

2. $I = Prt = 42{,}000 \cdot 0.13 \cdot 1 = \$5460$ interest owed.

3. Carolyn is compounding $125 for 12 periods at 1.5% per period.
   Thus $A = 125(1 + 0.015)^{12} \doteq \$149.45$ (i.e., principal and interest) and interest owed = $149.45 - 125 = \$24.45$.

4. The interest charged was $28,500 - 25,000 = \$3500$. Then $3500 = 25,000 \cdot r \cdot 4 = 100,000 \cdot r$.
   $r = \frac{3500}{100,000} = 3.5\%$.

5. In the expression for compound interest, $A = P(1 + i)^n$, the amount here is $50,000 and P is what we need to find. Thus,
   $P = \frac{A}{(1 + i)^n}$, where $i = \frac{0.09}{4} = 0.0225$ and $n = 20$. We now have: $P = \frac{50,000}{(1.0225)^{20}} = \$32,040.82$ to be invested now.

6. $I = 320,000 \cdot 0.135 \cdot \frac{18}{12} = \$64,800$

7. For the 1st 3 years, $P = 3000$, $i = \frac{0.05}{4} = 0.0125$ and $n = 12$. Thus $A = 3000(1.0125)^{12} \doteq \$3482.26$.
   For the 2nd 3 years, $P = 3482.26$, $i = \frac{0.08}{4} = 0.02$, and $n = 12$. Thus $A = 3482.26(1.02)^{12} \doteq \$4416.35$.
   Thus the balance in the account after six years was $4416.35.

8. $A = 4000(1 + \frac{0.09}{4})^{80} \doteq \$23,720.58$.

9. $P = 10,000$, $i = \frac{0.14}{365}$, and $n = 15 \cdot 365 = 5475$. Thus $A = 10,000(1 + \frac{0.14}{365})^{5475} \doteq \$81,628.82$ in the fund.

10. $I = 7200 \cdot 0.09 \cdot 3 = \$1944$ interest charged.

11. Suppose $1 were to be invested in each institution. Then:

    For New Age, $i = \frac{0.09}{365}$ and $n = 365$; thus $A = 1(1 + \frac{0.09}{365})^{365} \doteq \$1.094162$.
    Subtracting the $1 invested, we have earned about 9.4¢, corresponding to an effective rate of 9.4%.

    For Pay More, $i = \frac{0.105}{1}$ and $n = 1$; thus $A = 1(1 + 0.105) = \$1.105$.
    Subtracting the $1 invested, we have earned 10.5¢, corresponding to an effective rate of 10.5%.

    The Pay More bank has a higher effective interest rate.

12. (i)   Interest as a percentage of savings is $\frac{53.90}{980} = 5.5\%$.

    (ii) Interest as a percentage of savings is $\frac{55.20}{600} = 9.2\%$.

    (iii) Interest as a percentage of savings is $\frac{158.40}{1200} = 13.2\%$.

13. We are compounding at 11% annually for 6 years. Thus $A = 1.35(1 + 0.11)^6 = \$2.53$. A hamburger would cost $2.53 after six years if prices rise at 11% per year.

14. $A = 10,000(1 + 0.09)^{10} \doteq \$23,673.64$.

15. From problem 5, $P = \frac{A}{(1 + i)^n}$. We have $i = \frac{0.065}{4} = 0.01625$, $n = 16$, and $A = \$4650$. Thus,
    $P = \frac{4650}{(1.01625)^{16}} \doteq \$3592.89$ initial investment.

16. For problems involving compound depreciation, we can develop the formula: $A = P(1 - i)^n$.
    Thus $A = 15,000(1 - 0.10)^3 = \$10,935$ depreciated value.

17. At 1.1% per period (month) for 11 periods, $A = 300(1 + 0.011)^{11} \doteq \$338.36$, so Adrien and Jarrell will have $338.36 in their account on December 1. Interest earned will be $338.36 - 300.00 = \$38.36$.
    Thus interest as a percentage of the amount deposited will be $\frac{38.36}{300} = 12.8\%$ effective annual yield.

18. (a)   The value decreased.

    (b)   Using compound depreciation for the 1st 3 years: $A = 100\%(1 - 0.10)^3 = 72.9\%$ of original value.
           Using compound appreciation for the 2nd 3 years: $A = 72.9\%(1 + 0.10)^3 \doteq 97.03\%$ of original
           value, or a 2.97% decrease.

19.   We can develop a formula for compound decay:
       If we let A be the amount remaining after 1 year, r the rate of decay, and B the beginning amount,
       then after 1 year: $A = B - \text{decay} = B - rB = B(1 - r)$. After n periods, then, $A = B(1 - r)^n$.

       So in the rain forest, where $B = 2.34 \cdot 10^9$, $r = \frac{0.005}{12}$, and $n = 20 \cdot 12 = 240$, we have:
       $A = 2.34 \cdot 10^9 (1 - \frac{0.005}{12})^{240} \doteq 2.12 \cdot 10^9$ trees remaining after 20 years.

20.   If we want our money doubled, then $2 = 1(1 + 0,10)^n$, or $2 = 1.1^n$ and we are looking for n.
       We can find that $1.1^{7.3} \doteq 2.005$, so it would take about 7.3 years to double an investment at 10%
       compounded annually.

Problem Set 7-5

1.   Answers may vary. One such number could be 0.232233222333... .

2.   We line up the decimal points:
$$0.78 = 0.78000000...$$
$$0.\overline{7} = 0.77777777...$$
$$0.\overline{78} = 0.78787878...$$
$$0.788 = 0.78800000...$$
$$0.7\overline{8} = 0.78888888...$$
$$0.7\overline{88} = 0.78888888...\ (\text{Note that } 0.7\overline{88} = 0.7\overline{8})$$
$$0.77 = 0.77000000...$$
$$0.787787778... = 0.787787778...$$
       From least to greatest, then, we have: 0.77, $0.\overline{7}$, 0.78, 0.787787778..., $0.\overline{78}$, 0.788, $0.7\overline{8}$ and $0.7\overline{88}$.

3. We line up the decimal points:
$$0.9 = 0.90000000...$$
$$0.\overline{9} = 0.99999999...$$
$$0.\overline{98} = 0.98989898...$$
$$0.9\overline{88} = 0.98888888...$$
$$0.9\overline{98} = 0.99898989...$$
$$0.\overline{898} = 0.89889889...$$
       From greatest to least, then, we have: $0.\overline{9}$, $0.9\overline{98}$, $0.\overline{98}$, $0.9\overline{88}$, 0.9, $0.\overline{898}$.

4. (a)   Irrational. There is no number s such that $s^2 = 51$.

   (b)   Rational   (c)   Rational

   (d)   Irrational

   (e)   Irrational. There is no $s^2 = 2$; the sum of a rational number and an irrational number is irrational.

   (f)   Irrational. The quotient of a rational number and an irrational number is irrational.

5. (a) $15 \cdot 15 = 225$, so $\sqrt{225} = 15$.

   (b) $15.84 \cdot 15.84 \doteq 251$, so $\sqrt{251} \doteq 15.84$.

5. (c) $13 \cdot 13 = 169$, so $\sqrt{169} = 13$.

    (d) $22^2 = 484$; $23^2 = 529$; so $\sqrt{512}$ is between 22 and 23.
          $(22.6)^2 = 510.76$; $(22.7)^2 = 515.29$; so $\sqrt{512}$ is between 22.6 and 22.7.
          Continue in this manner to find $\sqrt{512}$ to the desired accuracy ($\sqrt{512} \doteq 22.627$).

    (e) $^-81$ has no square root. There is no number n such that $n^2 = {}^-81$.

    (f) $25 \cdot 25 = 625$, so $\sqrt{625} = 25$.

6. (a) $\sqrt{17}$ must have a value between $4(4^2 = 16)$ and $5(5^2 = 25)$, or $4 < \sqrt{17} < 5$. Now, squeezing:
          $4.1 < \sqrt{17} < 4.2$
          $4.12 < \sqrt{17} < 4.13$ [because $(4.12)^2 = 16.97$ and $(4.13)^2 = 17.06$]
          Since 17 is closer to 16.97 than to 17.06, $\sqrt{17} \doteq 4.12$ to the nearest hundredth.

    (b) $2 < \sqrt{7} < 3$. Squeezing:
          $2.6 < \sqrt{7} < 2.7$
          $2.64 < \sqrt{7} < 2.65$ [$(2.64)^2 = 6.9696$ and $(2.65)^2 = 7.0225$]
          Since 7 is closer to 7.0225 than to 6.9696, $\sqrt{7} \doteq 2.65$ to the nearest hundredth.

    (c) $4 < \sqrt{21} < 5$. Squeezing:
          $4.5 < \sqrt{21} < 4.6$
          $4.58 < \sqrt{21} < 4.59$ [$4.58^2 = 20.98$ and $(4.59)^2 = 21.07$]
          Since 21 is closer to 20.98 than to 21.07, $\sqrt{21} \doteq 4.58$ to the nearest hundredth.

    (d) $0.1 < \sqrt{0.0120} < 0.2$. Squeezing:
          $0.10 < \sqrt{0.0120} < 0.11$ [$(0.10)^2 = 0.0100$ and $(0.11)^2 = 0.0121$]
          Since 0.0120 is closer to 0.0121 than to 0.0100, $\sqrt{0.0120} \doteq 0.11$ to the nearest hundredth.

    (e) $4 < \sqrt{20.3} < 5$. Squeezing:
          $4.5 < \sqrt{20.3} < 4.6$
          $4.50 < \sqrt{20.3} < 4.51$ [$(4.50)^2 = 20.25$ and $(4.51)^2 = 20.34$]
          Since 20.3 is closer to 20.34 than to 20.25, $\sqrt{20.3} \doteq 4.51$ to the nearest hundredth.

    (f) $1 < \sqrt{1.64} < 2$. Squeezing:
          $1.2 < \sqrt{1.64} < 1.3$
          $1.28 < \sqrt{1.64} < 1.29$ [$(1.28)^2 = 1.6384$ and $(1.29)^2 = 1.6641$]
          Since 1.64 is closer to 1.6384 than to 1.6641, $\sqrt{1.64} \doteq 1.28$ to the nearest hundredth.

7. (a)   False. $2 + \sqrt{2}$ is an irrational number.

    (b)   False. $^-\sqrt{2} + \sqrt{2} = 0$, a rational number.

    (c)   False. $\sqrt{2} \cdot \sqrt{2} = 2$, which is a rational number.

    (d)   False. $\sqrt{2} - \sqrt{2} = 0$, a rational number.

8. No. For example, let $a = 9$ and $b = 16$.
    Then $\sqrt{a + b} = \sqrt{9 + 16} = \sqrt{25} = 5$, but $\sqrt{a} + \sqrt{b} = \sqrt{9} + \sqrt{16} = 3 + 4 = 7$.

9. Answers may vary. $\sqrt{2}$, $\sqrt{3}$, and $\sqrt{5}$ are three.

10. Answers may vary. $0.536336333633336\ldots$ is one.

11. No. $\frac{22}{7}$ is a rational number that can be represented by the repeating decimal $3.\overline{142857}$.

12. No. $\sqrt{13}$ is an irrational number, but $3.60\overline{5}$ is a repeating decimal, thus rational.

13. (a) We want the set of numbers that contains the set of rational numbers <u>or</u> the set of irrational numbers, <u>or</u> both. That set is R, the set of real numbers, or $Q \cup S = R$.

   (b) A rational number cannot be an irrational number, so $Q \cap S = \emptyset$.

   (c) The intersection of the set of rational numbers and the set of real numbers is the set of rational numbers (since Q is contained in R). Thus $Q \cap R = Q$.

   (d) No whole number can be irrational, so $S \cap W = \emptyset$.

   (e) The union of the set of whole numbers and the set of real numbers is the set of real numbers (since W is contained in R). Thus $W \cup R = R$.

   (f) Since the set of rational numbers is contained in the set of real numbers, $Q \cup R = R$.

14. (a) $5x - 1 \leq \frac{7}{2}x + 3$

     $5x - \frac{7}{2}x \leq 3 + 1$

     $\frac{3}{2}x \leq 4$

     $x \leq 4 \cdot \frac{2}{3}$, or $x \leq \frac{8}{3}$. The graph is:

   (b) $4 + 3x \geq \sqrt{5} - 7x$

     $3x + 7x \geq \sqrt{5} - 4$

     $10x \geq \sqrt{5} - 4$

     $x \geq \frac{\sqrt{5}-4}{10}$. The graph is:

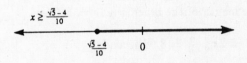

   (c) $\frac{2}{3}x + \sqrt{3} \leq {}^{-}5x$

     $\frac{2}{3}x + 5x \leq {}^{-}\sqrt{3}$

     $\frac{17}{3}x \leq {}^{-}\sqrt{3}$

     $x \leq {}^{-}\sqrt{3} \cdot \frac{3}{17}$, or $x \leq \frac{{}^{-}3\sqrt{3}}{17}$. The graph is:

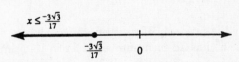

   (d) $(2x - 1)^2 = 4$
     $2x - 1 = 2$ or $2x - 1 = {}^{-}2$
     $2x = 3$ or $2x = {}^{-}1$
     $x = \frac{3}{2}$ or $x = \frac{{}^{-}1}{2}$. The graph is:

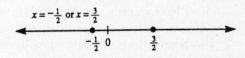

   (e) $|x| \geq 7$
     $x \geq 7$ or $x \leq {}^{-}7$. The graph is:

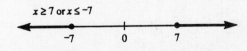

   (f) $|x| \leq 3$
     ${}^{-}3 \leq x \leq 3$. The graph is:

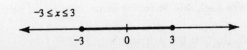
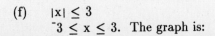

15. (a) $x^2 + 1 = 5$
         $x^2 = 4$
         $x = 2$, and 2 belongs to N, I, Q, and R.

    (b) $2x - 1 = 32$
         $2x = 33$
         $x = \frac{33}{2}$, and $\frac{33}{2}$ belongs to Q and R.

    (c) $x^2 = 3$
         $x = \sqrt{3}$, and $\sqrt{3}$ belongs to R and S.

    (d) $x^2 = 4$
         $x = 2$, and 2 belongs to N, I, Q, and R.

    (e) $\sqrt{x} = {}^-1$
         There is no solution to this equation, since by definition the principal square root of x is the nonnegative number a such that $a^2 = x$.

    (f) $\frac{3}{4}x = 4$
         $x = 4 \cdot \frac{4}{3} = \frac{16}{3}$, and $\frac{16}{3}$ belongs to Q and R.

16. (a) $x = 64$ (b) No real values.

    (c) $x = {}^-64$ (d) No real values.

    (e) All real numbers > 0.   (f) No real values.

17. The sides of the gate form the sides of a right triangle with the diagonal brace as the hypotenuse. If c is the length of the hypotenuse, then $c^2 = a^2 + b^2 = 4^2 + 5^2 = 16 + 25 = 41$. Thus the length of the brace $= \sqrt{41} \doteq 6.4$ feet.

18. (a) $T = 2\pi\sqrt{\frac{20}{9.8}} \doteq 8.98$ seconds.

    (b) $T = 2\pi\sqrt{\frac{100}{9.8}} \doteq 20.07$ seconds.

19. The sequence 0.13, 0.1313, 0.131313, ... , can be represented by the repeating decimal $0.\overline{13} = \frac{13}{99}$. Since any term of the repeating decimal $0.\overline{13}$ is less than $\frac{13}{99}$, that is the rational number for which we are looking.

20. Suppose $\sqrt{3}$ is rational. If so, then $\sqrt{3} = \frac{a}{b}$, where a and b are integers and $b \neq 0$. Therefore, $3 = \frac{a^2}{b^2}$, or $3b^2 = a^2$. a^2 has an even number of 3's in its prime factorization but $3b^2$ has an odd number of 3's in its prime factorization. If $3b^2 = a^2$, this is impossible. Thus, $\sqrt{3}$ cannot be a rational number and therefore must be irrational.

21. Suppose $\sqrt{p}$ is rational. If so, then $\sqrt{p} = \frac{a}{b}$, where a and b are integers and $b \neq 0$. Therefore $p = \frac{a^2}{b^2}$, or $pb^2 = a^2$. a^2 must have an even number of p's in its prime factorization, as must b^2. In pb^2, another factor of p is introduced, resulting in an odd number of p's in the prime factorization of pb^2 and hence of a^2. But p cannot appear both an odd number of times and an even number of times in the same prime factorization, so we have a contradiction. Consequently, $\sqrt{p}$ must be an irrational number.

22. (a) m such that $\sqrt{m} = n$, where n is a whole number and $n \cdot n = m$.

    (b) If n is a whole number and $n^2 = m$, then the prime factorization of n^2 and m must be the same. Since each will have the same number of prime factors, they are both rational numbers.

23. (a) $0.5 + \frac{1}{0.5} = 0.5 + 2 = 2.5 \geq 2$.

23. (b)   Suppose $x + \frac{1}{x} < 2$. Since $x > 0$, $x^2 + 1 < 2x$ so that $x^2 - 2x + 1 < 0$, or $(x - 1)^2 < 0$, which is false.

24. (a) $4.\overline{9}$ (b) $5.0\overline{9}$

     (c) $0.4\overline{9}$

25. $0.00024 = \frac{24}{100,000} = \frac{3}{12,500}$

26. $4.09 = 4.090000\ldots$
             $4.099 = 4.099000\ldots$
             $4.0\overline{9} = 4.099999\ldots$
             $4.09\overline{1} = 4.091111\ldots$

     So the numbers from least to greatest are 4.09, $4.09\overline{1}$, 4.099, $4.0\overline{9}$.

27. $100n = 24.\overline{24}$
             $\underline{-n = -.\overline{24}}$
             $99n = 24$, so $n = \frac{24}{99} = \frac{8}{33}$

28. (a) $208,000$ (b) 0.00038

29. 9% 0f $18,600 is $0.09 \cdot 18,600 = \$1674$ raise. $18,600 + 1674 = \$20,274$ as Joan's new salary.

30. $\frac{1200}{2000} = 60\%$ are females.

Problem Set 7-6

1.   (a) $\sqrt{180} = \sqrt{36 \cdot 5} = \sqrt{36} \cdot \sqrt{5} = 6\sqrt{5}$

     (b) $\sqrt{529} = 23$

     (c) $\sqrt{363} = \sqrt{121 \cdot 3} = 11\sqrt{3}$

     (d) $\sqrt{252} = \sqrt{36 \cdot 7} = 6\sqrt{7}$

     (e) $\sqrt{\frac{169}{196}} = \frac{\sqrt{169}}{\sqrt{196}} = \frac{13}{14}$

     (f) $\sqrt{\frac{49}{196}} = \frac{\sqrt{49}}{\sqrt{196}} = \frac{7}{14} = \frac{1}{2}$, or alternatively, $\sqrt{\frac{49}{196}} = \sqrt{\frac{1}{4}} = \frac{\sqrt{1}}{\sqrt{4}} = \frac{1}{2}$

2.   (a) $\sqrt[3]{^-27} = {^-3}$

     (b) $\sqrt[5]{96} = \sqrt[5]{32 \cdot 3} = 2 \cdot \sqrt[5]{3}$

     (c) $\sqrt[5]{32} = 2$

     (d) $\sqrt[3]{250} = \sqrt[3]{125 \cdot 2} = 5 \cdot \sqrt[3]{2}$

     (e) $\sqrt[5]{^-243} = {^-3}$

     (f) $\sqrt[4]{64} = \sqrt[4]{16 \cdot 4} = 2 \cdot \sqrt[4]{4} = 2 \cdot \sqrt{2}$

3.   (a) $2\sqrt{3} + 3\sqrt{2} + \sqrt{180} = 2\sqrt{3} + 3\sqrt{2} + 6\sqrt{5}$. (See problem 1(a) for $\sqrt{180}$) The sum cannot be simplified further.

3.   (b) $\sqrt[3]{4} \cdot \sqrt[3]{10} = \sqrt[3]{40} = \sqrt[3]{8 \cdot 5} = 2 \cdot \sqrt[3]{5}$

     (c) $\begin{aligned}(2\sqrt{3} + 3\sqrt{2})^2 &= (2\sqrt{3} + 3\sqrt{2}) \cdot (2\sqrt{3} + 3\sqrt{2}) \\ &= 2\sqrt{3} \cdot (2\sqrt{3} + 3\sqrt{2}) + 3\sqrt{2} \cdot (2\sqrt{3} + 3\sqrt{2}) \\ &= 4 \cdot 3 + 6\sqrt{6} + 6\sqrt{6} + 9 \cdot 2 \\ &= 12 + 12\sqrt{6} + 18 \\ &= 30 + 6\sqrt{6}\end{aligned}$

     (d) $\sqrt{6} \div \sqrt{12} = \sqrt{\frac{6}{12}} = \sqrt{\frac{1}{2}} = \frac{1}{\sqrt{2}}$

     (e) $\begin{aligned}5\sqrt{72} + 2\sqrt{50} - \sqrt{288} - \sqrt{242} &= 5\sqrt{36 \cdot 2} + 2\sqrt{25 \cdot 2} - \sqrt{144 \cdot 2} - \sqrt{121 \cdot 2} \\ &= 5 \cdot 6\sqrt{2} + 2 \cdot 5\sqrt{2} - 12\sqrt{2} - 11\sqrt{2} \\ &= 30\sqrt{2} + 10\sqrt{2} - 12\sqrt{2} - 11\sqrt{2} \\ &= 17\sqrt{2}\end{aligned}$

     (f) $\sqrt{8/7} \div \sqrt{4/21} = \sqrt{\frac{8}{7} \div \frac{4}{21}} = \sqrt{\frac{8}{7} \cdot \frac{21}{4}} = \sqrt{\frac{2}{1} \cdot \frac{3}{1}} = \sqrt{6}$

4.   (a) $16^{1/2} = \sqrt{16} = 4$

     (b) $27^{2/3} = (3^3)^{2/3} = 3^2 = 9$

     (c) $64^{5/6} = (2^6)^{5/6} = 2^5 = 32$

     (d) $3^{1/2} \cdot 3^{3/2} = 3^{1/2+3/2} = 3^2 = 9$

     (e) $32^{-2/5} = \frac{1}{32^{2/5}} = \frac{1}{(2^5)^{2/5}} = \frac{1}{2^2} = \frac{1}{4}$, and $\left(\frac{1}{16}\right)^{-3/2} = \left(\frac{16}{1}\right)^{3/2} = (2^4)^{3/2} = 2^6 = 64$

           So $\dfrac{(32)^{-2/5}}{\left(\frac{1}{16}\right)^{-3/2}} = \dfrac{\left(\frac{1}{4}\right)}{64} = \frac{1}{4} \cdot \frac{1}{64} = \frac{1}{256}$

     (f) $9^{2/3} \cdot 27^{2/9} = (3^2)^{2/3} \cdot (3^3)^{2/9} = 3^{4/3} \cdot 3^{2/3} = 3^{4/3+2/3} = 3^2 = 9$

     (g) $16^{-1/2} = \frac{1}{16^{1/2}} = \frac{1}{\sqrt{16}} = \frac{1}{4}$

     (h) $27^{-2/3} = \frac{1}{27^{2/3}} = \frac{1}{(3^3)^{2/3}} = \frac{1}{3^2} = \frac{1}{9}$

     (i) $32^{2/5} = (2^5)^{2/5} = 2^2 = 4$

     (j) $8^{3/2} \cdot 4^{1/4} = (2^3)^{3/2} \cdot (2^2)^{1/4} = 2^{9/2} \cdot 2^{1/2} = 2^5 = 32$

     (k) $(10^{1/3} \cdot 10^{-1/6})^6 = (10^{1/6})^6 = 10$

     (l) $16^{5/12} \cdot 16^{1/3} = 16^{9/12} = (2^4)^{9/12} = 2^3 = 8$

     (m) $64^{2/3} = (2^6)^{2/3} = 2^4 = 16$

     (n) $64^{-1/3} = \frac{1}{64^{1/3}} = \frac{1}{(2^6)^{1/3}} = \frac{1}{2^2} = \frac{1}{4}$

     (o) $(2 \cdot 64^{1/2})^{1/2} = (2 \cdot 8)^{1/2} = 16^{1/2} = 4$

5.   No. $\sqrt{x^2 + y^2} \neq x + y$.   (Note, though, that $\sqrt{x^2 \cdot y^2} = x \cdot y$)

6.   (a)   Sometimes (if $a \geq 0$).

6. (b)   Sometimes (if $x \leq 0$).

    (c)   Always.

    (d)   Sometimes (if $a + b \geq 0$).

    (e)   Sometimes (if $a \geq 0$).

7. Recall from Section 1-1 that in a geometric sequence each successive term is obtained from its predecessor by multiplying by a fixed number r (ratio). The ratio may thus be derived by dividing the *(n + 1)*th term by the *n*th term, or, in this problem, $r = 3 \div 3^{3/4} = 3^{1-3/4} = 3^{1/4}$. Thus $3^{3/4}$ (the first term) times $3^{1/4}$ (the ratio) equals $3^1 = 3$ (the second term), and so on.

    We find the that exponents are now in an arithmetic sequence: $\frac{3}{4}$, 1, $\frac{5}{4}$, ... , 6 (the last exponent is 6 becuse $729 = 3^6$).

    In an arithmetic sequence (again, from Section 1-1), the *n*th term, where *a* is the 1st term, is $a + (n - 1)d$. In this case, the 1st term is $\frac{3}{4}$, the *n*th term is 6, and the difference, *d*, is $\frac{1}{4}$. Solving for *n*, we have:
    $$6 = \tfrac{3}{4} + (n - 1)\tfrac{1}{4}$$

    $$6 = \tfrac{3}{4} + \tfrac{1}{4}n - \tfrac{1}{4}$$

    $$6 = \tfrac{1}{2} + \tfrac{1}{4}n$$

    $\frac{11}{2} = \frac{1}{4}n$, so n = 22 and there are 22 terms in the sequence.

8. (a) $E(0) = 2^{10} \cdot 16^0 = 2^{10}$.

    (b) $E(\frac{1}{4}) = 2^{10} \cdot 16^{1/4} = 2^{10} \cdot 2 = 2^{11}$.

    (c) $E(\frac{1}{2}) = 2^{10} \cdot 2^2 = 2^{12}$.

9. $(4/25)^{-1/3} = \dfrac{1}{(4/25)^{1/3}} = \dfrac{25^{1/3}}{4^{1/3}} = (25/4)^{1/3}$, and similarly, $(4/25)^{-1/4} = (25/4)^{1/4}$. Thus, in order from least to greatest, we have $(4/25)^{-1/4}$, $(4/25)^{-1/3}$, $(25/4)^{1/3}$.

10. (a) $\sqrt{3}$ (b) $\sqrt[3]{3}$

    (c) $3.46 < \sqrt{12} < 3.47$ and $3.74 < \sqrt{14} < 3.75$. Assuming that the root lies close to the midpoint of each interval, $\sqrt{12} + \sqrt{14}$ is about $3.465 + 3.745 = 7.21$.

    $3.31 < \sqrt{11} < 3.32$ and $3.87 < \sqrt{15} < 3.88$, so $\sqrt{11} + \sqrt{15}$ is about 7.19.

11. $\sqrt{2\sqrt{2\sqrt{2}}} = \sqrt{2\sqrt{2 \cdot 2^{1/2}}} = \sqrt{2\sqrt{2^{3/2}}} = \sqrt{2(2^{3/2})^{1/2}} = \sqrt{2 \cdot 2^{3/4}} = \sqrt{2^{7/4}} = (2^{7/4})^{1/2} = 2^{7/8}$

    and $2^{7/8} = \sqrt[8]{2^7}$.

12. (a) $81 = 3^4$, so if $3^x = 3^4$ then x = 4.

    (b) $(2^2)^x = 2^3$, so 2x = 3 and $x = \frac{3}{2}$.

    (c) $(2^7)^{-x} = 2^4$, so $^-7x = 4$ and $x = \frac{^-4}{7}$.

    (d) $[(\frac{2}{3})^2]^{3x} = (\frac{2}{3})^5$, so 6x = 5 and $x = \frac{5}{6}$.

13. $\sqrt[3]{(6-2)^{-2}} = \sqrt[3]{\frac{1}{16}} = \frac{1}{2 \cdot \sqrt[3]{2}}$

14. (a) n must be an odd number.

    (b)   If m is even, n can be any number except 0. If m is odd, n must be odd.

15. (a) $\sqrt{2} - \frac{2}{\sqrt{2}} = 0$, which is rational.   (b)   Rational

    (c)   Irrational   (d) $\frac{1}{1+\sqrt{2}} + 1 - \sqrt{2} = 0$; rational.

Chapter 7 Test

1. (a) $^{-}0.693$ (b)   31.564

   (c)   0.2284   (d)   0.032

   (e) $^{-}0.097$ (f)   0.00000016

2. (a) $3 \cdot 10 + 2 \cdot 1 + 1 \cdot 10^{-2} + 2 \cdot 10^{-3}$ (b) $1 \cdot 10^{-3} + 3 \cdot 10^{-5}$

3. If the denominator of a fraction in simplest form contains no prime factors other than 2 or 5, then the fraction can be written as a terminating decimal.

4. $442.4 \div 55.3 = 8$, so 8 shelves can be cut.

5. (a) $0.\overline{571428}$ (b)   0.125

   (c) $0.\overline{6}$ (d)   0.625

6. (a) $\frac{7}{25}$ (b) $\frac{1}{3}$

   (c) $\frac{94}{45}$

7. (a)   307.63   (b)   307.6

   (c)   308   (d)   300

8. (a) $0.2x - 0.75 \geq 0.5x - 1.75$ (b) $x = 0$
          $^{-}0.3x \geq ^{-}1.0$
          $x \leq 3.\overline{3}$

   (c) $x = \frac{4600}{0.23} = 20,000$ (d) $x = \left(100 \cdot \frac{10}{50}\right)\% = 20\%$

   (e) $x = \frac{17}{0.50} = 34$ (f) $x = 1 - 0.\overline{3} = 0.\overline{6}$

9. (a) $n = \left(100 \cdot \frac{6}{24}\right)\% = 25\%$ (b) $3.20 \cdot 60 = 192$

   (c) $n = \frac{17}{0.30} = 56.\overline{6}$ (d) $n = \left(100 \cdot \frac{0.2}{1}\right)\% = 20\%$

10. (a)   12.5%   (b)   7.5%

    (c)   627%   (d)   1.23%

    (e)   150%

11. (a) 0.60   (b) $0.00\bar{6}$

    (c) 1.00

12. (a) No. $^-\sqrt{2} + \sqrt{2}$ is not an irrational number.

    (b) No (see above).

    (c) No. Two irrational numbers multiplied together may be rational (i.e., $\sqrt{2}\cdot\sqrt{2} = 2$).

    (d) No. An irrational number divided by itself is rational.

13. 4.7958

14. (a) $4.26\cdot10^5$ (b) $2.37\cdot10^{-6}$

    (c) $3.2\cdot10^1$ (d) $3.25\cdot10^{-1}$

15. (a) Three   (b) Three

    (c) Two   (d) Three

16. (a) Irrational   (b) Irrational

    (c) Rational   (d) Rational

    (e) Irrational

17. Investment $= \frac{1020.80}{0.11} = \$9280$

18. Percent defective $= (100\cdot\frac{5}{150})\% = 3.\bar{3}\%$

19. Percent correct $= (100\cdot\frac{70-8}{70})\% \doteq 88.6\%$

20. Cost $= \frac{3450}{0.60} = \$5750$

21. There is no difference in the total discount, regardless of the order chosen.

22. Cost $+$ 30% of cost $= \$104$
     $1.3\cdot$Cost $= 104$
     Cost $= \frac{104}{1.3} = \$80$

23. $I = 30{,}000\cdot0.125\cdot4 = \$15{,}000$ interest due.

24. $A = 10{,}000(1 + \frac{0.14}{4})^{12} \doteq \$15{,}110.69$ in the account.

25. (a) $\sqrt{121\cdot2} = 11\sqrt{2}$ (b) $\sqrt{144\cdot2} = 12\sqrt{2}$

    (c) $\sqrt{36\cdot10} = 6\sqrt{10}$ (d) $\sqrt[3]{27\cdot6} = 3\cdot\sqrt[3]{6}$

26. (a) $(\frac{1}{2})^{11}$ (b) $5^{-20} = (\frac{1}{5})^{20}$

    (c) $(\frac{2}{3})^{-28} = (\frac{3}{2})^{28}$ (d) 3^{18}

CHAPTER 8 - PROBABILITY

Problem Set 8-1

1. (a) S = {Clinton, Bush, Reagan, Carter, Ford, Nixon, Johnson, Kennedy, Eisenhower, Truman}

   (b) S = {C|C is one of my classmates}

   (c) S = {M|M is a member of the U. S. House of Representatives from my State}

2. (a) {0, 1, 2, 3, 4, 5, 6, 7, 8, 9}.   (b) {0, 1, 2, 3, 4}.

   (c) {1, 3, 5, 7, 9}.   (d) {0, 1, 3, 4, 5, 6, 7, 8, 9}.

   (e) (i) $\frac{5}{10}$ (ii) $\frac{5}{10}$ (iii) $\frac{9}{10}$

3. (a) $P(1, 5, \text{ or } 7) = \frac{1}{8} + \frac{1}{8} + \frac{1}{8} = \frac{3}{8}$.   (b) $P(3 \text{ or } 6) = \frac{1}{8} + \frac{1}{8} = \frac{1}{4}$.

   (c) $P(2, 4, 6, \text{ or } 8) = \frac{1}{8} + \frac{1}{8} + \frac{1}{8} + \frac{1}{8} = \frac{1}{2}$.   (d) $P(6 \text{ or } 2) = \frac{1}{8} + \frac{1}{8} = \frac{1}{4}$.

   (e) $P(11) = 0$.   (f) $P(4, 6, \text{ or } 8) = \frac{1}{8} + \frac{1}{8} + \frac{1}{8} = \frac{3}{8}$.

   (g) $P(\text{Neither prime nor composite}) = P(1) = \frac{1}{8}$.

4. (a) $P(\text{Red}) = \frac{n(\text{Red})}{n(S)} = \frac{26}{52} = \frac{1}{2}$.   (b) $P(\text{Face card}) = \frac{n(\text{Face card})}{n(S)} = \frac{12}{52} = \frac{3}{13}$.

   (c) $P(\text{Red or ten}) = \frac{n(\text{Red})}{n(S)} + \frac{n(\text{Ten})}{n(S)} - \frac{n(\text{Red and ten})}{n(S)} = \frac{26}{52} + \frac{4}{52} - \frac{2}{52} = \frac{7}{13}$.

   (d) $P(\text{Queen}) = \frac{n(\text{Queen})}{n(S)} = \frac{4}{52} = \frac{1}{13}$.

   (e) $P(\text{Not a queen}) = 1 - P(\text{Queen}) = 1 - \frac{1}{13} = \frac{12}{13}$.

   (f) $P(\text{Face card or club}) = \frac{n(\text{Face card})}{n(S)} + \frac{n(\text{Club})}{n(S)} - \frac{n(\text{Face card and club})}{n(S)} = \frac{12}{52} + \frac{13}{52} - \frac{3}{52} = \frac{11}{26}$.

   (g) $P(\text{Face card and club}) = \frac{n(\text{Face card and club})}{n(S)} = \frac{3}{52}$.

   (h) $P(\text{Not a face card and not a club}) = 1 - P(\text{Face card or club}) = 1 - \frac{11}{26} = \frac{15}{26}$. (Note: Use a Venn diagram to verify this use of the complementary property.)

5. (a) There are 4 brown socks out of the total of 12 in the drawer, so $P(\text{Brown}) = \frac{n(\text{Brown})}{n(S)} = \frac{1}{3}$.

   (b) The events are mutually exclusive, so $P(\text{Black or green}) = \frac{n(\text{Black})}{n(S)} + \frac{n(\text{Green})}{n(S)} = \frac{6}{12} + \frac{2}{12} = \frac{2}{3}$.

   (c) There are no red socks in the drawer, so $P(\text{Red}) = 0$.

   (d) $P(\text{Not black}) = 1 - P(\text{Black}) = 1 - \frac{n(\text{Black})}{n(S)} = 1 - \frac{6}{12} = \frac{1}{2}$.

6. (a) $P(\text{Vowel}) = \frac{n(\text{Vowel})}{n(S)} = \frac{5}{26}$.

   (b) $P(\text{Consonant}) = 1 - P(\text{Vowel}) = 1 - \frac{5}{26} = \frac{21}{26}$.

7. $P(\text{Missing flight}) = 1 - P(\text{Boarding flight}) = 1 - 0.2 = 0.8$.

8. (a) $P(\text{English disk}) = \frac{n(\text{English disk})}{n(S)} = \frac{1}{6}$.

   (b) If English, French, and American History are courses in the humanities, then:

   $P(\text{Humanities disk}) = \frac{n(\text{Humanities disk})}{n(S)} = \frac{1}{2}$.

9.   (a)   There are 36 equally likely outcomes when rolling two dice. Of these 36, a 7 may be obtained in six different ways: (1, 6), (2, 5), (3, 4), (4, 3), (5, 2), or (6, 1). 11 may be obtained in only two ways: (5, 6) or (6, 5). These events are mutually exclusive, so:

$$P(7 \text{ or } 11) = \frac{n(7)}{n(S)} + \frac{n(11)}{n(S)} = \frac{6}{36} + \frac{2}{36} = \frac{2}{9}.$$

     (b)   Two may be obtained in only one way: (1, 1); three may be obtained in two ways: (1, 2) or (2, 1); and twelve may be obtained in only one way: (6, 6). These events are mutually exclusive, so:

$$P(\text{Loss on first roll}) = \frac{n(2)}{n(S)} + \frac{n(3)}{n(S)} + \frac{n(12)}{n(S)} = \frac{1}{36} + \frac{2}{36} + \frac{1}{36} = \frac{1}{9}.$$

     (c)   A 4 may be rolled in three ways: (1, 3), (2, 2), (3, 1).
           A 5 may be rolled in four ways: (1, 4), (2, 3), (3, 2), (4, 1).
           A 6 may be rolled in five ways: (1, 5), (2, 4), (3, 3), (4, 2), (5, 1).
           A 8 may be rolled in five ways: (2, 6), (3, 5), (4, 4), (5, 3), (6, 2).
           A 9 may be rolled in four ways: (3, 6), (4, 5), (5, 4), (6, 3).
           A 10 may be rolled in three ways: (4, 6), (5, 5), (6, 4).
           These events are mutually exclusive, so:

$$P(\text{Neither win nor loss}) = \frac{n(4)}{n(S)} + \frac{n(5)}{n(S)} + \frac{n(6)}{n(S)} + \frac{n(8)}{n(S)} + \frac{n(9)}{n(S)} + \frac{n(10)}{n(S)} = \frac{3}{36} + \frac{4}{36} + \frac{5}{36} + \frac{5}{36} + \frac{4}{36} + \frac{3}{36}$$

$$P(\text{Neither win nor loss}) = \frac{2}{3}.$$

     (d)   6 or 8, with probabilities of $\frac{5}{36}$, have the highest probability of occurring again. (7 has a probability of $\frac{6}{36}$.)

     (e)   It is not possible to roll a sum of 1 with two dice, so $P(1) = 0$.

     (f)   The largest number which can be rolled with two dice is 12, so $P(< 13) = 1$.

     (g)   There is a $\frac{6}{36} = \frac{1}{6}$ probability of rolling 7 on any one roll; in 60 rolls one would expect $\frac{1}{6} \cdot 60 = 10$ sevens.

10. 70%. $P(\text{No rain}) = 1 - P(\text{Rain}) = 1 - 0.30 = 0.70$, or 70%.

11. (a)   There are 18 black slots on the roulette wheel, so $P(\text{Black}) = \frac{n(\text{Black})}{n(S)} = \frac{18}{38} = \frac{9}{19}$.

     (b) $P(0 \text{ or } 00) = \frac{n(0 \text{ or } 00)}{n(S)} = \frac{2}{38} = \frac{1}{19}$.

     (c)   This problem is easier if we find the probability that the ball does land on a number 1 through 12, and then use the property of complementary events. Thus:

$$P(\text{Not 1-12}) = 1 - P(1\text{-}12) = 1 - \frac{n(1\text{-}12)}{n(S)} = 1 - \frac{12}{38} = \frac{13}{19}.$$

     (d)   Since there are no green numbers other than 0 and 00, the events are mutually exclusive. Thus:

$$P(\text{Odd or green}) = \frac{n(\text{Odd})}{n(S)} + \frac{n(\text{Green})}{n(S)} = \frac{18}{38} + \frac{2}{38} = \frac{10}{19}.$$

12. $P(0 \text{ or } 00) = \frac{1}{19}$, so in 190 spins one would expect the ball to land in one of these slots $\frac{1}{19} \cdot 190 = 10$ times.

13. (a) $P(\text{I win or you lose}) = P(H) + P(T) = \frac{1}{2} + \frac{1}{2} = 1$. Each player's probability of winning is not equal.

     (b)   Equal. $P(\text{Heads I win}) = P(H) = \frac{1}{2}$; $P(\text{Tails you win}) = P(T) = \frac{1}{2}$.

     (c)   Equal. $P(1; \text{I win}) = \frac{n(1)}{n(S)} = \frac{1}{6}$; $P(6; \text{you win}) = \frac{n(6)}{n(S)} = \frac{1}{6}$.

13. (d) Equal. $P(\text{Even; I win}) = \frac{n(\text{Even})}{n(S)} = \frac{3}{6}$; $P(\text{Odd; you win}) = \frac{3}{6}$.

(e) Not equal. $P(\geq 3; \text{I win}) = \frac{n(\geq 3)}{n(S)} = \frac{4}{6}$; $P(< 3; \text{you win}) = \frac{n(< 3)}{n(S)} = \frac{2}{6}$.

(f) Equal. $P(\text{1 on each; I win}) = \frac{1}{36}$; $P(\text{6 on each; you win}) = \frac{1}{36}$.

(g) Not equal. $P(3; \text{I win}) = \frac{n(3)}{n(S)} = \frac{2}{6}$; $P(2; \text{you win}) = \frac{n(2)}{n(S)} = \frac{1}{6}$.

(h) Not equal. Red greater than white can occur in 15 ways:

Red	White
2	1
3	2, 1
4	3, 2, 1
5	4, 3, 2, 1
6	5, 4, 3, 2, 1

There are also 15 ways in which the white die could be greater than the red die and 6 ways in which they could be equal. Thus: $P(\text{Red} > \text{white; I win}) = \frac{15}{36}$; $P(\text{White} \geq \text{red; you win}) = \frac{21}{36}$.

14. Assuming that the bowler's performance is consistent, and that 45 strikes in 150 frames is an unbiased empirical probability, then $P(\text{Strike}) = \frac{n(\text{Strikes})}{n(S)} = \frac{45}{150} = \frac{3}{10}$.

15. (a) The sample space, S, is $\{(H, H), (H, T), (T, H), (T, T)\}$. Exactly one head appears in two of the events, so:
$P(\text{Exactly 1 head}) = \frac{n(\text{1 head})}{n(S)} = \frac{2}{4} = \frac{1}{2}$.

(b) At least one head means 1 head or 2 heads. $P(\text{At least 1}) = \frac{n(\text{1 head})}{n(S)} + \frac{n(\text{2 head})}{n(S)} = \frac{2}{4} + \frac{1}{4} = \frac{3}{4}$.

(c) At most one head means 0 heads or 1 head. $P(\text{At most 1}) = \frac{1}{4} + \frac{1}{2} = \frac{3}{4}$.

16. $P(A \cup B) = P(A) + P(B) = 0.3 + 0.4 = 0.7$.

17. No. $P(A) + P(B) > 1$, thus cannot be mutually exclusive.

18. (a) The sample space, S, is $35 + 45 = 80$, so $P(\text{Female}) = \frac{n(\text{Female})}{n(S)} = \frac{35}{80} = \frac{9}{16}$.

(b) $P(\text{Computer Science}) = \frac{n(\text{Computer Science})}{n(S)} = \frac{10}{80} = \frac{1}{8}$.

(c) Since we know we have 20 mathematics majors, this problem is easier if we use the property of complementary events:
$P(\text{Not math}) = 1 - P(\text{Math}) = 1 - \frac{20}{80} = \frac{3}{4}$.

(d) Since these events are mutually exclusive, $P(\text{Computer Science or Math}) = \frac{10}{80} + \frac{20}{80} = \frac{3}{8}$.

Problem Set 8-2

1. (a)   (b)

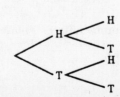

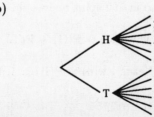

2. (a) $S = \{(1, 1), (1, 2), (1, 3), (2, 1), (2, 2), (2, 3)\}$

    (b) $A = \{(2, 2)\}$

    (c) $B = \{(1, 2), (2, 1), (2, 2), (2, 3)\}$ (d) $C = \{(1, 2), (2, 1), (2, 3)\}$

3. (a) $P(D) = \frac{1}{6}$; $P(A) = \frac{1}{6}$; $P(N) = \frac{1}{6}$. Thus $P(DAN) = \frac{1}{6} \cdot \frac{1}{6} \cdot \frac{1}{6} = \frac{1}{216}$.

    (b) $P(D) = \frac{1}{6}$; $P(A) = \frac{1}{5}$; $P(N) = \frac{1}{4}$. Thus $P(DAN) = \frac{1}{6} \cdot \frac{1}{5} \cdot \frac{1}{4} = \frac{1}{120}$.

4. (a) $P(HAT) = \frac{1}{4} \cdot \frac{1}{3} \cdot \frac{1}{2} = \frac{1}{24}$.   (b) $P(HAT) = \frac{1}{4} \cdot \frac{1}{4} \cdot \frac{1}{4} = \frac{1}{64}$.

    (c) $P(HAT) = \frac{1}{4} \cdot \frac{1}{3} \cdot \frac{1}{7} = \frac{1}{84}$.

    (d)   Box 1: $P(A) = \frac{1}{3} \cdot \frac{1}{4} = \frac{1}{12}$ (because the probability of choosing Box 1 is $\frac{1}{3}$ and the probability of choosing an A, given Box 1, is $\frac{1}{4}$.) Similarly:

    Box 2: $P(A) = \frac{1}{3} \cdot \frac{1}{3} = \frac{1}{9}$; Box 3: $P(A) = \frac{1}{3} \cdot 0 = 0$.

    Since these are mutually exclusive events, $P(A) = \frac{1}{12} + \frac{1}{9} + 0 = \frac{7}{36}$.

5. This problem is similar to that of drawing colored marbles out of a box without replacement; i.e., three woman-colored marbles from a box with four woman-colored and six man-colored in it. Thus: $P(3 \text{ women}) = \frac{4}{10} \cdot \frac{3}{9} \cdot \frac{2}{8} = \frac{1}{30}$.

6. (a)   (*i*)   If we choose Box 1: $P(SOS) = \frac{2}{3} \cdot \frac{1}{2} \cdot 1 = \frac{1}{3}$.

         (*ii*)   If we choose Box 2: $P(SOS) = \frac{4}{6} \cdot \frac{2}{5} \cdot \frac{3}{4} = \frac{1}{5}$.

    Thus we choose Box 1.

    (b)   (*i*)   If we choose Box 1: $P(SOS) = \frac{2}{3} \cdot \frac{1}{3} \cdot \frac{2}{3} = \frac{4}{27}$.

         (*ii*)   If we choose Box 2: $P(SOS) = \frac{4}{6} \cdot \frac{2}{6} \cdot \frac{4}{6} = \frac{4}{27}$.

    So we may choose either box.

7. (a)   This problem is best illustrated by a tree diagram showing four mutually exclusive paths for the probabilities of a white ball being drawn. For example, the first path would show probabilities of $\frac{1}{5}$ for drawing a white ball from the first box, $\frac{3}{5}$ of drawing a white ball from the second box given that white had been drawn from box one, and $\frac{2}{3}$ of drawing a white ball from the third box given that white had been drawn from boxes one and two. Other paths would be similarly drawn. Thus: $P(\text{White from 3}) = \frac{1}{5} \cdot \frac{3}{5} \cdot \frac{2}{3} + \frac{1}{5} \cdot \frac{2}{5} \cdot 1 + \frac{4}{5} \cdot \frac{2}{5} \cdot \frac{2}{3} + \frac{4}{5} \cdot \frac{3}{5} \cdot 1 = \frac{6}{75} \cdot \frac{2}{25} \cdot \frac{16}{75} \cdot \frac{12}{25} = \frac{64}{75}$

    (b) $P(\text{Black}) = 1 - P(\text{White}) = 1 - \frac{64}{75} = \frac{11}{75}$.

8. (*i*)   Billie-Bobby-Billie: Carolyn can win the prize only if she wins the first two games or the last two games.
    P(Beats Billie and Beats Bobbie) = (0.5)(0.8) = 0.4.
    P(Loses to Billie; beats Bobby and Billie) = (0.5)(0.8)(0.5) = 0.2.
    P(Wins prize) = 0.4 + 0.2 = 0.6.

8.   (*ii*)   Bobby-Billie-Bobby:
            P(Beats Bobby and beats Billie) = (0.8)(0.5) = 0.4.
            P(Loses to Bobby; beats Billie and Bobby) = (0.2)(0.5)(0.8) = 0.08.
            P(Wins prize) = 0.4 + 0.08 = 0.48.

            Carolyn should choose to play Billie-Bobby-Billie.

9.   (a)   P(White from box 1) = $\frac{3}{5}$; P(White from box 2) = $\frac{2}{6}$. P(Two whites) = $\frac{3}{5} \cdot \frac{2}{6} = \frac{1}{5}$.

     (b)   "At least 1" means either one or two; i.e., black from 1 and black from 2, or, black from 1 and white
           from 2, or, white from 1 and black from 2. These events are mutually exclusive, so:
           P(At least 1 black) = $\frac{2}{5} \cdot \frac{4}{6} + \frac{2}{5} \cdot \frac{2}{6} + \frac{3}{5} \cdot \frac{4}{6} = \frac{8}{30} + \frac{4}{30} + \frac{12}{30} = \frac{4}{5}$.

     (c)   "At most 1" means either zero or one. Since we can have a maximum of 2 black balls, it is easier to
           find the probability of 2 black balls and then use the property of complementary events. Thus:
           P(Two blacks) = $\frac{2}{5} \cdot \frac{4}{6} = \frac{4}{15}$. P(0 or 1 black) = 1 − P(Two blacks) = $1 - \frac{4}{15} = \frac{11}{15}$.

     (d)   P(Black-white or white-black) = $\frac{2}{5} \cdot \frac{2}{6} + \frac{3}{5} \cdot \frac{4}{6} = \frac{4}{30} + \frac{12}{30} = \frac{8}{15}$.

10. "At least 3 heads" means either 3 heads or 4 heads.
     There is only one way four heads can be tossed; there are four ways 3 heads can be tossed: HHHT, HHTH,
     HTHH, or THHH. Each of these events can occur with a probability of $\frac{1}{2} \cdot \frac{1}{2} \cdot \frac{1}{2} \cdot \frac{1}{2} = \frac{1}{16}$.

     Thus P(At least 3 heads) = $\frac{1}{16} + \frac{1}{16} + \frac{1}{16} + \frac{1}{16} + \frac{1}{16} = \frac{5}{16}$.

11. P(All boys) = $\frac{1}{2} \cdot \frac{1}{2} \cdot \frac{1}{2} \cdot \frac{1}{2} = \frac{1}{16}$.

12. (a)   There are five different ways of ascending four steps in either 1 or 2 strides: S = {(1, 1, 1, 1),
           (1, 2, 1), (1, 1, 2), (2, 1, 1), (2, 2)}, with probabilities of $\frac{1}{16}$, $\frac{1}{8}$, $\frac{1}{8}$, $\frac{1}{8}$, and $\frac{1}{4}$, respectively.
           Thus, P(2 strides) = $\frac{1}{4}$.

     (b)   P(3 strides) = $\frac{1}{8} + \frac{1}{8} + \frac{1}{8} = \frac{3}{8}$.   (c)   P(4 strides) = $\frac{1}{16}$.

13. Blond hair and blue eyes. Introducing another probability (red car) adds one more to the product of the
     probabilities; since each probability is less than 1 the product will be smaller.

14. (a)   P(3 plums) = $\frac{5}{20} \cdot \frac{1}{20} \cdot \frac{5}{20} = \frac{1}{320}$.   (b)   P(3 oranges) = $\frac{3}{20} \cdot \frac{6}{20} \cdot \frac{7}{20} = \frac{63}{4000}$.

     (c)   P(3 lemons) = $\frac{3}{20} \cdot \frac{0}{20} \cdot \frac{4}{20} = 0$ (d)   P(No plums) = $\frac{15}{20} \cdot \frac{19}{20} \cdot \frac{15}{20} = \frac{171}{320}$.

15. Each question has a $\frac{1}{2}$ probability of being right, and the results of each question have no effect on
     subsequent questions. Thus P(100%) = $\frac{1}{2} \cdot \frac{1}{2} \cdot \frac{1}{2} \cdot \frac{1}{2} \cdot \frac{1}{2} = \frac{1}{32}$.

16. The sample space consists of 8 events: S = {(black, black, black), (black, black, blue), (black, blue, black),
     (black, blue, blue), (blue, black, black), (blue, black, blue), (blue, blue, black), (blue, blue, blue)}.
     Since each event in the sample space has at least two socks of the same color, P(Matching pair) = 1.

17. (a)   P(Paxson loses) = P(Rattlesnake wins). Thus P(4 Paxson loses) = $\frac{2}{3} \cdot \frac{2}{3} \cdot \frac{2}{3} \cdot \frac{2}{3} = \frac{16}{81}$.

     (b)   There are six ways in which each school wins two games: D = {(PPRR), (PRPR), (PRRP), (RPPR),
           (RPRP), (RRPP)}. Each occurs with a probability $\frac{2}{3} \cdot \frac{2}{3} \cdot \frac{1}{3} \cdot \frac{1}{3} = \frac{4}{81}$.
           Thus P(Draw) = $6 \cdot \frac{4}{81} = \frac{8}{27}$.

18. The set of multiples of 9 = {0, 9, 18, 27, 36}. The set of multiples of 4 = {0, 4, 8, 12, 16, 20, 24, 28, 32,
     36}. There are 5 multiples of 9, 10 multiples of 4, and 40 numbers between 0 and 39.
     Thus P(9×, 9×, 4×) = $\frac{5}{40} \cdot \frac{5}{40} \cdot \frac{10}{40} = \frac{1}{256}$.

19. $P(\text{MISSISSIPPI}) = \frac{1}{11} \cdot \frac{4}{10} \cdot \frac{4}{9} \cdot \frac{3}{8} \cdot \frac{3}{7} \cdot \frac{2}{6} \cdot \frac{1}{5} \cdot \frac{2}{4} \cdot \frac{2}{3} \cdot \frac{1}{2} \cdot 1 = \frac{1152}{39916800} = \frac{1}{34650}.$

20.   (a)   The total area of the dart board is 5x by 5x, or $25x^2$. The area of A is x by x, or x^2. Thus:

$$P(\text{Section A}) = \frac{x^2}{25x^2} = \frac{1}{25}.$$

       (b)   The area of B is $(3x)^2 - x^2 = 8x^2$. Thus $P(\text{Section B}) = \frac{8x^2}{25x^2} = \frac{8}{25}.$

       (c)   The area of C is $(5x)^2 - (3x)^2 = 16x^2$. $P(\text{Section C}) = \frac{16}{25}.$

21.   (a)   Total area is 10 units by 10 units = 100 square units.

       (b)   (*i*) $P(\text{Area A}) = \frac{4}{100} = \frac{1}{25}$ (*ii*) $P(\text{Area B}) = \frac{12}{100} = \frac{3}{25}$

               (*iii*) $P(\text{Area C}) = \frac{20}{100} = \frac{1}{5}$ (*iv*) $P(\text{Area D}) = \frac{28}{100} = \frac{7}{25}$

               (*v*) $P(\text{Area E}) = \frac{36}{100} = \frac{9}{25}$

       (c)   20 points with two darts can only be scored if both land in Area A.
               Thus $P(\text{20 points}) = \frac{1}{25} \cdot \frac{1}{25} = \frac{1}{625}.$

       (d)   If the dart lands in neither D nor E, then it must land in either A, B, or C.
               $P(\text{A, B, or C}) = P(\text{Neither D nor E}) = \frac{4}{100} + \frac{12}{100} + \frac{20}{100} = \frac{9}{25}.$

22.   The total area of the earth is about 197,100,00 square miles. Thus:

$$P(\text{Hitting water}) = \frac{139,600,000}{197,100,000} = 0.7 \text{ (to the nearest tenth)}.$$

23.   Assuming that we have an analog and not a digital display, the second hand will cover the distance between 3 and 4 in five seconds. Thus $P(\text{Between 3 and 4}) = \frac{5}{60} = \frac{1}{12}.$

24.   There are 7 ways of infecting at least 3 children: (YNN), (NYN), (NNY), (YYN), (YNY), (NYY), (YYY).
       Each Y has probability 0.1; each N has probability 0.9.
       Thus $P(\text{At least 1}) = 3(0.1)(0.9)(0.9) + 3(0.1)(0.1)(0.9) + (0.1)^3 = 0.271.$

25.   Set A covers 2 units; set B covers 5. Thus $P(B \in A) = \frac{2}{5}.$

26.   There are two ways of drawing exactly one red sock in two draws: RB or BR. If there were 3 red socks in the drawer and 1 black, then $P(\text{1 red}) = P(\text{Red, black}) + P(\text{Black, red}) = \frac{3}{4} \cdot \frac{1}{3} + \frac{1}{4} \cdot \frac{3}{3} = \frac{1}{2}.$ The least number of each color in the drawer is 3 reds and 1 black. (Assume no replacement between draws.)

27.   The board should be designed so that the portion in which it is desired to hit with probability $\frac{3}{5}$ will have $\frac{3}{5}$ of the total area.

28.   The possible outcomes are HH, HT, TH, and TT. In only one of the four ways is it possible to obtain HH, so $P(\text{HH}) = \frac{1}{4}.$

29.   We want the probability that a randomly-selected patient has lung cancer, given that the patient smokes. We know that of the 30 smokers 25 have lung cancer, so :

$$P(\text{Cancer given smoker}) = \frac{n(\text{Cancer} \cap \text{Smoker})}{n(\text{Smoker})} = \frac{25}{30} = \frac{5}{6}.$$

30.   Of the ten secretaries two are male, so $P(\text{Secretary given male}) = \dfrac{n(\text{Male} \cap \text{Secretary})}{n(\text{Male})} = \frac{2}{28} = \frac{1}{14}.$

31.   The probability of red or black on the 27th spin was the same as for each of the preceding 26. If the wheel is fair, the probability of red or black on any roll is unchanged by whatever may have previously occurred.

32. A tree diagram would show three possibilities:
    (*i*)   First inspector will catch the defect, with a probability of 0.95; or
    (*ii*) First inspector will miss the defect and the second will catch it, with a probability of $(0.05)(0.99) = 0.0495$; or
    (*iii*) First inspector will miss the defect and the second will miss it, with a probability of $(0.05)(0.01) = 0.0005$.
The probability of a defect passing both inspectors is 0.0005.

33. As shown in Problem 29, the probability of an event given another happening, or P(A given B), is

$$P(A \text{ given } B) = \frac{P(A \cap B)}{P(B)}.$$ It follows, then, that $P(A \cap B) = P(B) \cdot P(A \text{ given } B)$. Thus:

$P(\text{Eaten} \cap \text{Sickly}) = P(\text{Sickly}) \cdot P(\text{Eaten given sickly}) = \frac{1}{20} \cdot \frac{1}{3} = \frac{1}{60}$;
$P(\text{Eaten} \cap \text{Not sickly}) = P(\text{Not sickly}) \cdot P(\text{Eaten given not sickly}) = \frac{19}{20} \cdot \frac{1}{150} = \frac{19}{3000}$;
and $P(\text{Eaten}) = \frac{1}{60} + \frac{19}{3000} = \frac{23}{1000}$.

34. (a)   Spinner B has a probability of beating A of $\frac{4}{9}$, or 4 times out of 9. Spinner C has a probability of beating A of $\frac{5}{11}$, or 5 times out of 11. Choose A.

    (b)   Choose C, with a winning probability of $\frac{35}{99}$.

35. The probabilities of Abe's winning the game are summarized in the table below. Of the 12 possible games, only 8 result in choices with eqully likely outcomes, i.e., fair games.

		Abe's choice			
		HH	HT	TH	TT
	HH	--	.50	.75	.50
Your	HT	.50	--	.50	.25
choice	TH	.25	.50	--	.50
	TT	.50	.75	.50	--

36. (*i*)   HS: $P(\text{Win}) = P(\text{1st in}) \cdot P(\text{Point}) + P(\text{1st out}) \cdot P(\text{2nd in}) \cdot P(\text{Point})$
                    $= (0.50)(0.75) + (0.50)(0.75)(0.50) = 0.5625$
    (*ii*) HH: $P(\text{Win}) = (0.50)(0.75) + (0.50)(0.50)(0.75) = 0.5625$
    (*iii*) SH: $P(\text{Win}) = (0.75)(0.50) + (0.25)(0.50)(0.75) = 0.46875$
    (*iv*) SS: $P(\text{Win}) = (0.75)(0.50) + (0.25)(0.75)(0.50) = 0.46875$
Jane should always serve hard the first time. It does not matter what her second serve is.

37. (a)   A certain event $\leftrightarrow$ (v) (A certain event has a probability of 1)

    (b)   An impossible event $\leftrightarrow$ (iii) (An impossible event has a probability of 0)

    (c)   A very likely event $\leftrightarrow$ (ii) (A very likely event has a probability close to 1)

    (d)   An unlikely event $\leftrightarrow$ (i) (An unlikely event has a probability close to 0)

    (e)   A 50% chance $\leftrightarrow$ (iv) (A 50% chance has a probability of $\frac{1}{2}$)

38. (a) $P(\text{April 7}) = \frac{1}{30}$ (b) $P(\text{April 31}) = 0$

    (c) $P(\text{Before April 20}) = \frac{19}{30}$

1. If trial 1 produces 2, 5, 1, 3, then Bridge #1 is open, Bridge #2 is closed, Bridge #3 is closed, and Bridge #4 is closed. There was no open route.

    If trial 2 produces 7, 4, 4, 6, then Bridge #1 is closed, Bridge #2 is open, Bridge #3 is open, and Bridge #4 is open. There was an open route.

    You may use a spinner, a random number generator, a table, or any other means of producing random numbers. Continue the experiment for 20 trials and record your results.

2. If there is an even chance of having a girl, shuffle the cards, draw, and let red cards be the birth of a girl.

3. (a) Let rain be 1, 2, ... , 9 on a card; let no rain be a 10. Then shuffle the cards and draw randomly.

    (b) Shuffle and draw a large number of times. Record the times a 10 occurs seven times in a row. Then

    $$P(\text{No rain for 7 days}) = \frac{n(\text{No rain for 7 times})}{n(\text{Total experiments})}$$

    (c) $P(\text{No rain for 7 days}) = (0.1)^7 = 0.0000001$.

4. (a) Let the numbers 1, 2, 3, 4, 5, 6 represent the numbers of the die and ignore the numbers 0, 7, 8, 9.

    (b) Pick 3 two-digit numbers at random. (Discard any that are more than 20 and draw again.) These are the numbers of the 3 out of 20 that will be chosen.

    (c) Let red be numbers 1, 2, 3, 4, 5; green be numbers 6, 7, 8; yellow be 9; and white be 0. Then pick a number at random; its value will the the color upon which the needle rests.

5. Assuming an unbiased random sample of fish in the pond are caught, then $\frac{50}{300} = \frac{1}{6}$ of the total population is marked. Let n be the fish population; then $\frac{1}{6}n = 200$. Solving, n = 1200 fish.

6. $\frac{3}{10}$

7. Pick a starting spot on the table and count the number of digits it takes before all the numbers 1 through 9 are obtained. Repeat this experiment many times and record the average number of boxes.

8. Pick 30 three-digit numbers at random. (Discard any that are more than 500 and draw again.) These are the numbers of the 30 out of 500 that will be chosen.

9. Monday: Pick 10 random numbers; let those 0 to 7 represent rain and 8, 9 represent dry.
    Tuesday: Pick 10 random numbers. If it rained on Monday let 0 to 7 represent rain; if not, let 0 to 2 represent rain.
    Wednesday through Saturday: Repeat.

10. $P(\text{Ace}) = \frac{1}{13}$. One would expect one ace every 13 cards.

11. (a) Since it is possible for the losing team to win three games in a series, the maximum number that could be played is 7.

    (b) Since the teams are evenly matched, use a table of random digits and let a number between 0 and 4 represent a win by Team A; let a number between 5 and 9 represent a win by Team B. Pick a starting spot and count the number of digits it takes before a Team A or Team B series win is recorded. Repeat the experiment many times and then base your answers on:

    $$P(\text{4-game series}) = \frac{n(\text{4-game series})}{n(\text{Total series})} \text{ and } P(\text{7-game series}) = \frac{n(\text{7-game series})}{n(\text{Total series})}.$$

    Given evenly matched teams, the probability of a 4-game series would be expected to be low.

12. Use a random digit table. Let the digits 1-8 represent a win and the digits 0 and 9 represent a loss. Mark off blocks of three. If only the digits 1-8 appear, then this represents 3 wins in a row. Repeat the experiment many times.

13. In a random-number table, mark off 100 three-digit blocks. Let numbers 000-014 represent contraction of strep throat. Pick one at random from the block of 100; if it is within 000-014 it simulates having caught the disease. Do the experiment three times to represent three children. Now repeat this procedure many times and record the number of times one, two or all three children catch strep throat. Then:

$$P(\text{At least one}) = \frac{n(1 \text{ child catches})}{n(\text{Total number of trials})} + \frac{n(2 \text{ children catch})}{n(\text{Total number of trials})} + \frac{n(3 \text{ children catch})}{n(\text{Total number of trials})}.$$

14. Let the ten ducks be represented by the digits 0-9. Then pick a starting point in a table of random digits and mark off ten digits to simulate which ducks the hunters shoot at. Count how many of the digits 0-9 are not in the ten digits and this represents the ducks that escaped. Do this experiment many times and take the average. The theoretical expectation of the number of escapees is 3.49.

15. (a) $\frac{1}{4}$ (b) $\frac{1}{52}$

     (c) $1 - \frac{4}{52} = \frac{48}{52} = \frac{12}{13}$ (d) $1 - \frac{1}{4} = \frac{3}{4}$

     (e) $\frac{1}{4} + \frac{1}{4} = \frac{1}{2}$ (f) $\frac{1}{52}$

     (g) $\frac{1}{13} + \frac{1}{4} - \frac{1}{13} \cdot \frac{1}{4} = \frac{4}{13}$ (h) $\frac{1}{2} + \frac{1}{2} = 1$

16. (a) $\frac{7}{19} + \frac{8}{19} = \frac{15}{19}$ (b) $\frac{7}{19} \cdot \frac{8}{19} = \frac{56}{361}$

     (c) $\frac{7}{19} \cdot \frac{8}{18} = \frac{28}{171}$

Problem Set 8-4

1. (a) $P(\text{Drawing a face card}) = \frac{12}{52} = \frac{3}{13}$, so Odds in favor $= \frac{P(\text{Face card})}{1 - P(\text{Face card})} = \frac{3}{13} \div \frac{10}{13} = 3{:}10.$

     (b) Since the odds in favor are 3:10, the odds against are 10:3.

2. $P(7) = \frac{1}{6}$, so the odds against are $\frac{1 - P(7)}{P(7)} = 5{:}1.$

3. If $P(\text{Boy}) = \frac{1}{2}$, then $P(4 \text{ boys}) = (\frac{1}{2})^4 = \frac{1}{16}$. Thus odds against $= \frac{1 - P(4 \text{ boys})}{P(4 \text{ boys})} = \frac{15}{16} \div \frac{1}{16} = 15{:}1.$

4. (a) $P(\text{Tail on 10th toss}) = \frac{1}{2}.$

     (b) $P(10 \text{ tails}) = (\frac{1}{2})^{10} = \frac{1}{1024}.$

     (c) Odds against $= \frac{1 - P(10 \text{ tails})}{P(10 \text{ tails})} = 1023{:}1.$

5. $\frac{1 - P(\text{Win})}{P(\text{Win})} = \frac{3}{5}$, given that the odds against are 3:5. Solving for $P(\text{Win})$: $5[1 - P(\text{Win})] = 3[P(\text{Win})]$, or $P(\text{Win}) = \frac{5}{8}.$

6. $S = \{\text{HHH, HHT, HTH, HTT, THH, THT, TTH, TTT}\}$. At least 2 heads appear in 4 of the 8 outcomes, so $P(\text{At least 2 heads}) = \frac{1}{2}$. Thus odds in favor $= \frac{P(\text{At least 2 heads})}{1 - P(\text{At least 2 heads})} = 1{:}1.$

7. Odds against raining $= \frac{1 - P(\text{Rain})}{P(\text{Rain})} = \frac{1 - 0.60}{0.60} = 2{:}3.$

8. $P(\text{Red slot}) = \frac{18}{38} = \frac{9}{19}$. Thus the odds against a red slot are $\dfrac{1 - \frac{9}{19}}{\frac{9}{19}} = 10:9$.

9. The possible outcomes are HH, HT, TH, TT, so $P(2 \text{ heads}) = \frac{1}{4}$. Then E, the expected outcome, is $\$1.00(\frac{1}{4}) = 25\cancel{c}$; this is what should be paid to make a fair game.

10. Each possible number of spots on the die occurs with a probability of $\frac{1}{6}$. Thus:
$E = 1(\frac{1}{6}) + 2(\frac{1}{6}) + 3(\frac{1}{6}) + 4(\frac{1}{6}) + 5(\frac{1}{6}) + 6(\frac{1}{6}) = \$3.50$.

11. $E = 1000(\frac{1}{500}) + 100(\frac{5}{500}) + 0(\frac{494}{500}) = \frac{1000}{500} + \frac{500}{500} = \$3.00$.

12. $E = 1(0.15) + 2(0.20) + 3(0.40) + 4(0.10) + 5(0.05) + 6(0.10) = 3$ hours.

13. $\dfrac{P(\text{Broken arm})}{1 - P(\text{Broken arm})} = \frac{1000}{1}$. Solving for P, the probability of a broken arm: $1 \cdot P = 1000(1 - P)$, or
$P = \frac{1000}{1001}$.

14. $E = 0.25(\frac{1}{5}) + 0.10(\frac{1}{5}) + 0.05(\frac{1}{5}) + 0.01(\frac{2}{5}) = 0.84$, or about $8\cancel{c}$.

15. If the odds in favor of winning are 5:2, then $\dfrac{P(\text{Win})}{1 - P(\text{win})} = \frac{5}{2}$. Solving, we find $P(\text{Win}) = \frac{5}{7}$.
Then $E = 14,000(\frac{5}{7}) = \$10,000$.

16. (a) There are two outcomes of further tossing that would provide Al with a win: H and TH, so
$P(\text{Al wins}) = \frac{1}{2} + \frac{1}{2} \cdot \frac{1}{2} = \frac{3}{4}$ and $P(\text{Betsy wins}) = 1 - P(\text{Al wins}) = \frac{1}{4}$. An equitable division, then, would be $\frac{1}{4}$ for Betsy and $\frac{3}{4}$ for Al, or \$25 and \$75.

(b) Odds against Betsy $= \dfrac{1 - P(\text{Betsy wins})}{P(\text{Betsy wins})} = 3:1$.

(c) There are 15 outcomes of further tossing that would give Al a win: HH, HTH, HTTH, HTTTH, HTTTTH, THH, THTH, THTTH, THTTTH, TTHH, TTHTH, TTHTTH, TTTHH, TTTHTH, TTTTHH. Thus $P(\text{Al wins}) = \frac{1}{4} + \frac{1}{8} + \frac{1}{16} + \frac{1}{32} + \frac{1}{64} + \frac{1}{8} + \frac{1}{16} + \frac{1}{32} + \frac{1}{64} + \frac{1}{16} + \frac{1}{32} + \frac{1}{64} + \frac{1}{32} + \frac{1}{64}$ $+ \frac{1}{64} = \frac{57}{64} \doteq 0.8906$. Rounding to the nearest dollar, Al should receive \$89 and Betsy \$11.

(d) Odds for Al $= \dfrac{P(\text{Al wins})}{1 - P(\text{Al wins})} = \dfrac{\frac{57}{64}}{1 - \frac{57}{64}} = 57:7$.

17. $P(2 \text{ heads}) = \frac{1}{4}$; $P(1 \text{ head}) = \frac{1}{2}$; $P(0 \text{ heads}) = \frac{1}{4}$. Accordingly, $E = 10(\frac{1}{4}) + 5(\frac{1}{2}) + 0(\frac{1}{4}) = \$5.00$. Because you pay the same as the expected gain, it is a fair game.

18. $E = 100(\frac{1}{200}) = \$0.50$. Since the expected gain is less than the cost, it is not a fair game.

19. $\dfrac{1 - P(\text{Win})}{P(\text{Win})} = \frac{1,000,000,000}{1}$, or $1,000,000,000 \cdot P(\text{Win}) = 1 - P(\text{Win})$. Solving, $P(\text{Win}) = \frac{1}{1,000,000,001}$.

20. Don't believe the report. If the odds of getting AIDS were 68,000 to 1, the probability of getting AIDS would be $\frac{68,000}{68,001}$. This would mean that your chances of getting AIDS would be almost a certainty.

21. If the odds are 26:1 that Gameylegs will lose, then $\dfrac{P(\text{Loss})}{1 - P(\text{Loss})} = \frac{26}{1}$, or $P(\text{Loss}) = \frac{26}{27}$. Thus the probability of Gameylegs winning is $1 - \frac{26}{27} = \frac{1}{27}$.

22. (a) $S = \{1, 2, 3, 4\}$ (b) $S = \{\text{Red, Blue}\}$

(c) $S = \{(1, R), (1, B), (2, R), (2, B), (3, R), (3, B), (4, R), (4, B)\}$

(d) $S = \{(R, 1), (R, 2), (R, 3), (R, 4), (R, 5), (R, 6), (B, 1), (B, 2), (B, 3), (B, 4), (B, 5), (B, 6)\}$

(e) $S = \{(1, 1), (1, 2), (1, 3), (1, 4), (2, 1), (2, 2), (2, 3), (2, 4), (3, 1), (3, 2), (3, 3), (3, 4), (4, 1),$
$(4, 2), (4, 3), (4, 4)\}$

22.   (f) $S = \{(R, R), (R, B), (B, R), (B, B)\}$

23.   The blue section must have $\frac{5}{6} \cdot 360° = 300°$; the red section must have $360° - 300° = 60°$.

24. $P(2 \text{ Vowels}) = \frac{5}{26} \cdot \frac{5}{26} = \frac{25}{676}$.

Problem Set 8-5

1.   Answers may vary. The fundamental counting principal says that if an event can occur in a fixed number of ways, and after it has occurred another event can happen in a fixed number of ways, then the total number of ways the two events can occur is the product of the number of ways of each. Permutations are the number of ways different arrangements of things can happen, if the order of the things is distinct. Combinations are the number of ways different arrangements of things can happen if the order of the things is not distinct.

2.   (a)   (i) $\frac{4!}{2!} = 12$ ways   (ii) $\frac{11!}{2!2!2!} = 4,989,600$ ways

       (b) $\frac{12!}{6!4!2!} = 13,860$ ways

3.   (a)   There are $10^6 = 1,000,000$ possible license plates.

       (b)   The 1990 census showed Montana, Wyoming, Alaska, Delaware, North and South Dakota, and Vermont with less than 1,000,000 automobiles.

       (c)   Answers may vary; one is to use numbers plus letters of the alphabet.

4.   There are $16 \cdot 14 = 224$ different ways of pairing 16 boys and 14 girls.

5.   Each coin toss will result in two possible outcomes (H or T). Five tosses will then result in $2^5 = 32$ different combinations of heads and tails.

6.   The number of ways the four digits may be arranged is $10^4 = 10,000$. Assuming all can be used, 10,000 numbers can be associated with each prefix.

7.   Assuming all letters after the first can be repeated, there are $2 \cdot 26 \cdot 26 = 1352$ three-letter call signs available (the factor 2 represents either K or W). There are $2 \cdot 26 \cdot 26 \cdot 26 = 35,152$ four-letter call signs available.

8.   There are $3 \cdot 15 \cdot 4 = 180$ different three-course meals.

9.   (a)   True. $6 \cdot 5! = 6 \cdot (5 \cdot 4 \cdot 3 \cdot 2 \cdot 1) = 6!$.

       (b)   False. $3! + 3! = 3 \cdot 2 \cdot 1 + 3 \cdot 2 \cdot 1 \neq 6!$.

       (c)   False. $\frac{6!}{3!} = \frac{6 \cdot 5 \cdot 4 \cdot 3 \cdot 2 \cdot 1}{3 \cdot 2 \cdot 1} = 6 \cdot 5 \cdot 4 \neq 2!$.

       (d)   False. $\frac{6!}{3} = \frac{6 \cdot 5 \cdot 4 \cdot 3 \cdot 2 \cdot 1}{3} \neq 2!$

       (e)   True. See (c).

       (f)   True. $\frac{6!}{4!2!} = \frac{6 \cdot 5 \cdot 4 \cdot 3 \cdot 2 \cdot 1}{(4 \cdot 3 \cdot 2 \cdot 1)(2 \cdot 1)} = \frac{6 \cdot 5}{2 \cdot 1} = 15$.

       (g)   True. $(n + 1) \cdot n! = (n + 1) \cdot n \cdot (n - 1) \cdot (n - 2) \cdot \cdots \cdot 3 \cdot 2 \cdot 1 = (n + 1)!$.

10. $8! = 40,320$ ways.

11. Since order is not distinct, the number of two-person committees is a combination of six things taken two at a time, or $_6C_2$. $_6C_2 = \frac{6!}{2!(6-2)!} = 15$ different committees.

12. (a) $\frac{4!}{2!} = 12$ ways.   (b) $\frac{7!}{4!} = 210$ ways.

     (c) $\frac{8!}{2!3!} = 3360$ ways.   (d) $\frac{11!}{4!4!2!} = 34{,}650$ ways.

     (e) $\frac{9!}{4!2!2!} = 3780$ ways.

13. (a)   Since order is distinct, this is a permutation of 30 things taken 3 at a time: $_{30}P_3 = \frac{30!}{27!} = 24{,}360$ ways.

     (b)   In this case order is not distinct; this is a combination: $_{30}C_3 = \frac{30!}{27!3!} = 4060$ ways.

14. The combination of 12 things taken 5 at a time is: $_{12}C_5 = \frac{12!}{7!5!} = 792$ different teams.

15. There are $9! = 362{,}880$ different ways of arranging the nine books.

16. Five volumes may be placed in $5! = 120$ different ways; only one will be in order. Thus $P(\text{In order}) = \frac{1}{120}$.

17. We want the number of ways of choosing 10 points, 2 at a time. Since a line may be drawn either way, order is not distinct; i.e., we have a combination. $_{10}C_2 = \frac{10!}{8!2!} = 45$ straight lines.

18. There are $10^3 = 1000$ possible combinations.

19. Sally can run $\frac{9!}{4!3!2!} = 1260$ nine-flag signals up the pole.

20. (a)   Each shortest path involves one face of the cube. Since there are 6 faces, there are 6 shortest paths.

     (b)   There are $6 \cdot 6 = 36$ total shortest paths.

21. If there were n people at the party, there were n combinations of people two at a time shaking hands. That is, $_nC_2 = \frac{n!}{(n-2)!2!} = \frac{n \cdot (n-1)}{2!} = 28$. If $n \cdot (n-1) = 56$, $n = 8$ and there were 8 people at the party.

22. (a)   The number of ways of selecting a committee of 3 from the group of 7 Americans is $_7C_3 = 35$. There are $_{15}C_3 = 455$ ways of selecting 3 members from the whole set. Thus $P(\text{3 Americans}) = \frac{35}{455} = \frac{1}{13}$.

     (b)   If no Americans are selected, there are $_8C_3 = 56$ ways of selecting the 3 members from among the French and English. Thus $P(\text{No American}) = \frac{56}{455} = \frac{8}{65}$.

23. (a) $_5C_3 = $ the third number in row 5, or 10.   (b) $_5C_5 = $ the fifth number in row 5, or 1.

     (c) $_6C_0 = $ the 0th number in row 6, or 1.   (d) $_3C_2 = $ the second number in row 3, or 3.

24. If six free throws are made, then four are missed. If the probability of making one is $\frac{2}{3}$, then the probability of missing is $\frac{1}{3}$. Thus $P(\text{6 made and 4 missed}) = (\frac{2}{3})^6 \cdot (\frac{1}{3})^4$. There are $_{10}C_6 = 210$ different ways of making 6 free throws out of 10, so $P(\text{Exactly 6 free throws}) = 210 \cdot (\frac{2}{3})^6 \cdot (\frac{1}{3})^4 = 0.23$ (rounded to the nearest hundredth).

25. If we treat this as 5 people to be seated in 5 chairs (since the couples cannot be separated), there are $5! = 120$ different ways of being seated. Each couple, though, can be alternated, and there are $2^5 = 32$ ways of doing this. $120 \cdot 32 = 3840$ possible combinations.

1. (a) S = {Monday, Tuesday, Wednesday, Thursday, Friday, Saturday, Sunday}

    (b) E = {Tuesday, Thursday}

    (c) P(Day starting with T) = $\frac{2}{7}$.

2. $\frac{4}{5} \cdot 1000 = 800$; $\frac{1}{8} \cdot 1000 = 125$. There must be 75 jelly beans that are neither blue nor red.

3. (a) P(Vote for Kennedy) = $\frac{34,226,731}{68,334,888}$, or about 0.501.

    (b) P(Vote for Nixon) = $\frac{34,108,157}{68,334,888}$, or about 0.499.

    (c) Odds against Nixon were $\frac{1 - 0.4991324}{0.4991324}$, or 1.0034764 to 1.

4. (a) P(Black) = $\frac{5}{12}$.   (b) P(Black or white) = $\frac{5}{12} + \frac{4}{12} = \frac{3}{4}$.

    (c) P(Neither red nor white) = P(Black) = $\frac{5}{12}$.

    (d) P(Red not drawn) = 1 − P(Red) = $1 - \frac{3}{12} = \frac{3}{4}$.

    (e) Since only one ball is drawn, P(Black and white) = 0.

    (f) P(Black or white or red) = 1.

5. (a) P(Club) = $\frac{1}{4}$.

    (b) P(Spade and 5) = $\frac{1}{52}$.

    (c) P(Heart or face card) = $\frac{1}{4} + \frac{12}{52} - \frac{1}{4} \cdot \frac{12}{52} = \frac{11}{26}$.

    (d) P(No jack) = 1 − P(Jack) = $1 - \frac{1}{13} = \frac{12}{13}$.

6. (a) $\frac{4}{9} \cdot \frac{4}{9} \cdot \frac{4}{9} = \frac{64}{729}$.   (b) $\frac{4}{9} \cdot \frac{3}{8} \cdot \frac{2}{7} = \frac{24}{504} = \frac{1}{21}$

7. $\frac{1}{5} \cdot \frac{2}{5} + \frac{4}{5} \cdot \frac{1}{5} = \frac{6}{25}$.

8. $\frac{1}{4} \cdot \frac{0}{2} + \frac{1}{4} \cdot \frac{1}{4} + \frac{1}{4} \cdot \frac{1}{4} + \frac{1}{4} \cdot \frac{1}{5} = \frac{7}{40}$.

9. P(Black) = $\frac{1}{3} \cdot \frac{3}{5} \cdot \frac{1}{3} + \frac{1}{3} \cdot \frac{2}{5} \cdot 0 + \frac{2}{3} \cdot \frac{2}{5} \cdot \frac{1}{3} + \frac{2}{3} \cdot \frac{3}{5} \cdot 0 = \frac{3}{45} + 0 + \frac{4}{45} + 0 = \frac{7}{45}$.

10. P(Jack) = $\frac{1}{13}$. Odds in favor of a jack are $\frac{\frac{1}{13}}{1 - \frac{1}{13}} = 1:12$.

11. P(Prime number) = $\frac{1}{2}$. Odds against are 1:1.

12. $\frac{P(Event)}{1 - P(Event)} = \frac{3}{5}$. Solving, P(Event) = $\frac{3}{8}$.

13. E = $7.20(\frac{1}{36}) + 3.60(\frac{1}{36}) = \$0.30$.

14. Fair price = E = $1000(\frac{1}{3000}) = \$0.33$ (rounded to the nearest cent).

15. $9 \cdot 10 \cdot 10 \cdot 1 = 900$ different numbers.

16. $_{10}C_3 = 120$ different ways.

17. $_{10}P_4 = 5040$ different ways.

18. P(Both blue) = $\frac{_2C_2}{_5C_2} = \frac{1}{10}$.

19. (a) $_5P_3 = 60$ different ways.

   (b)   P(Deadbeat 1st and Bandy 2nd) $= \frac{1}{_5P_2} = \frac{1}{20}$.

   (c)   P(Deadbeat, Egglegs, Cash) $= \frac{1}{60}$.

20. There are 15 different ways that Ruby can roll a higher number than Al; P(Ruby > Al) $= \frac{15}{36}$.

21. There are $_5C_3 = 10$ ways of selecting 3 questions out of 5. 6 of these would include question 1, so $\frac{4}{10} = \frac{2}{5}$ will exclude it.

22. P(All green) $= (0.3)^3 = 0.027$.

23. P(2nd stage success) $= \frac{7}{8}$; P(3rd stage success) $= \frac{9}{10}$. P(Success given stage 1) $= \frac{7}{8} \cdot \frac{9}{10} = \frac{63}{80}$.

24. (a)   Randomly select numbers 1-6 (discard numbers 0, 7-9).

   (b)   Pick 3 random two-digit numbers (discard numbers other than 01-12).

   (c)   Let random numbers 0-2 represent red; 3-5 represent white; 6-8 represent blue. Discard any 9's.

25. (a)   Divide the figure into 16 equal triangles; A represents 2 of them. P(A) $= \frac{2}{16} = \frac{1}{8}$.

   (b)   P(B) $= \frac{1}{4}$ (b)   P(C) $= \frac{1}{16}$

26. P(Between N and O) $= \frac{8}{20} = \frac{2}{5}$.

CHAPTER 9 - STATISTICS: AN INTRODUCTION

Problem Set 9-1

1.

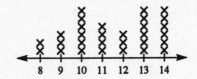

Glasses of Lemonade Sold

Friday
Thursday
Wednesday
Tuesday
Monday

🥤 represents 10 glasses

2. (a) 225 million   (b) 375 million

   (c) 675 million − 125 million = 550 million

3.   Student Ages at Washington School

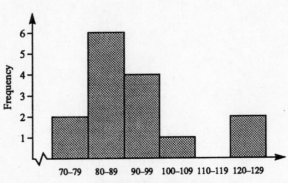

4. (a) 72, 74, 81, 81, 82, 85, 87, 88, 92, 94, 97, 98, 103, 123, 125

   (b) 72 pounds   (c) 125 pounds

5.

![Histogram of Weights of Students in East Junior High Algebra I Class, with frequency on the vertical axis and weight ranges 70-79, 80-89, 90-99, 100-109, 110-119, 120-129 on the horizontal axis. Bars: 70-79 = 2, 80-89 = 6, 90-99 = 4, 100-109 = 1, 110-119 = 0, 120-129 = 2]

Weights of Students in East Junior
High Algebra I Class

6. Data may vary.

   (a) A line plot will have two columns of x's; one for Heads and one for Tails.

   (b) A histogram will have two columns; one for Heads and one for Tails. The vertical axis will be partitioned to show numbers of each.

7. (a) Novenber, with approximately 30 cm of rain.

   (b) 15 (October) + 25 (December) + 10 (January) = 50 cm.

8. (a)   Ages of HKM Employees

   ```
   6 | 332
   5 | 8224
   4 | 8561511
   3 | 474224              3 | 4 represents
   2 | 14333617301365396      34 years old
   1 | 898
   ```

(b)   There are seven in their 40's; 4 in their 50's.

(c)   The total of teens and 20's is 20 employees.

(d)   There are 7 age 50 or more; that is $\frac{7}{40} = 0.175 = 17.5\%$ of the total.

9.   (a)   The Mississippi is approximately 3800 km long.

     (b)   The Columbia is approximately 1900 km long.

10.

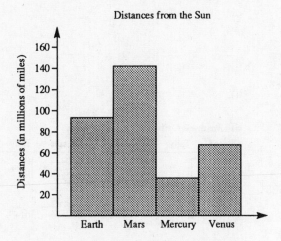

Distances from the Sun

11.

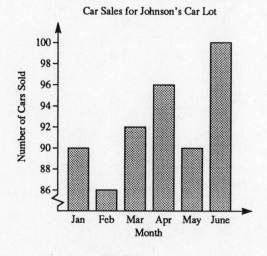

Car Sales for Johnson's Car Lot

12.

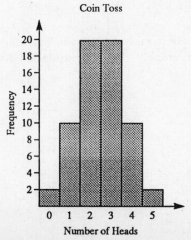

Coin Toss

13. (a)

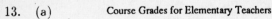

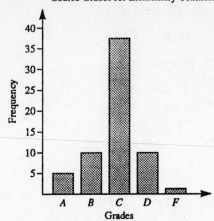

(b)

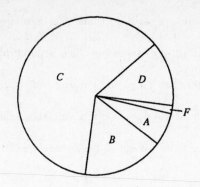

14. (a) <u>Fall</u> <u>Textbook</u> <u>Costs</u>

```
1 | 6
2 | 3 3
3 | 0 3 5 7 7 9 9
4 | 0 1 2 2 5 8 9
5 | 0 0 1 3 8
6 | 0 2 2            2 | 3 represents $23
```

(c) and (d) are shown on the same graph:

(b)

Fall Textbook Costs

Classes	Tally	Frequency	Classes	Tally	Frequency
$15–19	I	1	$40–44	IIII	4
$20–24	II	2	$45–49	III	3
$25–29		0	$50–54	IIII	4
$30–34	II	2	$55–59	I	1
$35–39	LHT	5	$60–64	III	3
					‾‾
					25

Text Costs

[Graph: Number of Students vs. Amount Paid for Books, showing bars and line graph for classes 15-19, 20-24, 25-29, 30-34, 35-39, 40-44, 45-49, 50-54, 55-59, 60-64]

15. The line graph is more helpful, since we can approximate the point midway between 8:00 and 12:00 noon and then draw a vertical line upward until it hits the line graph. An approximation for the 10:00 temperature can then be obtained from the vertical axis.

16. (a)   A line graph is more appropriate. We have continuous data changing over time.

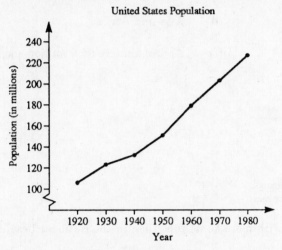

    (b)   The data falls into distinct categories and is not continuous. Use a bar graph.

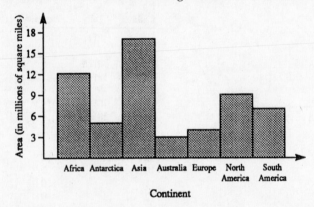

17. (a)   The chicken. It's graph has the shortest bar of the graph.

    (b)   10 miles per hour, where the length of the chicken's bar intersects 10 on the horizontal axis.

    (c)   The cheetah. Twice the rabbit's 35 mph is 70 mph, where the cheetah's bar ends.

    (d)   Yes. The lion's speed is 50 mph; the zebra's 40 mph.

18 (a)   Women.   (b)   Approximately two years.

    (c)   Approximately 7.5 years.

19. Answers may vary, but a circle graph would be more appropriate when it is desired to emphasize proportions.

20. Answers may vary, but a line graph is preferable when data is continuous.

21. Answers may vary, but a stem-and-leaf plot is more informative when exact data is needed.

22. (a)   Approximately 70% of $12,000 = $8400.   (b)   Approximately 70% of $20,000 = $14,000.

    (c)   Approximately 35% of $20,000 = $7000.   (d)   Between two and three years.

23. (a)   Asia.   (b)   Africa.

     (c)   It is about two-thirds as large.   (d)   Asia and Africa.

     (e)   About 5:16.   (f)   Approximately 58.6 million square miles.

24.

Home Run Leaders
1976–90

National League		American League
	2	2
9877761	3	22699
9887000	4	00123569
2	5	1

1 | 3 | represents | 3 | 2 represents
31 home runs   32 home runs

There is a pattern of American League leaders with more home runs than in the National League.

25. (a)   (b)

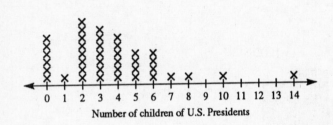

Number of children of U.S. Presidents

No. of Children	Tally	Frequency
0	ЖHТ I	6
1	I	1
2	ЖHТ III	8
3	ЖHТ II	7
4	ЖHТ I	6
5	IIII	4
6	IIII	4
7	I	1
8	I	1
9		0
10	I	1
11		0
12		0
13		0
14	I	1
		40

     (c)   The most frequent number of children is two.

Problem Set 9-2

1.   (a)   Ordering the data, we have 2, 5, 5, 7, 8, 8, 8, 10.

          (i)   Mean $= \frac{2 + 5 + 5 + 7 + 8 + 8 + 8 + 10}{8} = \frac{53}{8} = 6.625$.

          (ii)   Median: The midpoint is between 7 and 8, or $\frac{7 + 8}{2} = 7.5$.

          (iii) Mode: 8 occurs most frequently, so the mode $= 8$.

     (b)   Ordering the data, we have 10, 11, 12, 12, 12, 14, 14, 16, 20.

          (i)   Mean $= \frac{10 + 11 + 12 + 12 + 12 + 14 + 14 + 16 + 20}{9} = \frac{121}{9} = 13.\overline{4}$.

          (ii)   Median: The midpoint is at 12, so the median $= 12$.

          (iii) Mode: 12 occurs most frequently, so the mode $= 12$.

1.   (c)   Ordering the data, we have 12, 17, 18, 18, 22, 22, 30.

        (i)   Mean $= \frac{12 + 17 + 18 + 18 + 22 + 22 + 30}{7} = \frac{139}{7} \doteq 19.9$.

        (ii)   Median: The midpoint is at 18, so the median $= 18$.

        (iii)   Mode: 18 and 22 occur most frequently, so we have dual modes of 18 and 22.

   (d)   Ordering the data, we have 63, 75, 80, 80, 80, 80, 82, 90, 92, 92.

        (i)   Mean $= \frac{63 + 75 + 80 + 80 + 80 + 80 + 90 + 92 + 92}{10} = \frac{814}{10} = 81.4$.

        (ii)   Median: The midpoint is between 80 and 80, or the median $= 80$.

        (iii)   Mode: 80 occurs most frequently, so the mode $= 80$.

   (e)   (i)   Mean $= \frac{5 + 5 + 5 + 5 + 5 + 10}{6} = \frac{35}{6} = 5.8\overline{3}$.

        (ii)   Median: The midpoint is between 5 and 5, or the median $= 5$.

        (iii)   Mode: 5 occurs most frequently, so the mode $= 5$.

2.   (a)   (i)   Mean: Since all values are 80, the mean $= 80$.

        (ii)   Median: Since all values are 80, the median $= 80$.

        (iii)   Mode: Since all values are 80, the mode $= 80$.

   (b)   Answers may vary, but one set would be 70, 80, 80, 80, 90.

3. Since mean $= \frac{\text{sum of test scores}}{\text{number of test scores}}$, then $75 = \frac{\text{sum}}{20}$ or sum $= 20 \cdot 75 = 1500$.

4. If 50 people average $\frac{7500}{50} = 150$ pounds, the tram will be at capacity.

5. If the mean of 28 scores is 80, then the sum of the scores is $28 \cdot 80 = 2240$. Adding 60 and 50, the new sum is 2350. The new mean is thus $\frac{2350}{28 + 2} = 78.\overline{3}$.

6.   (a)   Mean $= \frac{40 + 36 + 8 + 6 + 2}{5} = \frac{92}{5} = 18.4$ years.

   (b)   Five years from now, the family's ages will be 45, 36, 13, 11, and 7.
       Mean $= \frac{45 + 36 + 13 + 11 + 7}{5} = \frac{117}{5} = 23.4$ years.

   (c)   Note that the mean five years from now is 5 more than the mean now. The mean ten years from now will thus be $18.4 + 10 = 28.4$.

   (d)   The mean in (b) is equal to the mean in (a) plus 5 years. The mean in (c) is equal to the mean in (a) plus 10 years, or the mean in (b) plus 5 years.

7. Select the mode; it is the size which sold most frequently.

8. The number of points for each course is the product of the number of credits and the point value of each, so Jon will have 15 points for math, 12 for english, 10 for physics, 3 for German, and 4 for handball; a total of 44 points. His GPA will thus be $\frac{44 \; points}{17 \; credits} = 2.59$.

9. Total lineman weight is $7 \cdot 230 = 1610$ pounds; total backfield weight is $4 \cdot 190 = 760$ pounds. Total player weight is $1610 + 760 = 2370$ pounds. The mean weight is thus $\frac{2370}{11} \doteq 215.5$ pounds per player.

10. 99 people with mean of $12,000 is $1,188,000 total income. Increased by $200,000, the new total income is $1,388,000. Mean income is now $\frac{1388000}{100} = \$13,880$. There has been an increase of $1880.

11. (a)   The total of salaries, in thousands of dollars, is:
$18 \cdot 2 + 22 \cdot 4 + 26 \cdot 4 + 35 \cdot 3 + 38 \cdot 12 + 44 \cdot 8 + 50 \cdot 4 + 80 \cdot 2 + 150$
$= 36 + 88 + 104 + 105 + 456 + 352 + 200 + 160 + 150 = 1651$, or $1,651,000.
There are a total of 40 players, so the mean annual salary is $\frac{1651000}{40} = \$41,275$.

   (b)   The median is between the 20th and 21st (in order, from smallest to largest) salaries. Since salaries between the 13th and 25th are all at $38,000, the median is $38,000.

   (c)   The largest number of salaries is 12 at $38,000, so the mode is $38,000.

12. (a)   Balance beam - Olga, with a score of 9.575. Uneven bars - Lisa, with a score of 9.85. Floor exercise - Lisa, with a score of 9.925.

   (b)   Lisa - 29.20.

13. The total miles of the trip were $43,390 - 42,800 = 590$ miles. The total amount of gasoline used was $12 + 18 = 30$ gallons. Her fuel mileage was thus $\frac{590 \ miles}{30 \ gallons} = 19\frac{2}{3}$ miles per gallon.

14. $\frac{45 \ miles}{1\frac{1}{2} \ hours} = 30$ miles per hour.

15. Mean hours per day was $\dfrac{5\frac{1}{2} + 3\frac{1}{2} + 5\frac{1}{4} + 6\frac{3}{4} + 8}{5} = \frac{29}{5} = 5\frac{4}{5}$ hours.

16. The oldest person is $24 + 34 = 58$ years old.

17. (a)   Set A: mean is $\frac{24}{4} = 6$; range is $9 - 3 = 6$.

   (b)   Set B: all elements are 11, so mean, median, and mode are all 11.
         Set C: mean $= \frac{77}{7} = 11$; median and mode are each 11.

   (c)   Set C: mean $= \frac{12}{4} = 3$; median $= \frac{2 + 4}{2} = 3$; there is no mode, since no value occurs more than once.

18. Ordering, Carl's scores are 85, 90, 90, 95.

   (a)   Mean $= \frac{360}{4} = 90$; median $= 90$, mode $= 90$.

   (b)   Either the median or the mode; either would remain unchanged by the lower score.

   (c)   The mean.

19. (a)   Answers may vary; one set would be 10, 30, 70, and 90.

   (b)   The smaller numbers are the same amount below the mean as the larger numbers are above it. That is, their mean is also 50.

   (c)   The mean of 10, 30, 70, and 90 is 50. See (b) above.

20. $\bar{x} = \frac{1281}{7} = 183$ cm. The summation of $(x - \bar{x})^2 = 64 + 1 + 49 + 9 + 81 + 121 + 49 = 374$.
Variance is thus $\frac{374}{7} \doteq 53.43$ and $s = \sqrt{53.43} \doteq 7.31$ cm.

21. The mean is increased by the value of the number added; all values have been shifted the same amount. The standard deviation is unchanged; the spread between the numbers has remained constant.

22. (a)   s = 0 (there are no deviations from the mean).

     (b)   Yes. Otherwise, there would be some differences from the mean and the standard deviation would therefore not be zero.

23. (a) $\bar{x} = \dfrac{96+71+43+77+75+76+61+83+71+58+97+76+74+91+74+71+77+83+87+93+79}{21} \doteq 76.8.$

     (b)   Ordering, the scores are:
           43, 58, 61, 71, 71, 71, 74, 74, 75, 76, 76, 77, 77, 79, 83, 83, 87, 91, 93, 96, 97.
           The median is the 11th score, or 76.

     (c)   The mode is 71, or the most frequent score.

     (d)

x	x − $\bar{x}$	$(x - \bar{x})^2$
96	19.2	368.64
71	⁻5.8	33.64
43	⁻33.8	1142.44
77	0.2	0.04
75	⁻1.8	3.24
76	⁻0.8	0.64
61	⁻15.8	249.64
83	6.2	38.44
71	⁻5.8	33.64
58	⁻18.8	353.44
97	20.2	408.04
76	⁻0.8	0.64
74	⁻2.8	7.84
91	14.2	201.64
74	⁻2.8	7.84
71	⁻5.8	33.64
77	0.2	0.04
83	6.2	38.44
87	10.2	104.04
93	16.2	262.44
79	2.2	4.84
		3293.24

$v = \dfrac{3293.24}{21} \doteq 156.8$

     (e) $s = \sqrt{156.8} \doteq 12.5$

24. If S is the score needed on the fifth exam, then $\dfrac{84 + 95 + 86 + 94 + S}{5} = 90$, or $394 + S = 450$.
     Solving, S = 91.

25. If we let Ginny's three scores be represented by F (first), S (second), and T (third), then:
           S = 90 (the median);

           $\dfrac{F + S + T}{3} = 92$ (the mean), or F + S + T = 376;

           F − T = 6 (the range).
     Solving as a system of equations, we find: F = 96, S = 90, and T = 90.

26. If the mean of 5 numbers is 6, then the sum of the numbers = 5·6 = 30. Removing a number, n, then
     means that $\dfrac{30 - n}{4} = 7$, or n = 2.

27. No. To find the average speed we divide the distance traveled by the time it takes to drive it. The first part of the trip took $\frac{5 \; miles}{30 \; mph} = \frac{1}{6}$ hours. The second part of the trip took $\frac{5 \; miles}{50 \; mph} = \frac{1}{10}$ hours. To find the average speed we then compute $\frac{5 \text{ miles} + 5 \text{ miles}}{\frac{1}{6} \text{ hour} + \frac{1}{10} \text{ hour}} = 37.5$ mph.

28.

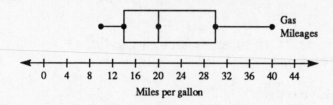

29. (a) The median in a box plot is the middle line through the box. The median of Theater A is thus 25; that of Theater B is 50.

(b) The greatest range is that of Theater B: $80 - 15 = \$65$.

(c) The highest price of either is the upper value at Theater B, $80.

(d) Answers may vary. Some observations are that there is significantly more variation and generally higher prices at Theater B.

30. The lower extreme is 40; the upper extreme is 95.
The lower quartile is 70; the upper quartile is 90.
The median is 80.
There is an outlier at 20.

31. (a) Minneapolis: Lower extreme = 366   Los Angeles: Lower extreme = 516
Lower quartile = 416   Lower quartile = 571
Median $= \frac{447 + 561}{2} = 504$ Median $= \frac{620 + 625}{2} = 622.5$
Upper quartile = 668   Upper quartile = 735
Upper extreme = 950   Upper extreme = 858

The box plot is shown below:

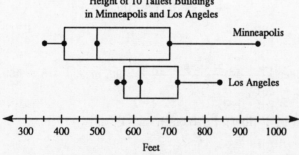

Height of 10 Tallest Buildings
in Minneapolis and Los Angeles

(b) In Minneapolis, the IQR $= 668 - 416 = 252$. There are no values more than $1.5 \cdot$IQR $= 378$ feet above the upper quartile or more than 378 feet below the lower quartile, so there are no outliers. In Los Angeles there are no values more than $1.5 \cdot$IQR $= 1.5(735 - 571) = 246$ feet above the upper quartile or more than 246 feet below the lower quartile, so there are no outliers.

32. (a) (i)   The mean increases by $1000.   (ii)   The median increases by $1000.

(iii) The extremes increase by $1000.   (iv)   The quartiles increase by $1000.

(v)   The standard deviation is unchanged.

32. (b)   (i)   The mean increases by 5%.   (ii)   The standard deviation increases by 5%.

33. (a)   (i)   Mean $= \dfrac{1 + 3 + 5 + 7 + 9}{5} = 5$. Median is the middle value, or 5.

     (ii) $199 = 1 + (n - 1)2$, so $n = 100$; i.e., there are 100 terms in the sequence.
            The sum of 100 terms of this sequence is $\frac{100}{2}(1 + 199) = 10{,}000$.
            The 50th term is $1 + (50 - 1)2 = 99$.

            Thus the mean $= \dfrac{10{,}000}{100} = 100$; the median is between term 50 and 51, or $\dfrac{99 + 101}{2} = 100$.

     (iii) $607 = 7 + (n - 1)3$, so $n = 201$ and there are 201 terms in the sequence.
            The sum of 201 terms of this sequence is $\frac{201}{2}(7 + 607) = 61{,}707$.
            The 101st term is $7 + (101 - 1)3 = 307$.

            Thus the mean $= \dfrac{61{,}707}{201} = 307$; the median is the 101st term, or 307.

     (b)   The mean and median of an arithmetic sequence are the same.

34. $v = \dfrac{(x_1 - \bar{x})^2 + (x_2 - \bar{x})^2 + \cdots + (x_n - \bar{x})^2}{n}$

     $= \dfrac{(x_1^2 - 2\bar{x}x_1 + \bar{x}^2) + (x_2^2 - 2\bar{x}x_2 + \bar{x}^2) + \cdots + (x_n^2 - 2\bar{x}x_n + \bar{x}^2)}{n}$

     $= \dfrac{(x_1^2 + x_2^2 + \cdots + x_n^2) - 2\bar{x}(x_1 + x_2 + \cdots + x_n) + n\bar{x}^2}{n}$

     $= \dfrac{x_1^2 + x_2^2 + \cdots + x_n^2}{n} - \dfrac{2\bar{x}(x_1 + x_2 + \cdots + x_n)}{n} + \dfrac{n\bar{x}^2}{n}$

     $= \dfrac{x_1^2 + x_2^2 + \cdots + x_n^2}{n} - 2\bar{x}^2 + \bar{x}^2 = \dfrac{x_1^2 + x_2^2 + \cdots + x_n^2}{n} - \bar{x}^2$.

35. (a)   Mount Everest is the highest mountain, at approximately 8500 meters.

     (b)   Mounts Aconcagus, Everest, and McKinley.

36. (a)

History Test Scores

5	5
6	48
7	2334679
8	0255567889
9	00346

7 | 2 represents
a score of 72

(b)

History Test Scores

Classes	Tallies	Frequency
55–59	I	1
60–64	I	1
65–69	I	1
70–74	IIII	4
75–79	III	3
80–84	II	2
85–89	IIII III	8
90–94	IIII	4
95–99	I	1

(c)

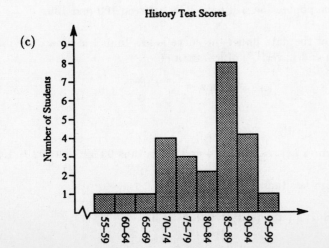

History Test Scores

(d)

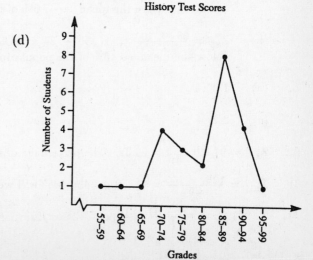

History Test Scores

36. (e) Eight of the 25 scores are in the 85-89 range. This would be represented by $\frac{8}{25}(360) \doteq 115°$.

Problem Set 9-3

1. (a) 85 is one standard deviation below the mean; 115 is one standard deviation above the mean. That is: $Z_{85} = \frac{85 - 100}{15} = {}^-1$, and $Z_{115} = \frac{115 - 100}{15} = 1$.
Since $34 + 34 = 68\%$ of the area under the curve lies within ± 1 standard deviation from the mean, 68% of the students will have IQ's between 85 and 115. 68% of 1500 is 1020 students in that range.

   (b) 70 is two standard deviations below the mean; 130 is two standard deviations above the mean. 95% of the area under the curve lies within ± 2 standard deviations from the mean, and 95% of 1500 = 1425 students with IQ's between 70 and 130.

   (c) 145 is three standard deviations above the mean; only 0.1% of the area under the curve is more than three standard deviations from the mean. 0.01% of 1500 = 1.5, so one or two students will have an IQ of more than 145.

2. $Z_{16} = \frac{16 - 16.1}{0.05} = {}^-2$, so 16 ounces is 2 standard deviations below the mean. $13.5 + 34 + 50 = 97.5\%$ of the area under the curve is more than 2 standard deviations below the mean; i.e., 97.5% of the boxes will actually contain more than 16 ounces.

3. $Z_{4.50} = \frac{4.50 - 5.00}{0.50} = {}^-1$ and $Z_{5.50} = \frac{5.00 - 5.00}{0.50} = 1$.
The amount of data between ± 1 standard deviations is 68%, so there is a 68% chance that a worker picked at random will earn between $4.50 and $5.50 per hour.

4. (a) $Z_{verbal} = \frac{90 - 84}{10} = 0.60$; $Z_{quan} = \frac{133 - 118}{18} = 0.8\bar{3}$; $Z_{reason} = \frac{18 - 14}{4} = 1$.

   (b) (i) She performed relatively the highest on the logical reasoning test.

   (ii) She performed relatively the lowest on the verbal exam.

   (iii) Mean $= \frac{0.60 + 0.8\bar{3} + 1}{3} \doteq 0.8\bar{1}$.

5. $Z_{2\ min} = \frac{2 - 4}{2} = {}^-1$. Only $50 - 34 = 16\%$ of the data under the curve is less than 2 standard deviations below the mean, so 16% of the calls will last less than 2 minutes.

6. The mean and median are the same in a normal distribution.

7. (a) $Z_{130} = \frac{130 - 100}{15} = 2$. $34 + 13.5 = 47.5\%$ of the data under the curve lies within 2 standard deviations above the mean, so 47.5% of the population will have IQ's between 100 and 130.

   (b) $Z_{85} = \frac{85 - 100}{15} = {}^-1$. $50 - 34 = 16\%$ of the data under the curve is less than 1 standard deviation below the mean, so 16% of the population will have IQ's of less than 85.

8. (a) 1.07%   (b) 95.54%

   (c) 2.27%

9. $Z_{1.4} = 91.92$; $Z_{1.5} = 93.32$. The percentage of scores between $Z = 1.4$ and 1.5 is thus $93.32 - 91.92 = 1.4\%$.

10. $Z_{125} = \frac{125 - 105}{20} = 1$. $50 + 34 = 84\%$ will weigh less than 125 ounces.

11. $Z = {}^-1.25 = \frac{53 - 63}{s} = \frac{10}{s}$, or ${}^-1.25s = 10$. Solving, s (standard deviation) $= 8$.

12. Two standard deviations above the mean is a score of $72 + 2 \cdot 9 = 90$. The lowest score for an A is thus 90.

13. 95% of all data under a normal curve is within $\pm$ 2 standard deviations of the mean. The range corresponding to $\pm$ 2 standard deviations is between $65.5 - 2 \cdot 2.5 = 60.5$ inches to $65.5 + 2 \cdot 2.5 = 70.5$ inches.

14. $Z_{23,000} = \frac{23,000 - 28,000}{2500} = {}^-2$. The amount of data less than 2 standard deviations below the mean is 2.5%, and 2.5% of 2000 = 50 tires.

15. $Z_{440} = \frac{440 - 500}{60} = {}^-1$. A z-score of $^-1$ represents the 16th percentile, so $0.16 \cdot 10,000 = 1600$ students rated deficient.

16. (a)

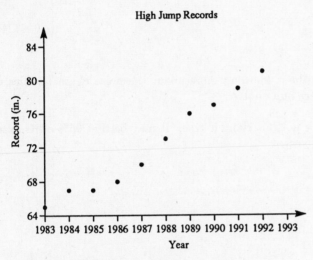

High Jump Records

(b) There is a positive correlation between the data.

17. (a) The trend of the line slopes downward to the right, so there is a negative correlation.

    (b) Approximately 10.   (c) Approximately 22 years old.

18. (a) $\bar{x} = \frac{43 + 91 + 73 + 65 + 56 + 77 + 84 + 91 + 82 + 65 + 98 + 65}{12} \doteq 74.17$.

    (b) Ordering, the scores are 43, 56, 65, 65, 65, 73, 77, 82, 84, 91, 91, 98.
Median $= \frac{73 + 77}{2} = 75$.

    (c) The mode is 65.

    (d) The sum of the $(x - \bar{x})^2$ terms is 2855.68. The variance is $\frac{2855.68}{12} \doteq 237.97$.

    (e) $s = \sqrt{237.97} \doteq 15.43$.

19. If the mean is 27, then the total of the scores is $36 \cdot 27 = 972$. Adding the two additional scores, the new total is 1054. Mean $= \frac{1054}{38} \doteq 27.74$.

20. If the mean of 10 papers is 70 there are $10 \cdot 70 = 700$ points. Of 20 papers, there are 1600 points. The combined mean $= \frac{2300}{30} = 76.\bar{6}$.

21.   Men's Olympic
       100 meter Run Times
            1896-1964

```
1 0 | 0 2 3 3 3 4
  * | 5 6 8 8 8 8
1 1 | 0 0
  * |                    1 0 | 0  represents 10.0 seconds
12  | 0
```

Problem Set 9-4

1.   Answers may vary.

   (a)   The claim cannot be substantiated without knowing more about the noise characteristics of the car
          and glider in question. Many gliders are quite noisy.

   (b)   There is no way of knowing whether or not this claim is true. It may be that 95% of its cycles sold in
          the United States were sold in the last year.

   (c)   10% more than 10% is not very much.

   (d)   Fresher than what?

   (e)   "Up to" can cover a multitude of sins.

   (f)   Brighter than what?

   (g)   How many dentists responded? Who paid them?

   (h)   This is an example of carrying an argument to a ridiculous extreme.

   (i)   Is there another airline flying to the city?

2.   Answers may vary. One possibility is that people might think the temperature is always 25°. Another is
      that, unfamiliar with the metric system, people would think it to be always cold (25° C = 77° F).

3.   She could have taken a different number of quizzes during the first part of the quarter than in the second
      part.

4.   When the radius of a circle is doubled, the area is quadrupled. This is misleading since the population has
      only doubled.

5.   The horizontal axis does not have uniformly-sized intervals, and neither the horizontal axis nor the graph are
      labeled.

6.   There were more scores above the mean than below, but the mean was affected more by low scores.

7.   No. It could very well be that most of the pickups sold in the past 10 years were actually sold during the
      last two years. In such a case most of the pickups have been on the road for only two years, and therefore
      the given information would not imply that the average life of a pickup is around ten years.

8.   Answers may vary, but General Cooster was assuming that there were no deep holes in the river where he
      was crossing.

9.   The three-dimensional drawing distorts the graph. The result of doubling the radius and the height of the can are to increase the volume by a factor of 8.

10. There are no labels by which to compare actual sales.

11. One would need more information; e.g., is the graph in percentage or actual numbers?

12. (a)   False. Prices vary by only $30.

     (b)   False. The bar has four times the area but the price is only 3.5% higher.

     (c)   True.

13. (a)   This bar graph would have perhaps 20 accidents as the baseline. Then 38 in 1992 would appear to be almost double the 24 of 1988, when in fact it is only 58% higher.

     (b)   This bar graph would have 0 accidents as its baseline.

14. Answers may vary, but one such would be 5, 5, 5, 5, 5, 5, 100, 100. The mean would be 28.75 and the median 5.

15. It is not clear what is meant by "margin" and it is not clear whether the dollar amounts are for units or some other quantity (such as thousands of dollars).

Chapter 9 Test

1.   If the average is 2.41 children, then the mean is probably being used. If the average is 2.5, then the mean *or* the median might have been used.

2.   10 part-timers with an average salary of $50 means a total part-time payroll of $500. That leaves $3450 for full-timers; $\frac{3450}{150} = 23$ full-time employees.

3.   (a)   Mean $= \frac{10 + 50 + 30 + 40 + 10 + 60 + 10}{7} = 30$. Ordering, we have 10, 10, 10, 30, 40, 50, 60.
           The median is 30. The mode is 10.

     (b)   Mean $= \frac{5 + 8 + 6 + 3 + 5 + 4 + 3 + 6 + 1 + 9}{10} = 5$. Ordering, we have 1, 3, 3, 4, 5, 5, 6, 6, 8, 9.
           The median is 5. The modes are 3, 5, and 6.

4.   (a)   The range is $60 - 10 = 50$. The sum of the $(x - \bar{x})^2$ terms is 2600; the variance is $\frac{2600}{7} \doteq 371.4$.
           The standard deviation is $\sqrt{371.4} \doteq 19.3$.

     (b)   The range is $9 - 1 = 8$. The sum of the $(x - \bar{x})^2$ terms is 52; the variance is $\frac{52}{10} = 5.2$.
           The standard deviation is $\sqrt{5.2} \doteq 2.28$.

5.   (a)   Miss Rider's Class   (b)   Miss Rider's Class
                           Masses in Kilograms   Masses in Kilograms

3	99	
4	001122223345678999	4 | 0 represents
		40 kg

5.   (c)

Miss Rider's Class
Masses in Kilograms

Mass	Tally	Frequency
39	II	2
40	II	2
41	II	2
42	IIII	4
43	II	2
44	I	1
45	I	1
46	I	1
47	I	1
48	I	1
49	III	3
		20

(d)

Miss Rider's Class
Masses in Kilograms

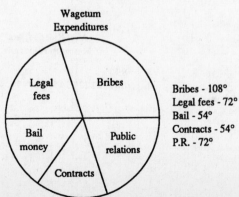

6.   (a)

Test Grades

Classes	Tally	Frequency
61–70	IIII I	6
71–80	IIII IIII I	11
81–90	IIII II	7
91–100	IIII I	6
		30

(b) and (c) are shown on the same graph below.

Grade Distribution

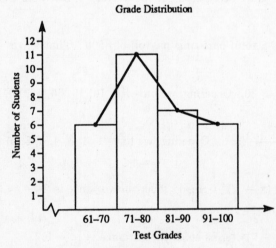

7.

Wagetum
Expenditures

Bribes - 108°
Legal fees - 72°
Bail - 54°
Contracts - 54°
P.R. - 72°

8.   The width of the bars is not uniform and the graph has no title.

9.   The total salary is $24 \cdot 9000 = \$216{,}000$. An additional \$80,000 salary makes the total \$296,000. The new mean is $\frac{296{,}000}{25} = \$11{,}840$. The mean was increased by \$2840.

10.

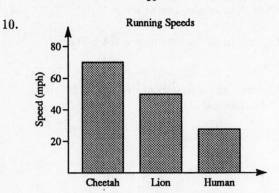

11. (a)

Life Expectancy
for Males and Females

Females		Males
	67	1446
	68	28
	69	156
	70	0049
	71	0223458
	72	
	73	
7	74	
9310	75	
86	76	
88532	77	
54332211	78	
	79	

7 |74| represents |67| 1 represents
   74.7 years old   67.1 years old

(b)

Life Expectancies

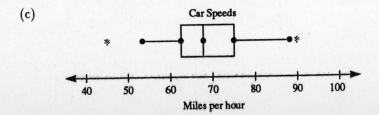

12. Larry's GPA is $\dfrac{4\cdot 4 + 4\cdot 4 + 3\cdot 3 + 3\cdot 2 + 1\cdot 2}{4 + 4 + 3 + 3 + 1} = 3.2\overline{6}$. Moe's is $\dfrac{4\cdot 2 + 4\cdot 2 + 3\cdot 3 + 3\cdot 4 + 1\cdot 4}{4 + 4 + 3 + 3 + 1} = 2.7\overline{3}$.
     Larry is correct.

13. (a)   Ordering, the lengths are 160, 180, 330, 350, 360, 380, 450, 460, 480. The median is 360 yards.

    (b)   There is no mode.

    (c)   The mean is $\dfrac{160 + 180 + 330 + 350 + 360 + 380 + 450 + 460 + 480}{9} = 350$ yards.

    (d)   The sum of the $(x - \bar{x})^2$ terms is 105,600. The standard deviation is $\sqrt{\dfrac{105{,}600}{9}} \doteq 108.2$.

14. (a)   Ordering, the speeds are:
          45, 54, 56, 58, 58, 60, 62, 64, 64, 64, 65, 65, 65, 66, 67, 67, 67, 67, 68, 68, 69, 72, 74, 74, 75, 75, 82,
          86, 88, 90. The median is 67.

    (b)   The upper quartile is 74; the lower is 64.

    (c)

Car Speeds

14. (d)   By definition, 50% of the scores are in the interquartile range.

     (e) $\frac{9}{30} = 30\%$ of the drivers received tickets.

     (f)   No. There are fewer speeds close to 67 in the 3rd quartile than in the 2nd quartile.

15. (a) $Z_{68} = \frac{68 - 64}{2} = 2$. 2.5% of the data is more than 2 standard deviations above the mean; 2.5% of 1000 = 25 girls over 68 inches tall.

     (b) $Z_{60} = \frac{60 - 64}{2} = ^-2$; 47.5% of the data is between the mean and 2 standard deviations below the mean. 47.5% of 1000 = 475 girls between 60 and 64 inches tall.

     (c) $Z_{66} = \frac{66 - 64}{2} = 1$. $50 - 34 = 16\%$ of the girls are over 66 inchs tall.

16. $Z_{750} = \frac{750 - 600}{75} = 2$. 47.5% scored between 600 and 750, or 475 students.

17. $Z_{725} = \frac{725 - 600}{75} = 1.\bar{6}$.

18. Answers may vary. With 95% certainty, Company A's products will have a life of between 130 hours and 170 hours; Company B's products will have a life of between 141 and 149 hours. One's chances of knowing how long the product will really last would seem to be better with Company B.

19. (a)   A positive correlation exists.   (b)   Approximately 170 pounds.

     (c)   Approximately 67 inches.   (d)   64 inches.

     (e) $170 - 120 = 50$ pounds.

20. Answers may vary.

     (a)   One way would be to leave the television on, even if no one was watching.

     (b)   They show very popular shows during "ratings sweeps" periods.

21. Answers may vary. Graphs may show area or volume instead of relative size; another is to select a horizontal baseline that will support the point trying to be made.

CHAPTER 10 - INTRODUCTORY GEOMETRY

<u>Problem</u> <u>Set</u> <u>10-1</u>

1.   (a) $\overleftrightarrow{AB}$ (b) $\overline{AB}$

     (c) $\overrightarrow{AB}$ (d) $\overrightarrow{AB}$

     (e) $\overleftrightarrow{AB} \| \overleftrightarrow{CD}$ (f) $\overline{AB}$

     (g) $\overleftrightarrow{AB} \perp \overleftrightarrow{CD}$ (h) $m(\angle ABC) = 30°$

2.   (a)   {C}   (b) $\emptyset$

     (c)   {C}   (d)   {C}

     (e) $\overline{CE}$ (f) $\overrightarrow{AB}$

     (g) $\overrightarrow{BA}$ (h) $\overleftrightarrow{AD}$

3.   No. The symbol is a finite collection of points.

4.   (a) $\emptyset$ (b) $\angle$ A-BD-E

     (c)   {C}   (d)   {A}

     (e)   {A}   (f)   {A}

     (g) $\overleftrightarrow{AD}$ and $\overleftrightarrow{BE}$, $\overleftrightarrow{AC}$ and $\overleftrightarrow{BE}$, ...   (h) $\overleftrightarrow{AD}$ and $\overleftrightarrow{CE}$; $\overleftrightarrow{AC}$ and $\overleftrightarrow{DE}$

     (i)   Plane ABE or CBD

5.   (a)   True   (b)   True

     (c)   False. Three points may define a plane with the fourth not on that plane.

     (d)   False. They may be skew.   (e)   True

     (f)   True

     (g)   False. In fact, no plane contains both, which is what makes them skew.

     (h)   False. Think of the baseboard and a horizontal window sill on the same wall. They are parallel lines both parallel to the ceiling, yet their plane (the wall) is in this case perpendicular to the ceiling.

     (i)   False. Three points may define a plane, but try putting a line through three corners of a table top.

     (j)   True   (k)   True

     (l)   True

6.   See 5.(c), (d), (g), (h), and (i).

7.   20 pairs. Adjacent angles share a common vertex and a common side, and have nonoverlapping interiors.

8.   Answers may vary.

(a)   Edges of a room; vertical and horizontal parts of a window frame.

(b)   Branches in a tree; clock hands at 7:30.

(c)   The top angle of intersection of a guy wire and telephone pole; clock hands at 7:15.

(d)   An open book resting on a lap; intersection at the peak of a rooftop.

(e)   The peak of an army tent; an opened cabinet.

(f)   Any two teeth of a zipper; buttons on a shirt.

(g)   Ends of the legs of a tripod and the camera atop; the tips of any four prongs of a child's jack.

9.   (a)   Yes. l and m cannot intersect since $\alpha \| \beta$, and they cannot be skew since γ contains both.

(b)   No. The sloped sides of any A-frame structure would intersect the ground in two parallel lines, but the sides are not parallel to each other.

(c)   Yes. If the planes were not parallel they would intersect in a line m and at least one of the given lines would intersect m and would then intersect plane α, which contradicts the fact that the given lines are parallel to α.

10.   (a) $110°$ (b) $40°$

(c) $20°$ (d) $130°$

11.   (a)   Approximately $36°$.   (b)   Approximately $120°$.

12.   (a)   (i) $41° 31' 10''$ (ii) $79° 48' 47''$

(b)   (i) $54'$ (ii) $15° 7' 48''$

13.   (a)   Draw a line with 3 points labeled A, B, and C. Then there are four rays determined by the three points: $\overrightarrow{AB}$, $\overrightarrow{BC}$, $\overrightarrow{CB}$, and $\overrightarrow{BA}$ (remember that $\overrightarrow{AB} = \overrightarrow{AC}$, but $\overrightarrow{AB} \neq \overrightarrow{BA}$).

(b)   Draw a line with 4 points labeled A, B, C, and D. Then there are six rays: $\overrightarrow{AB}$, $\overrightarrow{BC}$, $\overrightarrow{CD}$, $\overrightarrow{DC}$, $\overrightarrow{CB}$, and $\overrightarrow{BA}$.

(c)   With 5 colinear points A, B, C, D, and E, there are eight rays: $\overrightarrow{AB}$, $\overrightarrow{BC}$, $\overrightarrow{CD}$, $\overrightarrow{DE}$, $\overrightarrow{ED}$, $\overrightarrow{DC}$, $\overrightarrow{CB}$, $\overrightarrow{BA}$

(d)   There are 4, 6, and 8 rays for 3, 4, and 5 points, respectively. The general term for the number of rays given n points is thus $2(n - 1)$.

14.   (a)   3; if the points are labeled A, B, and C, the lines are $\overleftrightarrow{AB}$, $\overleftrightarrow{AC}$, $\overleftrightarrow{BC}$.

(b)   6; $\overleftrightarrow{AB}$, $\overleftrightarrow{AC}$, $\overleftrightarrow{AD}$, $\overleftrightarrow{BC}$, $\overleftrightarrow{BD}$, $\overleftrightarrow{CD}$.

(c)   10   (d) $1 + 2 + \cdots + (n - 1) = \dfrac{n(n - 1)}{2}$

15. (a)

Number of Intersection Points

		0	1	2	3	4	5
Number of lines	2			Not Possible	Not Possible	Not Possible	Not Possible
	3					Not Possible	Not Possible
	4			Not Possible			
	5			Not Possible	Not Possible		
	6			Not Possible	Not Possible	Not Possible	

(b) The maximum number of intersections is the number of possible pairings of two lines: $\frac{n(n-1)}{2}$, or $_nC_2$.

16. Any three points are always coplanar, with the floor being the plane that the three leg ends determine (though the seat may not be parallel to the floor). Any given four points may be non-coplanar.

17. (a) No. If $\angle$ BDC were a right angle, then both $\overleftrightarrow{BD}$ and $\overleftrightarrow{BC}$ would be perpendicular to $\overleftrightarrow{DC}$ and thus be parallel.

(b) No. Consider some line $\overleftrightarrow{QP}$ with $\overleftrightarrow{QP} \perp \alpha$ and Q on the same side of α as D. Then $\angle$ QPC is a right angle. $\overrightarrow{PD}$ divides $\angle$ QPC into two angles ($\angle$ QPD and $\angle$ DPC) which then must both be less than a right angle.

(c) Yes. Two planes are perpendicular if and only if one plane contains a line perpendicular to the other plane.

18. (a) Yes. Consider the rafters on a roof truss. Each is perpendicular to the peak of the roof (which is in planes containing the rafters), yet neither is perpendicular to the other's side of the roof.

(b) Yes. It could lie in the plane.

(c) Yes. The line will form two right angles with lines in the plane and thus may not "lean" in any direction.

19. (a)

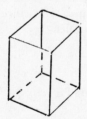

(b)

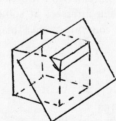

(c)

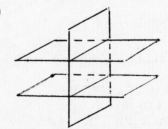

(d)

20. (a)   3   (b)   4

    (c)   4   (d)   6

21. (*i*)   (b) is empty because lines cannot be both skew and coplanar.

    (*ii*)   (d) is empty because lines cannot be both skew and parallel.

    (*iii*)   (e) is empty; lines cannot be skew, coplanar, and parallel.

    (*iv*)   (g) is empty because lines cannot be parallel without being coplanar.

22. $\overrightarrow{AB}$ begins at point A and extends in the direction of point B. $\overrightarrow{BA}$ begins at point B and extends in the direction of point A.

23. (a)   No. Skew lines do not intersect, thus cannot be perpendicular.

    (b)   No. Obtuse angles are greater than 90°, so their sum is greater than $90 + 90 = 180°$.

    (c)   No. As in (b), but "less than 90°" and "less than 180°."

24. There are not. Planes extend indefinitely in two directions and are either parallel or they will eventually intersect.

25. Segments do not extend beyond their endpoints and can be separate without being parallel.

26. The measure of an angle involves only the rotation from one side to the other and has nothing to do with the length of the sides. Lengthening the sides only increases the area needed to make a replica of the drawn angle.

27. By definition, a point has no size; i.e., the is no "smallest" point. No matter how close the two points are, another point can be placed between them, leading to an infinite number of points on a segment.

28. No. The only possibilities are to have all four collinear, exactly three collinear, and no three collinear. These cases give rise to 1, 4, and 6 lines, respectively.

29. Suppose the lines of intersection are not parallel. They cannot be skew since they are both in the third plane. They must then intersect at some point x which must be in both parallel planes. But since parallel planes cannot have a common point, this too is impossible. Thus the lines must be parallel.

30. Answers may vary.

    (a)   TO ANGLE :SIZE   (b)   TO SEGMENT :LENGTH
           FD 100 BK 100   FD :LENGTH
           RT :SIZE FD 100   BK :LENGTH
           BK 100 LT :SIZE   END
           END

    (c)   TO PERPENDICULAR :LENGTH1 :LENGTH2   (d)   TO PARALLEL :LENGTH1 :LENGTH2
           FD :LENGTH1 BK :LENGTH1/2   DRAW
           RT 90 FD :LENGTH2   FD :LENGTH1 PENUP
           BK :LENGTH2 LT 90   RT 90 FD 10 RT 90
           BK :LENGTH1/2   PENDOWN FD :LENGTH2
           END   PENUP HOME
                                                       RT 180 PENDOWN
                                                       END

1. (a)   By definition, polygonal curves are made entirely of line segments. Thus 1, 2, 3, 6, 7, 8, 9, 11, and 12 are polygonal curves.

    (b)   "Simple" adds the restriction that the polygonal curves may not cross themselves, leaving 1, 2, 7, 8, 9, and 11.

    (c)   Closed polygonal curves are those that when traced have the same starting and stopping points. Thus the closed polygonal curves are 1, 2, 3, 6, 7, 8, 9, and 11.

    (d)   Polygons are polygonal curves which are both simple and closed. The polygons are then 1, 2, 7, 8, 9, and 11.

    (e)   If all segments connecting any two points of a polygon are inside the polygon (i.e., the region is not dented inwards anywhere) then the polygon is a convex polygon. The convex polygons are 7 and 8.

    (f)   If part of any segment joining two points of a polygon is outside the polygon (i.e., it is "caved in" somewhere), then it is concave. The concave polygons are 1, 2, 9, and 11.

2. D and O.

3. (a)   The straight path from X crosses the curve six times (an even number). This indicates that X is outside the curve.

    (b)   The straight path from X crosses the curve twice; it is outside the curve.

4. (a)   Yes.

    (b)   No. One of the curves connecting diagonal numbers must cross the curve connecting the 2's.

5. A segment can pass through at most two sides of a triangle. With each side of the quadrilateral passing through two sides of the triangle, there can be eight intersections.

6. (a) and (c) are convex; (b) and (d) are concave.

7. Answers may vary.

    (a)   (b)

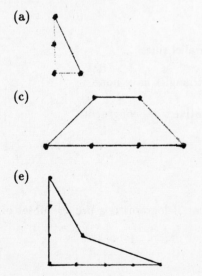

    (c)   (d)

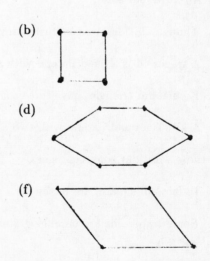

    (e)   (f)

8. (a)   Possible; three sides of different lengths with an obtuse angle.

    (b)   Possible; three sides of different lengths with three acute angles.

    (c)   Possible; three sides of different lengths with a right angle.

    (d)   Impossible; an equilateral triangle has three 60° angles.

    (e)   Impossible. An equilateral triangle has three 60° angles.

    (f)   Possible; two sides of equal length forming an obtuse angle.

    (g)   Possible; two sides of equal length forming an acute angle.

    (h)   Possible; two sides of equal length forming a right angle.

9. From "Looking Back" in Section 10-2 example problem 2, the number of diagonals is $\frac{n(n-3)}{2}$.

    (a) $\frac{10(7)}{2} = 35$ diagonals   (b) $\frac{20(17)}{2} = 170$ diagonals

    (c) $\frac{100(97)}{2} = 4850$ diagonals

10. (a)   Equilateral and isosceles.   (b)   Isosceles.

    (c)   Scalene.

11. (a)   False. Isosceles triangles might have only two congruent sides.

    (b)   True. If three sides are congruent, then "at least two" are.

    (c)   True. A square is a rectangle with all sides congruent.

    (d)   True. Those that are squares are rhombuses.

    (e)   True. All have four sides.

    (f)   False. Though all sides are congruent, angles may not be.

    (g)   True. A trapezoid is a quadrilateral with at least one pair of parallel sides.

    (h)   False. Equilateral triangles have three congruent sides; scalene triangles have none.

    (i)   True. A kite is a quadrilateral with two distinct pairs of consecutive sides congruent.

    (j)   True; those with four congruent sides.

    (k)   False. In fact, all squares are rectangles.

    (l)   False. Some trapezoids are parallelograms, because the set of parallelograms is a proper subset of the set of trapezoids.

    (m)   True. Right triangles may have two congruent sides.

    (n)   False. An isosceles trapezoid that is a square is also a kite.

    (o)   False. (See (n) above)

12. A square may be classified as a square but is still a rectangle, just as she, being a female, is still a human.

13. Angles must also be congruent as is the case only in special rhombuses; i.e., squares.

14. (a) and (b) represent rhombuses and rectangles, respectively.

15. (a)   T, Q, R, H, G, I, F, J   (b)   Y, Z, E

    (c)   W, D, A, Z, U, E   (d)   Q, J, F, G, H

    (e)   Y

16.

Nr. of Toothpicks	Triangles Possible	Types of Triangles
8	3-3-2	Isosceles
9	3-3-3, 4-4-1, 4-3-2	Equilateral, Isosceles, Scalene
10	4-4-2, 3-3-4	Isosceles
11	5-3-3, 4-4-3, 5-5-1, 5-4-2	Isosceles, Scalene
12	4-4-4, 5-5-2, 5-4-3	Equilateral, Isosceles, Scalene

17. Answers may vary.

18. Answers may vary.

    (a)   TO SQUARE :SIDE   (b)   TO RECTANGLE :WIDTH :LENGTH
              REPEAT 4 [FD :SIDE RT 90]   REPEAT 2 [FD :WIDTH RT 90 FD
           END   :LENGTH RT 90]
                                                           END

19. The angles are formed by any two rays. The number of angles is the number of pairs of rays; i.e., the combinations of all rays taken two at a time.

    (a) $_{10}C_2 = \frac{10!}{2!(10-2)!} = 45.$

    (b) $_nC_2 = \frac{n(n-1)(n-2)\cdots(1)}{2\cdot 1\cdot[(n-2)(n-3)\cdots(1)]} = \frac{n(n-1)}{2}.$

20. $\emptyset$, 1 point, 2 points, a ray.

21. (a) $\{C\}$ is the only point of intersection.   (b) $\overline{BD}$; $\overline{CD}$ adds nothing to $\overline{BD}$.

    (c) $\overline{AB}$, $\overline{AC}$, and $\overline{AD}$ all contain $\{A\}$.   (d) $\{D\}$ is the only point of intersection.

22. (a)   False.   A ray has one endpoint, continuing forever in the other direction.

    (b)   True.

    (c)   False. By definition, skew lines are non-coplanar.

    (d)   False. The two rays have different endpoints and go in opposite directions.

    (e)   True.

    (f)   False. Their intersection is a line.

1. (a)   ∠ 1 and ∠ 2 are adjacent; ∠ 3 and ∠ 4 are vertical.

   (b)   ∠ 1 and ∠ 2 are vertical; ∠ 3 and ∠ 4 are adjacent.

   (c)   ∠ 1 and ∠ 2 are neither vertical nor adjacent, since they are not formed by two intersecting lines and do not have a common side.

   (d)   ∠ 1 and ∠ 2 are adjacent.

2. Lay a ruler on the steps and measure the angle of inclination between a step and the ruler.

3. (a)    (b)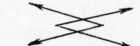

   (c)    (d)

   (e)

4. Every pair of lines forms two pairs of vertical angles, so there are $2[_5C_2] = 2 \cdot 10 = 20$ pairs.

5. The angles of every triangle add to 180°; subtract the given angles to find the third angle.

   (a) $60° \left(180 - (70 + 50) = 60\right)$ (b) $45° \left(180 - (90 + 45) = 45\right)$

   (c) $60° \left(180 - (90 + 30) = 60\right)$ (d) $60° \left(180 - (60 + 60) = 60\right)$

6. (a)   Yes. A pair of corresponding angles are 50° each.

   (b)   Yes. A pair of corresponding angles are 70° each.

   (c)   Yes. A pair of alternate interior angles are 40° each.

   (d)   Yes. A pair of corresponding angles are 90° each.

7. (a)   No. Two or more obtuse angles would produce a sum of more than 180°, the sum of all angles in a triangle.

   (b)   Yes. For example, each angle may have measure 60°.

   (c)   No. The sum of the measures of the three angles would be more than 180°.

   (d)   No. It may have an obtuse or right angle as well.

8. (a)   70°   (b)   70°

   (c)   65°   (d)   45°

9. (a)   Using congruent vertical angles, x = 40°. y = 180 − (90 + 40) = 50°.

   (b)   Using complementary interior angles, x + 4x = 90; x = 18°.

   (c)   Using supplementary interior angles formed by parallel lines, m∠ ACD = 110°. m∠ BCD = 50° from vertical angles. Thus y = 110 − 50 = 60°, so x = 180 − (70 + 60) = 50°.

9. (d) Using supplementary angles, one vertex of the triangle $= 180 - 125 = 55°$. Using vertical angles, the other vertex of the triangle $= 42°$. Thus the interior angle of the triangle vertical to x is $180 - (55 + 42) = 83°$, so, using vertical angles, x $= 83°$.

10. (a) $A = 2(90 - A) \Rightarrow A = 60°$.   (b) $180 - 90 = 90°$.

11. The ratio could be written 7x:2x. The angles must add to $90°$, so $7x + 2x = 90 \Rightarrow x = 10$. The angles are $7(10) = 70°$ and $2(10) = 20°$.

12. $(3x + 15) + (5x - 15) + (2x + 30) = 180 \Rightarrow x = 15$. The angles all measure $60°$.

13. (a) The six angles surrounding the center point add to $360°$. The angles contained by triangles equal those not contained (vertical angles); the contained angles must then add to $\frac{1}{2}(360) = 180°$. The three triangles total $3(180) = 540°$. The numbered angles must then add to $540 - 180 = 360°$.

(b) $m\angle 1 + m\angle 3 + m\angle 5 = 180°$ (the sum of a triangle's interior angles); likewise, $m\angle 2 + m\angle 4 + m\angle 6 = 180°$. The sum of the angles is $180 + 180 = 360°$.

(c) $360°$ (same as (b)).

14. If the two distinct lines are both perpendicular, then the measures of $\angle$ B and $\angle$ C are both $90°$. This would force the sum of the measures of the angles of $\triangle$ ABC to be greater than $180°$, which is impossible.

15. (a) Each exterior angle is $180 - 162 = 18°$. Since exterior angles add to $360°$, there must be $360 \div 18 = 20$ angles and hence 20 sides.

(b) A dodecagon has 12 exterior angles so each is $360 \div 12 = 30°$. The interior angles are then $180 - 30 = 150°$ each.

16. (a) $5 \cdot 180 - 360 = 540°$.

(b) If n is the number of sides of the regular n-gon, then by the method in (a) the sum of the measures of the angles is $180n - 360 = 180(n - 2)$.

17. (a) Drawing diagonals from one vertex gives three triangles, for a total of $3 \cdot 180 = 540°$.

(b) There are always two less triangles than sides, so the sum of the measures of the angles is $(n - 2 \text{ triangles}) \cdot (180° \text{ each}) = (n - 2) \cdot 180°$.

18. (a) True.   (b) False.

(c) False.   (d) True.

(e) False.

19. (a) The measures of the angles are the same.

(b) $m(\angle 4) + m(\angle 3) = 180°$ (straight line). $[m(\angle 1) + m(\angle 2)] + m(\angle 3) = 180°$ (the sum of the angles in a triangle). Since both $m(\angle 4)$ and $[m(\angle 1) + m(\angle 2)]$ plus $m(\angle 3) = 180°$, they must be equal.

20. The angles are 60, $60 + d$, $60 + 2d$, $60 + 3d$, and $60 + 4d$. Their sum is $300 + 10d = 540 \Rightarrow d = 24$. The angles measure $60°$, $84°$, $108°$, $132°$, and $156°$.

21. Vertical angles are formed by two intersecting lines. In this case, angle 1 is formed by a line and a ray.

22. No. Regular hexagons fit because the measure of each vertex angle is 120° and three hexagons fit to form 360°; thus the plane can be filled. The measure of each vertex angle in a pentagon is 108°, and 108° is not divisible by 360°, so penatagons will not fill the plane.

23. The measure of an octogon's interior angle is $\frac{(n-2)180}{n} = \frac{(6)180}{8} = 135°$. By using supplementary angles, the measure of each of the triangle's interior angles is $180 - 135 = 45°$. Since the two interior angles of the isosceles triangle are each 45°, $\angle 1 = 180 - (45 + 45) = 90°$.

24. Yes. The sum of the angles in a triangle must be 180°. Hence the measure of the third angle in each triangle must be 180° minus the sum of the measures of the two angles.

25. The angles must be supplementary.

26. The sum of the interior angles in this convex hexagon is 720°.
$\angle x = 720 - (110 + 105 + 142 + 122 + 130) = 111°$.

27. $m(\angle 1) = 90 - 30 = 60°$. $m(\angle 2) = 180 - (90 + 60) = 30°$. $m(\angle 3) = 180 - (30 + 40) = 110°$.

28. Home plate is a pentagon with a total of interior angles of 540°. The two congruent angles add to $540 - 3 \cdot 90 = 270°$, so must be 135° each.

29. (*i*)   Theorem 10-1(a):
Let both $\angle 2$ and $\angle 3$ be supplements of $\angle 1$.
Then: $m(\angle 2) + m(\angle 1) = 180°$
$m(\angle 3) + m(\angle 1) = 180°$
$m(\angle 2) + m(\angle 1) = m(\angle 3) + m(\angle 1)$
$m(\angle 2) = m(\angle 3)$, so $\angle 2 \simeq \angle 3$.
Let $\angle 3$ be the supplement of $\angle 1$, and $\angle 4$ be the supplement of $\angle 2$, and $\angle 1 \simeq \angle 2$.
Then: $m(\angle 3) + m(\angle 1) = 180°$
$m(\angle 4) + m(\angle 2) = 180°$
$m(\angle 3) + m(\angle 1) = m(\angle 4) + m(\angle 2)$
$\angle 1 \simeq \angle 2$ implies $m(\angle 1) = m(\angle 2)$
$m(\angle 3) + m(\angle 2) = m(\angle 4) + m(\angle 2)$
$m(\angle 3) = m(\angle 4)$, so $\angle 3 \simeq \angle 4$.

(*ii*)   The proof of Theorem 10-1(b) is similar to that of Theorem 10-1(a), using 90° in place of 180°.

30. If two lines are perpendicular to the same line, then congruent corresponding angles of 90° each are formed, and hence the lines are parallel.

31. Mark point F on ray $\overrightarrow{AB}$ past point B, and mark point E on ray $\overrightarrow{CB}$ past point B, as shown below:

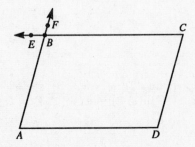

(a)   m($\angle$ A) = m($\angle$ FBC) (corresponding angles)
       m($\angle$ FBE) + m($\angle$ FBC) = 180° (supplementary angles)
       m($\angle$ FBE) = m($\angle$ ABC) (vertical angles)
       Then m($\angle$ ABC) + m($\angle$ A) = 180° (substitution)

(b)   m($\angle$ A) = m($\angle$ ABE) (alternate interior angles)
       m($\angle$ ABE) = m($\angle$ C) (corresponding angles)
       Then m($\angle$ A) = m($\angle$ C), and likewise m($\angle$ B) = m($\angle$ D).

32. Considering spaces between hands gives $3\frac{2}{5} - \frac{37}{60}$ spaces at 30°, or $(3\frac{2}{5} - \frac{37}{60})\cdot 30 = 83.5°$.

33. Answers may vary.

(a)   TO PARALLELOGRAM :L :W :A
         REPEAT 2[FD :L RT 180 − :A FD :W RT :A]
       END

(b)   TO RECTANGLE :L :W
         PARALLELOGRAM :L :W 90
       END

(c)   TO RHOMBUS :L :L :A
         PARALLELOGRAM :L :L :A
       END

(d)   Execute PARALLELOGRAM 50 50 90.

(e)   Execute RHOMBUS 50 90.

34. $_4C_2 = 6$ points.

35. No. The union of two rays will always extend indefinitely in at least one direction.

36. Answers may vary; one example is ⧖.

37. Crease a large piece of cardboard and lay it on the roof with the crease along $\overline{BC}$ and extending past B. Measure the dihedral angle of the folded cardboard.

38. Sketches may vary, but the possibilities are the empty set, a single point, a segment, a quadrilateral (various types possible), a triangle, a pentagon, and a hexagon.

39. (a)   Hexagon.   (b)   Rectangle or pentagon.

     (c)   Two intersecting segments.   (d)   Rectangle.

     (e)   Square or rectangle.

40. (a)   All rectangles have four right angles and congruent diagonals.

     (b)   All sides are the same length and all angles are right angles.

     (c)   Impossible. All squares are parallelograms.

1. (a) Quadrilateral pyramid.   (b) Quadrilateral prism.

    (c) Pentagonal pyramid.

2. (a) A, D, R, W   (b) $\overline{AR}, \overline{RD}, \overline{AD}, \overline{AW}, \overline{WR}, \overline{WD}$

    (c) △ ARD, △ AWD, △ AWR, △ WDR   (d) {R}

3. Answers may vary, but examples are: square prism (saltine crackers), rectangular prism (cereal), circular cylinder (canned corn), triangular prism (candy bar).

4. (a) 5 (triangular prism).   (b) 4 (triangular pyramid).

    (c) 4 (tetrahedron)

5. (a) True. This is the definition of a right prism.

    (b) False. No pyramid is a prism; e.g., a pyramid has one base and a prism two bases.

    (c) True. The definition of a pyramid starts with the fact that it is a polyhedron.

    (d) False. They lie in parallel planes.

    (e) False. The base can be any simple closed curve.

    (f) False. They have two bases.

    (g) False. They are parallelograms; if they were rectangles they would be right prisms.

    (h) True, by definition.

6. 3 pairs. For example, a box has three pairs of opposite, congruent faces.

7. (a)   (b)

    (c)

8. (a)    (b)

9. (a) Hexagonal pyramid.   (b) Quadrilateral (square) pyramid.

   (c) Cube.   (d) Rectangular prism.

   (e) Hexagonal prism.

10. (a) (*iv*)   (b) (*iii*)

11. (a) (*iv*)   (b) (*ii*)

12. (a) (*i*), (*ii*), and (*iii*)   (b) (*ii*), (*iii*), and (*iv*)

13.

Prism	Vertices per Base	Diagonals per Vertex	Total Number of Diagonals
Quadrilateral	4	1	4
Pentagonal	5	2	10
Hexagonal	6	3	18
Heptagonal	7	4	28
Octagonal	8	5	40
⋮			
n-gonal	n	(n − 3)	n(n − 3)

14. Both could be drawings of a quadrilateral pyramid.

   (a) We are directly above the pyramid.   (b) We are directly below the pyramid.

15. (a)   (b)

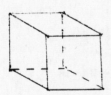 

   (c)   (d)

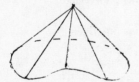 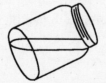

16. (a)   (b)

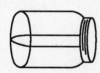

   (c)

17. (a) Object 2. Note the relationship between numbered faces.

   (b) Object 4. The two figures cannot be on adjoining faces.

18.   (a)   (b)

(c)   (d)

                                   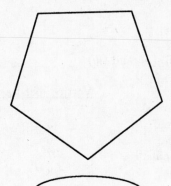

(e)   (f)

19.   (a)   V = 5; E = 8; F = 5.   V + F − E = 5 + 5 − 8 = 2.

(b)   V = 8; E = 12; F = 6.   8 + 6 − 12 = 2.

(c)   V = 6; E = 10; F = 6.   6 + 6 − 10 = 2.

20.   (a)   (*i*)   A pyramid has n + 1 faces.   (*ii*)   A prism has n + 2 faces.

(b)   (*i*)   A pyramid has n + 1 vertices.   (*ii*)   A prism has 2n vertices.

(c)   (*i*)   A pyramid has 2n edges.   (*ii*)   A prism has 3n edges.

(d)   (*i*)   Pyramids: (n + 1) + (n + 1) − 2n = 2.

(*ii*)   Prisms: (n + 2) + 2n − 3n = 2.

21.   Using Euler's formula to find the missing value:

(a)   6 vertices   (b)   48 edges

(c)   11 faces

22.   (a)   Yes. 10 vertices, 7 faces, and 15 edges; 10 + 7 − 15 = 2.

(b)   Yes. 9 vertices, 9 faces, and 16 edges; 9 + 9 − 16 = 2.

23.   (a)   A cone might be described as a many-sided pyramid.

(b)   A cylinder might be described as a many-sided prism.

24.   (a)   Yes. If the base is an 11-gon the number of edges is 3n; thus if 3n = 33 then n = 11 and an 11-gon has exactly 33 edges.

24. (b)   No. If the base of a pyramid is an n-gon the number of edges is 2n. Because 2n is even, the number of edges cannot be 33.

25.   A parallelogram. Try it and see.

26.   m($\angle$ BCD) = 60°.

27.   A nonogon has nine sides. Thus the interior angle measurement is $\frac{(9-2)180}{9} = 140°$.

28. (a)   True.   (b)   True.

    (c)   False. All three may be acute; e.g., an equilateral triangle.

29. (a)   A right triangle.

    (b)   The sum of the measures of complementary angles is 90°. Thus the measure of the third angle must be 90° and the triangle is a right triangle.

Problem Set 10-5

1. (a)   (b)

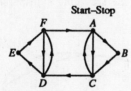

Path:
ABCACDEFDFA;
any point can be a
starting point.

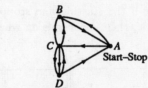

Path:
ABACBCDCDA;
any point can be a
starting point.

   (c)   (d)   Not traversable; has more than two odd vertices.

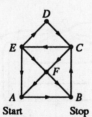

Start   Stop
Path:
ABCFAEDCEFB;
only points A and B
can be starting points.

   (e)   (f)   Not traversable; has more than two odd vertices.

Start
Path:
ABCBDCAD;
only points A and D
can be starting points.

1. (g)

    Path:
    FADABCBGFEDCHEHG;
    only points *F* and *G*
    can be starting points.

    (h)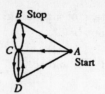

    Path:
    ACBCDCDAB;
    only points *A* and *B*
    can be starting points.

    (i) Not traversable; has more than two odd
         vertices.

    (j)

2. All are possible if the starting and stopping points are not the same. If the traveling salesperson must start
    and return home, then it depends on where home is.

3.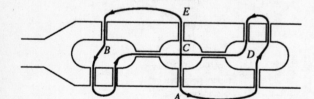

4. (a) (*i*)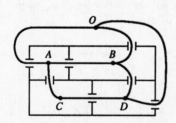

         (*ii*)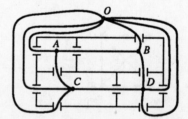

    (b) Network (*i*) is not traversable, since it has four odd vertices. Network (*ii*) has two odd vertices, so it
         is traversable, as shown below.

         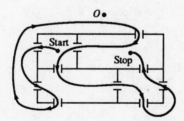

5.   Yes. See figure.

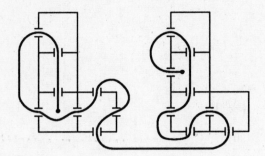

6.   It is not possible.

7.
Network	R	V	A	R + V − A
(a)	6	6	10	2
(b)	7	4	9	2
(c)	6	6	10	2
(d)	4	4	6	2
(e)	5	4	7	2
(f)	8	8	14	2
(g)	9	8	15	2
(h)	6	4	8	2
(i)	7	7	12	2
(j)	8	12	18	2

8.   Considering states as vertices and borders as arcs connecting them, all states are even vertices. The trip is thus possible; it does not matter in which state it begins.

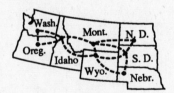

9.   To be non-traversable, a network must have more than two odd vertices. An example is below.

10. The bridge could be built anywhere and we would have two odd vertices. Thus the network would be traversable.

Problem Set 10-6

1.   (a)   TO RECTANGLE :LENGTH :WIDTH
            PARALLELOGRAM :LENGTH :WIDTH 90
         END

     (b)   TO RHOMBUS :SIDE :ANGLE
            PARALLELOGRAM :SIDE :SIDE :ANGLE
         END

2. TO SQUARE :SIDE
   RHOMBUS :SIDE 90
END

3. TO CUBE :SIDE
   REPEAT 3 [RHOMBUS :SIDE 60 RIGHT 120]
END

4. (a)   60°

     (b) $\left(\frac{360}{7}\right)°$

     (c)   45°

     (d)   30°

5. Execute on the computer.

6. No. The methods of this section yield an equilateral triangle if a 6-pointed star is attempted.

7. Answers may vary.

   (a)   TO HEXSTACK :SIDE
       REPEAT 3 [LEFT 30 HEXAGON :SIDE FD :SIDE RT 60 FD :SIDE LT 60]
     END
     TO HEXAGON :SIDE
       REPEAT 6 [FD :SIDE RIGHT 60]
     END

   (b)   TO HONEYCOMB :SIDE
       REPEAT 3 [HEXAGON :SIDE RT 120]
     END

8. Answers may vary.
   TO THIRTY
     FD 100 BK 100 RT 30
     FD 100 BK 100 LT 30
   END

9. Answers may vary.

   (a)   TO SEG
       RT 45 FD 50 BK 100
       FD 50 LT 45
     END

   (b)   TO PAR
       PENUP FD 50 PENDOWN
       SEG
     END

10. It will draw a 30-gon that looks like a circle on the screen. It will have perimeter 120 units.

11. Answers may vary.
   TO FILL.RECT :WIDTH :LENGTH
     IF :WIDTH < 0 STOP
     REPEAT 4[FD :WIDTH RT 90 FD :LENGTH RT 90]
     FILL.RECT :WIDTH − 1 :LENGTH − 1
     HT
   END

12. TO POLYGON :NUM :LEN
        REPEAT :NUM [FD :LEN RT 360/:NUM]
     END

13. Answers may vary.
     TO COUNT.ANGLES :NUMBER
        IF :NUMBER = 1 OUTPUT 0 STOP
        OUTPUT :NUMBER − 1 + COUNT.ANGLES :NUMBER − 1
     END

Chapter 10 Test

1.   Answers may vary.

2.   (a) $\overleftrightarrow{AB}$, $\overleftrightarrow{BC}$, $\overleftrightarrow{AC}$ (b) $\overrightarrow{BC}$, $\overrightarrow{BA}$

     (c) $\overline{AB}$ (d) $\overrightarrow{AB}$

     (e) $\overline{AB}$

3.   (a) $\overleftrightarrow{PQ}$ and $\overleftrightarrow{AB}$ are skew (i.e., they do not intersect and are non-coplanar)

     (b)   Any plane containing $\overleftrightarrow{PQ}$ is perpendicular to α. From the diagram, planes APQ and BPQ are two
           such.

     (c)   The planes have $\overleftrightarrow{AQ}$ in common.

     (d)   No. $\overleftrightarrow{AB}$ and $\overleftrightarrow{PQ}$ are skew lines, and no single plane contains them.

4.   Answers may vary.

5.   Answers may vary.

6.   (a)   No. The sum of the measures of two obtuse angles is greater than 180°, which is the sum of the
           measures of the angles of any triangle.

     (b)   No. The sum of the measures of the four angles in a parallelogram must be 360°. If all the angles are
           acute, the sum would be less than 360°.

7.   18°, 36°, and 126°.

8.   (a)   Given any convex n-gon, pick any vertex and draw all possible diagonals from this vertex. This will
           determine n − 2 triangles. Because the sum of the measures of the angles in each triangle is 180°, the
           sum of the measures of the angles in the n-gon is (n − 2)180°.

     (b)   90 sides.

9.   (a)   Answers may vary.

     (b)   12 + 8 − 18 = 2; Euler's formula holds.

10. Answers may vary.

11. Sketches may vary; the possibilities are a point, a segment, a triangle, a quadrilateral, or an empty set.

12. x = 6

13. 35° 8′ 35″

14. (a)   60°   (b)   120°

    (c)   120°

15. There are as many lateral faces as sides; thus an octogonal pyramid has 8 lateral faces.

16. 48°

17. (a)   (i), (ii), and (iv) are traversable.

    (b)   (i)   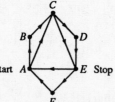   Path:
                  ABCDEFACEA;
                  any point can be usd
                  as a starting point.

           (ii)   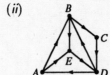   Path:
                  ABCDAEDBE;
                  points *A* and *E* are
                  possible starting points.

           (iv)   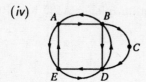   Path:
                  BDEABAEDBCD;
                  points *B* and *D* are
                  possible starting points.

18. Answers may vary.
    TO PERPENDICULAR :SEG1 :SEG2
        FD :SEG1 RT 90
        FD :SEG2
    END

19. Answers may vary.
    TO ISOS :LEG :ANGLE
        HOME
        FD :LEG
        RT 180 − :ANGLE
        FD :LEG
        HOME
    END

CHAPTER 11 - CONSTRUCTIONS, CONGRUENCE, AND SIMILARITY

<u>Problem Set 11-1</u>

1. (a) One such triangle is:

    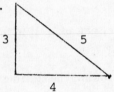

    Then BC > AC.

    (b) The triangle in (a) satisfies the condition. The angle opposite $\overline{BC}$ is larger than the angle opposite $\overline{AC}$ [m($\angle$ A) > m($\angle$ B)].

    (c) The side of greater length is opposite the angle of greater measure.

2. (a) See Figures 11-4 and 11-11.   (b)

    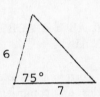

    (c) Scalene right triangle.   (d) Not possible; 10 > 4 + 5

    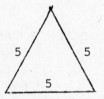

    (e)   (f)

    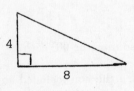   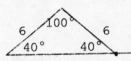

    (g)   (h)

    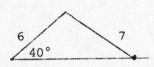

    (i)

3. (b) Yes; SSS.   (c) Yes; SSS.

    (d) No triangle.   (e) Yes; SSS.

    (f) Yes; SAS.   (g) No; SSA can be ambiguous.

    (h) Yes; SAS. With one angle given in an isosceles triangle, others are determined.

    (i) Yes; SAS.

4. 22 (5-5-5, 5-5-4, 5-5-2, 5-5-1, 5-4-4, ... , 1-1-1)

5. (a) Yes. The given information satisfies SAS.

5. (b)   Yes; SSS.

    (c)   No. Not SAS since the angles are non-included. SSA is not sufficient to ensure a congruent triangle.

6. The diagonals form congruent triangles, which are rigid structures and thus make the gate stronger. They also prevent cows from squeezing through.

7. The lengths must be the same since they are corresponding parts of congruent triangles.

8. The construction makes $\triangle$ ABC $\simeq$ $\triangle$ DBC by SAS, so AB = DB.

9. (a)   See Figure 11-11.

    (b)   Use the procedure in Figure 11-9 with all sides the length of $\overline{AB}$.

    (c)   Any angle in an equilateral triangle is 60°. Follow the procedure in (b) to construct a 60° angle.

    (d)   Copy $\angle$ A, the mark off the desired length for the congruent sides on each side of the angle. Connect the two marked points.

10. (a)   Use the "copy an angle" procedure, marking the span of $\angle$ B from the point where the span of $\angle$ A fell on the arc.

    (b)   Same as (a), except mark the span of $\angle$ A back toward the starting point from where the span of $\angle$ B fell on the arc.

11. (a) $\triangle$ ABC $\simeq$ $\triangle$ ABC; $\triangle$ ACB $\simeq$ $\triangle$ ABC; $\triangle$ BAC $\simeq$ $\triangle$ ABC; $\triangle$ BCA $\simeq$ $\triangle$ ABC; $\triangle$ CAB $\simeq$ $\triangle$ ABC; $\triangle$ CBA $\simeq$ $\triangle$ ABC.

    (b)   Consider the correspondence $\triangle$ BCA $\simeq$ $\triangle$ ABC. Then $\angle$ B $\simeq$ $\angle$ A, $\angle$ C $\simeq$ $\angle$ B, and $\angle$ A $\simeq$ $\angle$ C; i.e., all angles are congruent to each other. Thus, $\triangle$ ABC (and any equilateral triangle) is equiangular.

12. (a) $\overline{AD} \simeq \overline{CD}$.

    (b) $\triangle$ ABD $\simeq$ $\triangle$ CBD by SAS, so $\overline{AD} \simeq \overline{CD}$ by CPCTC.

    (c)   Both are 90°.

    (d)   The two angles are congruent and add to 180° (a straight angle) so must be 90° each.

13. If the non-included angles of existing triangles are obtuse or right. When the non-included angle is acute, it is sometimes possible to construct two triangles satisfying the given measures. With obtuse and right angles, only one triangle is possible.

14. (a)   F is the midpoint of both diagonals.

    (b) $\triangle$ ABC $\simeq$ $\triangle$ ADC by SSS, so $\angle$ DAF $\simeq$ $\angle$ BAF. Then $\triangle$ BAF $\simeq$ $\triangle$ DAF by SAS, and $\overline{BF} \simeq \overline{DF}$ by CPCTC. Thus F is the midpoint of $\overline{BD}$. A similar argument shows that F is the midpoint of $\overline{AC}$.

    (c)   90°.

    (d)   Since $\triangle$ BAF $\simeq$ $\triangle$ DAF [from (b)], $\angle$ BFA $\simeq$ $\angle$ DFA. These angles also add to 180° (straight angle), so they must be 90° each.

15. (a)   Parallelogram.

15. (b)   Let QRST be the quadrilateral; point N be the intersection of the diagonals. $\triangle$ QRN $\simeq$ $\triangle$ STN and $\triangle$ RSN $\simeq$ $\triangle$ TQN by SAS (congruent sides from bisection and vertical angles). Then $\angle$ RQN $\simeq$ $\angle$ TSN and $\angle$ SRN $\simeq$ $\angle$ QTN by CPCTC. With these alternate interior angles congruent, the opposite sides must be parallel. Nothing forces sides to be congruent or angles right, so a more specific classification than parallelogram cannot be made.

16. (a)   Diagonals of rhombuses meet at right angles.

    (b)   Let ABCD be the rhombus; point E be the intersection of the diagonals. $\triangle$ ABC $\simeq$ $\triangle$ ADC by SSS. Then $\angle$ BCE $\simeq$ $\angle$ DCE by CPCTC, making $\triangle$ BCE $\simeq$ $\triangle$ DCE by SAS. Then $\angle$ BEC and $\angle$ DCE must be right angles as in 12.(d). If $\overline{BC} \not\simeq \overline{DC}$, the argument is not possible; i.e., this is not true for non-rhombus parallelograms.

17. (a)   Parallelogram.

    (b)   Let QRST be the parallelogram. $\triangle$ SRT $\simeq$ $\triangle$ QTR by SSS. Then $\angle$ SRT $\simeq$ $\angle$ QTR and $\angle$ QRT $\simeq$ $\angle$ STR by CPCTC. With these alternate interior angles congruent, the opposite sides must be parallel. With no further restrictions no more specific classifications than parallelogram can be made.

18. With $\overline{AB} \simeq \overline{AC}$ and $\angle$ A $\simeq$ $\angle$ A, $\triangle$ BAC $\simeq$ $\triangle$ CAB by SAS. Then $\angle$ B $\simeq$ $\angle$ C by CPCTC; i.e., the base angles of an isosceles triangle are congruent.

19. Answers may vary.
    TO EQUITRI :SIDE
      REPEAT 3 [FD :SIDE RT 120]
    END

20. (a) and (b)   Execute the programs.

21. They produce basically the same results.

22. (a)   A triangle is constructed because the computer does not know the difference in an angle measure and a compass heading.

    (b)   No, because no triangle has one angle with measure 190°.

    (c)   Add the following:
           IF NOT (:ANGLE < 180) PRINT [NO TRIANGLE IS POSSIBLE.] STOP

Problem Set 11-2

1. (a)   (b)

   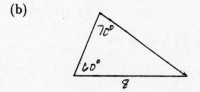

    (c)   (d)   Infinitely many are possible.

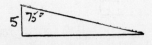

2. (a)   No. The triangle is unique by ASA.   (b)   No. The triangle is unique by AAS.

    (c)   No. The triangle is unique by ASA.

    (d)   Yes. AAA determines a unique shape, but not size.

3. (a)   Yes. The triangles are congruent by ASA.

    (b)   Yes. The triangles are congruent by AAS.

    (c)   No. SSA does not assign congruence.

    (d)   No. AAA does not assure congruence.

4. Drawing $\overleftrightarrow{AD}$ forms $\triangle$ ADC $\simeq \triangle$ DAB by SSS. $\angle$ ABD and $\angle$ CDB are alternate interior angles formed by $\overleftrightarrow{AB}$ and $\overleftrightarrow{DC}$ with transversal $\overline{BD}$, so $\overline{AB}\|\overline{DC}$.

5. If diagonals of a quadrilateral besect each other, it must be a parallelogram. Connecting the legs at their midpoint will then ensure that the board and the floor are opposite sides of the parallelogram and are thus parallel to each other.

6. (a)   Parallelogram

    (b)   None. One must know it is a parallelogram before it can be known that it is a rectangle. Otherwise it could be an isosceles triangle.

    (c)   None. It could be a kite if parallelogram is not specified.

    (d)   Rectangle   (e)   Rhombus

    (f)   Square   (g)   Parallelogram

7. (a)   True.   (b)   True.

    (c)   True.   (d)   True.

    (e)   True.

    (f)   False. A trapezoid may have only one pair of parallel sides.

    (g)   True.

    (h)   False. A square is both a rectangle and a rhombus.

    (i)   False. A square can be a trapezoid.

    (j)   True. In fact, all are.

8. (a)   Possibilities include:

    (b)   The sum of all four angles is 360°. If three are right angles, the fourth is $360 - 3 \cdot 90 = 90$, a fourth right angle.

8. (c) No. Since opposite angles are congruent and all angles add to 360°, making any two right angles forces the other two to be right as well.

9. There are five possibilities; one parallelogram and four kites.

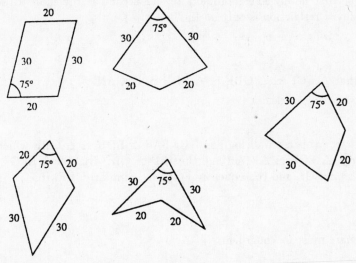

10. The triangle formed by Stan's head, his feet, and the opposite bank is congruent to the triangle formed by Stan's head, his feet, and the spot just obscured by the bill of his cap. These triangles are congruent by ASA since the angle at Stan's feet is 90° in both triangles, Stan's height is the same in both triangles, and the angle formed by the bill of his cap is the same in both triangles. The distance across the river is approximately equal to the distance he paced off by CPCTC.

11. (a) $\overline{OP} \simeq \overline{OQ}$

(b) $\angle$ PDO $\simeq$ $\angle$ QBO; alternate interior angles formed by the transversal $\overleftrightarrow{DB}$ and parallel lines $\overleftrightarrow{DC}$ and $\overleftrightarrow{AB}$. $\angle$ DPO $\simeq$ $\angle$ BQO because $\overleftrightarrow{PQ}$ is a transversal of $\overleftrightarrow{CD}$ and $\overleftrightarrow{AB}$. $\overline{DO} \simeq \overline{BO}$; diagonals of a parallelogram bisect each other. $\triangle$ POD $\simeq$ $\triangle$ QOB by AAS. Thus $\overline{PO} \simeq \overline{QO}$ by CPCTC.

12. (a) $\triangle$ ABC $\simeq$ $\triangle$ ADC by SSS, so $\angle$ BCA $\simeq$ $\angle$ DCA and $\angle$ BAC $\simeq$ $\angle$ DAC. Therefore $\overleftrightarrow{AC}$ bisects $\angle$ A and $\angle$ C.

(b) The diagonals intersect at right angles. $\triangle$ BCM $\simeq$ $\triangle$ DCM by SAS, so $\angle$ BMC $\simeq$ $\angle$ DMC. These two add to 180°, so must be 90° each.

(c) $\triangle$ BCM $\simeq$ $\triangle$ DCM by SAS, so $\overline{BM} \simeq \overline{DM}$ by CPCTC.

13. Let ABCD be an isosceles trapezoid with $\angle$ A $\simeq$ $\angle$ D and $\overline{BC} \| \overline{AD}$.

(a) Sides opposite congruent angles in an isosceles trapezoid are congruent.

(b) The diagonals are congruent.

(c) (i) Draw $\overline{BX}$ and $\overline{CY}$ perpendicular to $\overline{AD}$. Since $\overline{BC} \| \overline{AD}$, the distances between them must be constant; i.e., $\overline{BC} \simeq \overline{CY}$. Then $\triangle$ ABX $\simeq$ $\triangle$ DCY by AAS, so $\overline{AB} \simeq \overline{DC}$ by CPCTC.

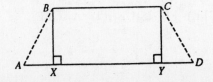

13. (c) (*ii*) △ ABD ≃ △ DCA by SAS (given ∠ BAD ≃ ∠ CDA, $\overline{AB}$ ≃ $\overline{DC}$, and $\overline{AC}$ common).
Thus $\overline{BD}$ ≃ $\overline{AC}$ by CPCTC.

14. There are two possibilities: (*i*) The first kite is a rhombus, the second is another rhombus with different angles; or (*ii*) the first is any non-rhombic kite, the second is the same kite with the more blunt point indented (i.e., the convex restriction is only on the first kite).

15. (a) Rhombus.

(b) Use SAS to prove that △ ECF ≃ △ GBF ≃ △ EDH ≃ △ GAH.

(c) Parallelogram.

(d) Suppose ADCB in part (a) is a parallelogram. By SAS △ EDH ≃ △ GBF which implies that $\overline{EH}$ ≃ $\overline{GF}$. Similarly, △ ECF ≃ △ GAH and thus $\overline{EF}$ ≃ $\overline{GH}$. By SSS △ EFG ≃ △ GHE. Therefore ∠ GEH ≃ ∠ EGF and consequently $\overline{FG}\|\overline{EH}$. Similarly, $\overline{EF}\|\overline{HG}$.

(e) Parallelogram.

16. (a) One side of each square must be congruent.

(b) Two adjacent sides of one must be congruent to those of the other.

(c) Two adjacent sides and an angle of one must be congruent to those of the other.

17. (a) ∠ ABD ≃ ∠ CDB and ∠ CBD ≃ ∠ ADB (alternate interior angles with respect to parallel lines), so △ ABD ≃ △ CDB (ASA). Thus ∠ BAD ≃ ∠ DCB (CPCTC); similarly, ∠ ABC ≃ ∠ CDA.

(b) △ ABD ≃ △ CDB, so $\overline{AB}$ ≃ $\overline{CD}$ and $\overline{AD}$ ≃ $\overline{CB}$.

(c) ∠ BAC ≃ ∠ DCA and ∠ ABD ≃ ∠ CDB (alternate interior angles), and $\overline{AB}$ ≃ $\overline{DC}$ (from (b)), so △ BAF ≃ △ DCF and thus $\overline{AF}$ ≃ $\overline{CF}$ and $\overline{BF}$ ≃ $\overline{DF}$.

(d) As for any triangle, in △ ABD m(∠ BAD) + m(∠ ABD) + m(∠ ADB) = 180°.
From (a), ∠ CBD ≃ ∠ ADB; substitution gives m(∠ BAD) + m(∠ ABD) + m(∠ CBD) = 180°.
Since m(∠ ABC) = m(∠ ABD) + m(∠ CBD), then m(∠ BAD) + m(∠ ABC) = 180°.
Thus ∠ ABC and ∠ BAD are supplementary.

18. (a) Execute the program.

(b) (*i*) Two intersecting line segments.

(*ii*) Three segments that do not close into a triangle.

(c) Add the following:
IF NOT (ALLOF (:ANGLE1 + :ANGLE2 < 180) (:ANGLE 1 > 0) (:ANGLE2 > 0))
PRINT [NO TRIANGLE IS POSSIBLE.] STOP

19. (a) Answers may vary.
TO RHOMBUS :SIDE :ANGLE
  REPEAT 2 [FD :SIDE RT (180 − :ANGLE) FD :SIDE RT :ANGLE]
END

(b) They are congruent.

19. (c)   TO SQ. RHOM :SIDE
                 RHOMBUS :SIDE 90
              END

20. Answers may vary.
     TO ISOSTRI :SIDE :ANGLE
       HOME FD :SIDE
       RIGHT (2∗:ANGLE)
       FD :SIDE RIGHT :ANGLE
       HOME
     END

21. Use the procedure in Figure 11-9.

22. Same as 21.

23. (a)   Yes; SAS.   (b)   Yes; SSS.

     (c)   No; SSA is not a congruous relation.

Problem Set 11-3

1. (a) and (b).   Use Figure 11-23.

2. (a)   Match up the sides of ∠ A and crease, being sure that the fold passes through A.

     (b)   Match vertices A and B, then fold making sure to keep the halves of $\overline{AB}$ flush with each other.

     (c)   Fold the paper so that *l* lands upon itself while being sure to make the crease pass through P.

3. (a)   See Figure 11-25.

     (b)   See Figure 11-27.

     (c)   See Figure 11-26.

4. See "Paper folding and Mira Construction" in the text.

5. Given ∠ BAC, put one strip of tape so that an edge of the tape is along $\overline{AB}$ and another strip of tape so that one of its edges is on $\overline{AC}$. Two edges of the strips of tape intersect in the interior of the angle; connect A with this point and you will have the angle bisector.

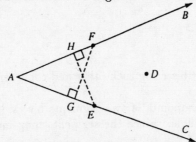

6. (a), (b), and (c).   Use the methods of Figures 11-30 and 11-31.

     (d)   The lines containing the altitudes meet at a point inside the triangle.

6.   (e)   The lines containing the altitudes meet at the vertex of the right angle.

     (f)   The lines containing the altitudes meet outside the triangle.

7.   (a)   The perpendicular bisectors meet at a point inside the triangle.

     (b)   The perpendicular bisectors meet at the midpoint of the hypotenuse of the right triangle.

     (c)   The perpendicular bisectors meet at a point outside the triangle.

8.   (a)   The perpendicular bisector of a chord passes through the center of the circle.

     (b)   The perpendicular bisector of a segment contains all points equidistant to the segment's endpoints. It must then contain the center, since it is equidistant to the endpoints of any chord (equal radii).

     (c)   Construct two non-parallel chords and find their perpendicular bisectors. The intersection of the bisectors is the center of the circle.

9.   Construct as described.

10.   Measure $\overline{AB}$ and use it to mark off vertices after a right angle has been constructed at one end of $\overline{AB}$.

11.   Answers may vary. One possibility is to:
    (*i*)   Draw a line segment (10¢).
    (*ii*)   Draw two intersecting arcs (20¢) to construct a perpendicular segment (10¢).
    (*iii*)   With compass point at the intersection of the two segments, sweep a wide arc (10¢) intersecting both segments.
    (*iv*)   Maintain the same compass setting and measure an arc from each of these points to determine the fourth point (20¢).
    (*v*)   Draw the two segments to complete the square (20¢).
    The total is 90¢.

12.   Make an arc of radius BC with center A and one with radius AB and center C so that the two intersect. This intersection is the location of the fourth vertex.

13.   (a)   PQ is the perpendicular bisector of AB.

     (b)   Q is on the perpendicular bisector of AB because AQ $\simeq$ QB. Similarly, P is on the perpendicular bisector of AB. Because a unique line contains two points, the perpendicular bisector contains PQ.

     (c)   PQ is the angle bisector of $\angle$ APB; QC is the angle bisector of $\angle$ AQB.

     (d) $\triangle$ APQ $\simeq$ $\triangle$ BPQ by SSS; thus $\angle$ APQ $\simeq$ $\angle$ BPQ by CPCTC. Similarly, $\triangle$ AQC $\simeq$ $\triangle$ BQC so so $\angle$ AQC $\simeq$ $\angle$ BQC.

14.   (a)   See problem 10.

     (b)   Construct two perpendicular segments bisecting each other and congruent to the given diagonal.

     (c)   There is no unique rectangle. The endpoints of two segments bisecting each other and congruent to the given diagonal determine a rectangle. Since the segments may intersect at any angle, there are infinitely many such rectangles.

     (d)   Without the angle between the sides, there is no unique parallelogram.

     (e)   Construct two perpendicular segments bisecting each other and congruent to the given diagonals.

14. (f)   Not possible; the sum of the measures of the angles would be greater than 180°.

     (g)   Not possible; the fourth angle must also be a right angle.

     (h)   Not possible; the kite would not be unique without knowing lengths of some sides.

     (i)   The kite would not be unique, but would be a square.

     (j)   Consider △ ABC and the angle bisector $\overline{CD}$. Since $\overline{AC} \simeq \overline{BC}$, then $\overline{CD} \perp \overline{AB}$. It is possible to construct △ ADC, since $\overline{AD}$ is half as long as the base and m(∠ DAC) = 90° − $\frac{1}{2}$m(∠ ACB).

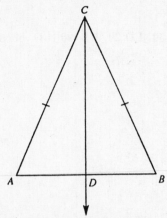

     (k)   There is no unique trapezoid unless two sides are designated as parallel. If this is the case, consider the trapezoid ABCD. Through B, construct $\overline{BE}\|\overline{CD}$. It follows that $\overline{BE} \simeq \overline{CD}$. Also, AE = AD − ED = AD − BC. Thus, △ ABE can be constructed by SSS. Now extend $\overline{AE}$ so that $\overline{ED} \simeq \overline{BC}$, and through B draw $\overline{BC}$ parallel to $\overline{AE}$. If the four given sides, though, are such that △ ABE cannot be constructed, the trapezoid cannot be constructed.

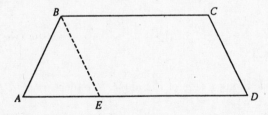

15. (a)   Construct a 60° angle (equilateral triangle) and bisect it.

     (b)   Bisect a 30° angle.

     (c)   Add 30° and 15° angles.

     (d)   Add 60° and 15° angles.

     (e)   Add 90° and 15° angles.

16. Make arcs of the same radius from A and B above $\overline{AB}$ and label their intersection C. Repeat the process with a new radius, labeling this intersection D. $\overleftrightarrow{CD}$ is the perpendicular bisector of $\overline{AB}$.

17. (a)   Since the triangles are congruent, the acute angles formed by the hypotenuse and the line are congruent. Since the corresponding angles are congruent, the hypotenuses are parallel (the line is formed by the top of the ruler).

17. (b) Beginning with the given line containing the hypotenuse, slide the triangle along the ruler until the hypotenuse passes through P.

18. Align the ruler with *l* and place the triangle with one leg on the ruler; slide the triangle until the other leg passes through P. Tracing along this leg will produce the desired line.

19. Let *l* be the given line and P a point not on *l*. Through P draw any line k intersecting *l*. That line forms ∠ 1 with *l*. Construct ∠ 2 congruent to ∠ 1 so that the two angles are alternate interior angles. Line *m* (which contains a side of ∠ 2) is parallel to *l*.

20. Answers may vary.
    TO ALTITUDES
      REPEAT 3 [RT 30 FD 60 RT 90 FD 110 BK 130 FD 20 LT 90 FD 60 RT 90]
    END

21. Answers may vary.

    (a) TO ANGBIS :MEAS
          REPEAT 3 [FD 75 BK 75 RT :MEAS/21]
        END

    (b) TO PERBIS :SIZE
        FD :SIZE/2 RT 90 FD :SIZE BK
        :SIZE/2 FD :SIZE RT 90 FD
        :SIZE/2
        END

    (c) TO PARALLEL :SEG1 :SEG2
        FD :SEG1 PENUP RT 90
        FD 20 RT 90 PENDOWN
        FD :SEG2
        END

22. △ ABC ≃ △ DEC by ASA. $\overline{AC} \simeq \overline{DC}$ by CPCTC.

23. (a) Copy the angle, then measure off each side along a side of the angle. Connect.

    (b) Copy $\overline{AB}$. Make arcs from A and B, one with radius AC, the other with radius BC. Their intersection is C. Connect.

    (c) Copy the side; copy the angles at opposite ends, extending their sides until they meet to form the triangle.

24. (a) No.

    (b) Yes.
        (*i*)   △ LYC ≃ △ UCY by SAS.
        (*ii*) △ ULY ≃ △ LUC by SAS.
        (*iii*) △ LOY ≃ △ UOC by ASA.

Problem Set 11-4

1. Folding the circle over on itself in two different directions will locate the center.

2.   No. The tangent line to any inner circle will intersect the outer circle in two points.

3.   (a)   90°   (b)   90°

      (c)   90°

      (d)   Any angle with its vertex on a circle and sides intersecting the endpoints of a diameter of that circle is
             a right angle.

      (e)   △ AOC and △ BOC are isosceles (radii are concruent), with ∠ OAC ≃ OCA and
             ∠ OAC ≃ ∠ OBC. All angles of a triangle add to 180°; here then ∠ OAC + ∠ OCA + ∠ OCB +
             ∠ OBC = 180°. Substituting for the congruent angles gives ∠ OCA + ∠ OCA + ∠ OCB + ∠ OCB
             = 180°, or 2(∠ OCA + ∠ OCB) = 180°; thus ∠ OCA + ∠ OCB (i.e., ∠ ACB) = 90°.

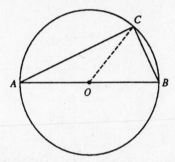

4.   Inscribe a regular hexagon as shown in Figure 11-38. Then bisect vertical angles either formed by diagonals
      or sides (the same lines serve both purposes) to locate the additional vertices on the circle.

5.   Inscribe a square as described in Figure 11-39. Then bisect either the vertical angles or the sides (both
      processes result in the same lines) to locate the additional vertices in the circle.

6.   (a)   Construct as described.   (b)   Measure as described.

      (c)   Opposite angles of inscribed quadrilaterals add to 180°.

7.   The circle will touch the midpoints of all sides. Bisect two opposite sides to locate the center of the circle;
      measure from the located center to the midpoint of a side for the radius.

8.   No. It is only possible if the sides are equidistant from some point.

9.   Construct a perpendicular from O to *l* to obtain the radius. Then draw the circle with the compass.
      (Construct the perpendicular as in Figure 11-28)

10.   Bisect either pair of interior angles on the same side of the transversal. The center of the circle is the point
      of intersection of the angle bisectors.

11.   (a)   Isosceles.

      (b)   m(∠ 1) + m(∠ 2) = m(∠ 3). Angles 1 and 2 add with ∠ BOC to 180° (total of angles of a
             triangle), and ∠ 3 also adds with ∠ BOC to 180° (straight line). The two quantities must then be
             equal.

      (c)   m(∠ 1) = ½m(∠ 3). m(∠ 1) + m(∠ 2) = m(∠ 3), and m(∠ 1) = m(∠ 2) (base angles of isosceles
             triangle OBC).

      (d)   In (c), ∠ 1 is formed by two chords and ∠ 3 is formed by radii from O to points opposite ∠ 1. In
             both circles (a) and (b), α and β have the same relationship. Thus in each case, α = ½β.

11. (e)   Angles 1, 2, and 3 are all formed by chords intersecting the same points on the major arc.
            Thus m($\angle$ 1) = m($\angle$ 2) = m($\angle$ 3).

12. (a)   0, 1, or 2, depending on how the line is chosen.

    (b)   0, 1, or infinitely many, depending on how the plane is chosen.

13. (a)   270° (three right angles).

    (b)   180° (two right angles).

14. Given that $\overline{AB} \simeq \overline{CD}$ (see below), then $\overline{AM} \simeq \overline{MB}$ and $\overline{CN} \simeq \overline{ND}$. $\triangle$ AOB $\simeq \triangle$ COD, so $\angle$ A $\simeq \angle$ C.
    $\triangle$ AMO $\simeq \triangle$ CNO (by SAS), so $\overline{OM} \simeq \overline{ON}$.

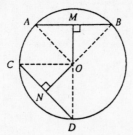

15. The radius r of the circle is half the distance between the parallel lines. The center of the circle is on line n
    parallel to the given lines and equidistant from these lines. The center of the circle can be obtained by
    finding the point of intersection of line n with the circle whose center is at P and whose radius is r.

16. Answers may vary.
    TO FILL.CIRCLE :RADIUS
      REPEAT 360 [FD :RADIUS BK :RADIUS RT 1]
    END

17. Answers may vary.
    TO DIAMETER
      REPEAT 360 [FD 1 RT 1] RT 90 FD 100
    END

18. $\overline{AB}$

19. In $\triangle$ ABC, $\angle$ B is included between $\overline{AB}$ and $\overline{BC}$.

20. If $\angle$ A is not the right angle, the triangles are congruent. If $\angle$ A is the right angle, the triangles are not
    necessarily congruent.

21. The bisector of one of a pair of vertical angles bisects the other if extended, forming two new pairs of vertical
    angles.

Problem Set 11-5

1. (a)   Similar by AAA, since all angles are 60°.

   (b)   Similar. Sides are proportional and angles congruent.

   (c)   Not always similar.   (d)   Not always similar.

1.   (e)   Similar; radii are proportional.

      (f)   Not always similar.

      (g)   Similar. Sides are proportional and angles congruent.

2.   Make all dimensions three times as long; e.g., in (c) each side would be three diagonal units long.

   (a)

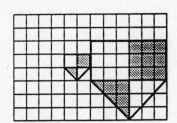

   (b)

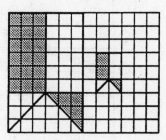

   (c)

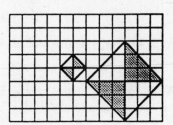

   (d)

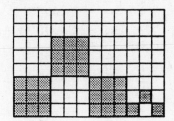

3.   Yes. The scale factor is 1 and the angles are congruent.

4.   (a) and (b)   Construct triangles as outlined.

      (c)   The triangles are similar when corresponding sides are proportional.

5.   (a) and (b)   Construct triangles as outlined.

      (c)   The triangles are similar when, for example, in $\triangle$ ABC and $\triangle$ DEF, $\frac{AB}{DE} = \frac{AC}{DF}$ and $\angle$ A $\simeq$ $\angle$ D.

6.   Answers may vary, but possibilities are:

      (a)   Two rectangles, one of which is a square and the other is not.

      (b)   Two rhombuses with the same length sides but with differing angles.

7.   The ratio of the perimeters is the same as the ratio of the sides.

8.   (a)   (*i*) $\triangle$ ABC $\sim$ $\triangle$ DEF by AA   (*ii*) $\triangle$ ABC $\sim$ $\triangle$ EDA by AA

           (*iii*) $\triangle$ ACD $\sim$ $\triangle$ ABE by AA   (*iv*) $\triangle$ ABE $\sim$ $\triangle$ DBC by AA

      (b)   (*i*)   2:3   (*ii*)   1:2

           (*iii*)   3:4   (*iv*)   3:4

9.   (a) $\frac{\text{short side}}{\text{long side}} = \frac{5}{10} = \frac{x}{x + 7}$. Solving, $5(x + 7) = 10x$, or $x = 7$.

      (b) $\frac{3}{x} = \frac{7}{8}$. Solving, $7x = 3\cdot8$, or $x = \frac{24}{7}$.

      (c) $\frac{x}{6} = \frac{x + 4}{14}$. Solving, $14 x = 6(x + 4)$, or $x = 3$.

9. (d) $\frac{x}{12-x} = \frac{8}{5}$. Solving, $8(12-x) = 5x$, or $x = \frac{96}{13}$.

10. Follow the procedure illustrated in Figure 11-49.

11. Lay the licorice diagonally on the paper so that it spans a number of spaces equal to the number of children. Cut on the lines. Equidistant parallel lines will divide any transversal into congruent segments.

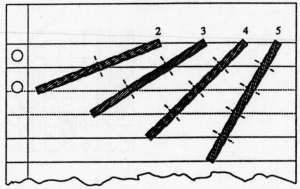

12. (a)   (i) $\triangle$ ABC $\sim$ $\triangle$ ACD by AA since $\angle$ ADC and $\angle$ ACB are right angles and $\angle$ A is common to both.

        (ii) $\triangle$ ABC $\sim$ $\triangle$ CBD by AA since $\angle$ CDB and $\angle$ ACB are right angles and $\angle$ B is common to both.

        (iii) $\triangle$ ACD $\sim$ $\triangle$ CBD by the transitive property.

    (b)   (i)   AC:AB = CD:CB = AD:AC   (ii) CB:AB = CD:AC = DB:CB

        (iii) AC:CB = AD:CD = CD:DB

13. No. The maps are similar and even though the scales may change, the actual distances do not.

14. $\frac{6}{x} = \frac{4}{10}$, so $x = 15$.

15. The setup forms similar triangles with proportional sides satisfying $\frac{150}{300} = \frac{x}{1800}$, where x is the height of the tree. Solving, $300x = 150 \cdot 1800$, or $x = 900$ cm. We could have as easily converted all measurements to meters, finding $x = 9$ m.

16. (a)   (i)   45°-45°-90°. Bisecting a 90° angle forms two more 45°-45°-90° triangles.

        (ii) 36°-72°-72°. Bisecting a 72° angle forms another 36°-72°-72° triangle and a 36°-36°-108° triangle.

    (b)   (i)   The two smaller triangles are congruent by ASA. All three triangles are similar by AA.

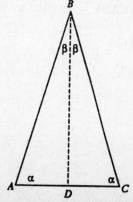

16. (b) (*ii*) The two 36°-72°-72° triangles are similar. No triangles are congruent.

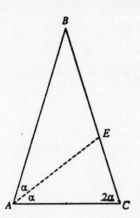

17. Converting all measurements to inches (3 feet = 36 inches; 7 feet = 84 inches) and using similar triangles gives $\frac{36}{13} = \frac{x}{84}$. Solving, 13x = 36·84, or x $\doteq$ 232.6 inches $\doteq$ 19.38 feet.

18. $\frac{3/4}{3} = \frac{72}{x}$. Solving, x = 288; i.e., the projector should be placed so that the slide is 288 inches, or 23 feet 9 inches, from the screen.

19. CF = 13 m; AE = 12 m.
Construct $\overline{BP}$ perpendicular to $\overline{CF}$. $\triangle$ CBP $\simeq$ $\triangle$ DFE by AAS because $\overline{BC} \simeq \overline{FD}$ (opposite sides of a rectangle) and $\angle$ DEF $\simeq$ $\angle$ CPB (right angles). From $\angle$ FDE $\simeq$ $\angle$ CFD (alternate interior angles between the parallels $\overleftrightarrow{CF}$ and $\overleftrightarrow{DE}$ and the transversal $\overleftrightarrow{DF}$) and $\angle$ CFD $\simeq$ $\angle$ BCP (alternate interior angles between $\overleftrightarrow{FD}\|\overleftrightarrow{BC}$ and the transversal $\overleftrightarrow{CF}$) it follows that $\angle$ FDE $\simeq$ $\angle$ BCP. By CPCTC, $\overline{CP} \simeq \overline{DE}$ and hence CP = DE = 4 m. CF = PF + CP; because ABPF is a rectangle, PF = BA = 9 m, and thus CF = 9 + 4 = 13 m. $\overline{AF} \simeq \overline{BP}$ (ABPF is a rectangle) and $\overline{FE} \simeq \overline{BP}$ (CPCTC in $\triangle$ CBP and $\triangle$ DFE). Consequently $\overline{AF} \simeq \overline{FE}$. $\triangle$ ABF $\sim$ $\triangle$ EFD (by AA since $\angle$ AFB and $\angle$ FDE are complements of $\angle$ DFE and each triangle has a right angle.) Consequently AF:EF = AF:ED, or 9:EF = AF:4, or EF·AF = 36. Because $\overline{EF} \simeq \overline{AF}$, we have $(EF)^2 = 36$, or EF = 6. Because AE = 2(EF), AE = 12 m.

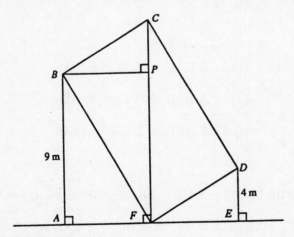

20. Answers may vary.

(a) TO RECTANGLE :LEN :WID
      REPEAT 2 [FD :LEN RT 90 FD :WID RT 90]
    END

    TO SIM.RECT :LEN :WID
      RECTANGLE :LEN∗2 :WID∗2
    END

20.   (b)   TO SIM.RECTANGLE :LEN :WID :SCALE
              RECTANGLE :LEN*:SCALE :WID*:SCALE
          END

      (c)   TO PARALLELOGRAM :LEN :WID :ANGLE
              REPEAT 2 [FD :LEN RT 180 − :ANGLE FD :WID RT :ANGLE]
          END

            TO SIM.PAR :LEN :WID :ANGLE :SCALE
              PARALLELOGRAM :LEN*:SCALE :WID*:SCALE :ANGLE
          END

21.   Answers may vary.

      (a)   TO TRISECT :LEN
              REPEAT 3 [MARK FD :LEN/3]
          END

            TO MARK
              RT 90 FD 5 BK 5 LT 90
          END

      (b)   TO PARTITION :LEN :NUM
              REPEAT :NUM [MARK FD :LEN/:NUM]
          END

22.   No. The image is two-dimensional while the person is three-dimensional.

23.   Copy the base and construct its perpendicular bisector. Measure the length of the altitude and mark it off
      on the bisector from the midpoint of the base. Connect endpoints of the base with the end of the altitude.

No solutions exist for Problem Set 11-6, for answers see your Instructor's Resource Guide.

Chapter 11 Test

1.   (a)   △ ADB ≃ △ CDB by SAS   (b)   △ GAC ≃ △ EDB by SAS

      (c)   △ ABC ≃ △ EDC by SAA   (d)   △ BAD ≃ △ EAC by ASA

      (e)   △ ABD ≃ △ CBD by ASA or by SAS   (f)   △ ABD ≃ △ CBD by SAS

      (g)   △ ABD ≃ △ CBE by SSS

      (h)   △ ABD ≃ △ ADC by SSS; △ ABE ≃ △ ADE by SSS or SAS; △ EBC ≃ △ EDC by SSS or SAS

2.   A parallelogram. △ EDA ≃ △ FBC by SAS, so ∠ DAE ≃ ∠ BCF. Thus $90° − ∠ EAD = 90° − ∠ FCB$
      $= ∠ BFC$ (i.e., ∠ EAF ≃ ∠ CFB). With these corresponding angles congruent, $\overline{AE} \| \overline{FC}$; $\overline{EC} \| \overline{AF}$ from the
      square. Two pairs of parallel opposite sides implies a parallelogram.

3.   (a)   (i)   See Figure 11-25.

            (ii)   Fold the angle down the middle so the sides match and the crease passes through A.

      (b)   (i)   See Figure 11-27.

            (ii)   Fold the line on top of itself so that the crease passes through B.

3.   (c)   (*i*)   See Figure 11-28.

        (*ii*)   Same as (b).

      (d)   (*i*)   See Figure 11-22 or 11-23.

        (*ii*)   Make line $k \perp l$ through P as in (b) and (c), then make $m \perp k$ through P as in (b).   Then $m \parallel l$.

4.   (a) $x = 8; y = 5$ (b) $x = 6$

5.   See Figure 11-49.

6. $\frac{a}{b} = \frac{c}{d}$.   In $\triangle$ ABC, $\frac{a}{b} = \frac{x}{y}$; in $\triangle$ ACD, $\frac{x}{y} = \frac{c}{d}$.   Using the transitive property, $\frac{a}{b} = \frac{c}{d}$.

7. $\overline{AB}$ must be a chord of the circle.   The perpendicular bisector of a chord passes through the center, so construct this line to locate the center on *l*.   Measure the radius to A or B and draw the circle with your compass.

8.   (a) $\triangle$ ACB $\sim$ $\triangle$ DEB by AA; $x = \frac{24}{5}$.

      (b) $\triangle$ AED $\sim$ $\triangle$ ACB by AA; $\frac{4}{6} = \frac{y + 6}{11}$, so $y = \frac{4}{3}$; $\frac{6}{5} = \frac{11}{x}$, so $x = \frac{55}{6}$.

9.   (a)   False.   A chord has both endpoints on the circle.

      (b)   False.   A diameter intersects a circle at two points; a tangent at only one.

      (c)   True.   (d)   True.

      (e)   True.

10.   12 m high.

11.   (a)   (*iii*) and (*iv*).

      (b)   Any regular convex polygon can be inscribed in a circle.

12.   h = 6 m.

13. $\frac{d}{64} = \frac{16}{20}$, so d = $\frac{256}{5}$ m.

14.   (a)   Sometimes.   If the diagonals bisect each other, then the quadrilateral is a square.   If they do not bisect each other, then it is not a square.

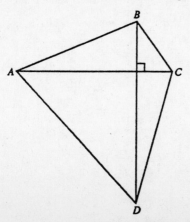

14. (b)   Always true. The intersection of the perpendicular bisectors of the two non-parallel sides is also on the perpendicular bisector of the bases and thus determines the center of the circle.

CHAPTER 12 - MOTION GEOMETRY AND TESSELLATIONS

1. (a) A skier skiing straight down a slope moves in a translation because there is no accompanying twisting or turning.

   (b) A floating leaf would include both translation and rotating.

2. (a) 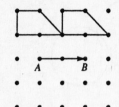   (b)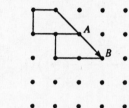

3. Reverse the translation so that the image completes a slide from X′ to X (to what is called its pre-image). Then check by carrying out the given motion in the "forward" direction; i.e., see if $\overline{AB}$ goes to A′B′.

   (a) 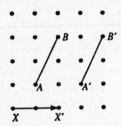   (b)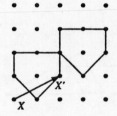

4. (a) Complete as shown in Figure 12-2.

   (b) Construct a parallelogram as in Figure 12-4.

5. Answers may vary. Some are ceiling fans, clock hands, or compact discs.

6.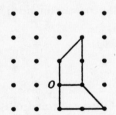

7. Reverse the rotation (to the counterclockwise direction) to locate $\overline{AB}$; i.e., the pre-image.

   (a) 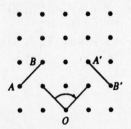   (b)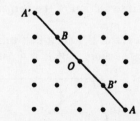

8. (a)   Answers may vary, but H, I, N, O, S, X, or Z could appear in such rotational words. Examples include SOS. Variations could use M and W in rotational images; e.g., MOW.

    (b)   1, 8, 11, 69, 88, 96, 101, 111, 181, 609, 619, 689, 808, 818, 888, 906, 916, 986, 1001, 1111, 1691, 1881, 1961, 6009, 6119, 6699, 6889, 6969, 8008, 8118, 8698, 8888, 8968, 9006, 9116, 9696, 9886, 9966.

9. (a)   (b)

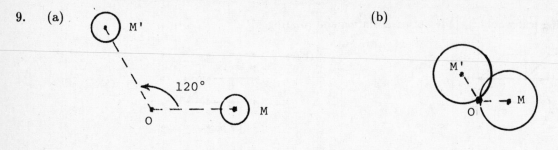

10. (a)   (b)

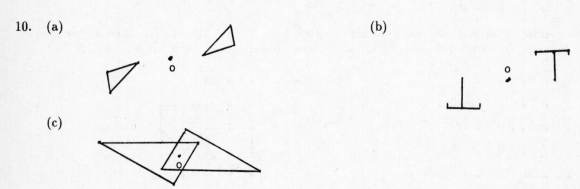

    (c)

11. Step 1: Draw $\overline{PP'}$. Step 2: Find the midpoint of $\overline{PP'}$ — call this midpoint X. Step 3: Draw the line through Q and X. Step 4: Measure off the distance from Q to X, then mark off the same distance on the opposite side of Q. Call this point Q′. Q′ is the image of Q under the half-turn.

12. (a)   Complete as indicated.

    (b)   A rotation in the direction of the larger of α and β, having their difference as magnitude.

    (c)   No.   (d)   Yes, as in (b).

13. (a)   A circle.

    (b)   The vertices A and B trace an identical path if and only if OA = OB; i.e., if and only if O is on the perpendicular bisector of $\overline{AB}$. Thus all points O for which two vertices trace an identical path are the points on the perpendicular bisectors of the sides of the triangle.

    (c)   Yes. The intersection of the perpendicular bisectors (center of the circumscribed circle).

14. (a)   A parallelogram. Under a half-turn the image of a line is parallel to the line. Thus $\overline{AB} \parallel \overline{CD}$ and $\overline{AC} \parallel \overline{DB}$; therefore ABCD is a parallelogram.

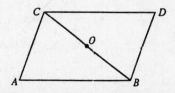

14. (b) A parallelogram. The image of $\overline{AB}$ is $\overline{FE}$ and thus $\overline{AB} \parallel \overline{EF}$. Consequently $\overline{BF} \parallel \overline{AE}$ and ABFE is a parallelogram.

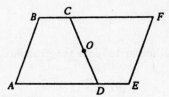

     (c) A square. Because the image of A is C and the image of B is D, the image of ABCD is CDAB.

15. (a) $l' = l$ (b) $l' \parallel l$

     (c) $l' \perp l$ (d) l' and l intersect at a 60° angle.

16. (a) Construct the image m' of m under a half-turn about P. Point A is the intersection of m' and l. Draw from A through P to locate B on m.

     (b) No. In fact, it will work only if P is on a third parallel line midway between l and m.

17. (a) Execute the program.

     (b) TO SLIDE :DIRECTION :DISTANCE :SIDE
      EQUILATERAL :SIDE
      SETHEADING :DIRECTION
      FORWARD :DISTANCE
      PENDOWN
      SETHEADING 0
      EQUILATERAL :SIDE
    END

    TO EQUILATERAL :SIDE
      REPEAT 3 [FORWARD :SIDE RIGHT 120]
    END

18. TO ROTATE :A :SIDE
  SQUARE :SIDE
  RIGHT :A
  SQUARE :SIDE
 END

 TO SQUARE :SIDE
  REPEAT 4 [FORWARD :SIDE RIGHT 90]
 END

19. (a) TO TURN.CIRCLE :A
      CIRCLE
      LEFT :A
      CIRCLE
    END

    TO CIRCLE
      REPEAT 360 [FORWARD 1 RT 1]
    END

     To produce the desired transformation, execute TURN.CIRCLE 180.

19.   (b)   To produce the desired transformation, execute TURN.CIRCLE 90.

Problem Set 12-2

1.   Locate the image of vertices directly across (perpendicular to) *l* on the geoboard.

(a)   (b)

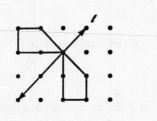   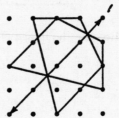

2.   (a)

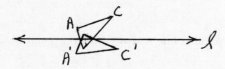

(b)   Yes. Find the images of A and C (A′ and C′). Label the point of intersection of $\overline{AB}$ and line *l* as point P; label the point of intersection of $\overline{BC}$ and line *l* as point Q. Draw $\overline{A'P}$ and $\overline{C'Q}$. The intersection of these lines is B′.

3.   Find the image of the center of the circle and one point on the circumference of the circle to determine the image of the circle.

4.   Reflecting lines are described for each.

(a)   All diameters (infinitely many).

(b)   Perpendicular bisector and line containing the segment.

(c)   Line containing the ray.

(d)   Perpendicular bisectors of sides and lines containing diagonals.

(e)   Perpendicular bisectors of pairs of parallel sides.

(f)   None.

(g)   Perpendicular bisector of the side that is not congruent to the other two.

(h)   Perpendicular bisectors of each of the sides.

(i)   None.

(j)   Perpendicular bisector of parallel sides.

(k)   Perpendicular bisector of the chord connecting the endpoints of the arc.

(l)   The diagonal determined by vertices of the noncongruent angles.

(m)   The diagonals.

4. (n)   Perpendicular bisectors of parallel sides and three diameters determined by vertices on circumscribed circle.

    (o)   Same as (n). There will be *n* reflecting lines in all.

5. As directed.

6. The original figure.

7. The images are congruent but in different locations.

8. (a)   Same as in problem 7.

    (b)   For *l* ⊥ *m*, the images are the same regardless of order of reflection.

9.

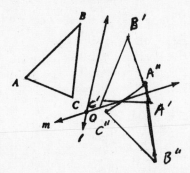

10. (a)   Examples include MOM, WOW, TOOT, HAH.

    (b)   Examples include BOX, HIKE, CODE, etc. B, C, D, E, H, I, K(depending on construction), O, X may be used.

    (c)   1, 8, 11, 88, 101, 181, 808, 818, 888, 1001, 1111, 1881, 8008, 8118, 8888.

11. (a)   If AB = BC then the perpendicular bisector of $\overline{AC}$ is the required line. Because a point is on the perpendicular bisector of $\overline{AC}$ if and only if it is equidistant from A and C, the image of B when reflected in L is B and the image of A is C. Hence the image of △ ABC is △ CBA.

    (b)   Equilateral triangles. Each side could be considered as the base.

    (c)   No. Since no sides (or angles) are congruent, bisecting any side or angle will leave non-congruent portions of the triangle on opposite sides of the bisector.

    (d)   All lines containing diameters will satisfy this situation. Diameters divide a circle into two congruent semicircles.

12. See Figure 12-34 in the text.

13. (a)   For glide reflections with the translation parallel to the reflection line, the images are the same regardless of order.

    (b)   Reflections and translations are commutative only for the conditions described in (a).

14. None of the images has a reverse orientation, so there are no reflections or glide reflections involved. Thus:
    1 to 2 is a counterclockwise rotation.
    1 to 3 is a clockwise rotation.
    1 to 4 is a translation down.
    1 to 5 is a rotation (with an exterior point as the center of rotation).
    1 to 6 is a translation (sides are parallel to 1).
    1 to 7 is a translation (sides are parallel).

15. Construct as suggested.

16. Reflect B about lines containing the sides of contact in reverse order to obtain B''', B'', and B'. Align A and B''' to locate the point to aim at (call this A'). To draw the path of the ball, align A' and B'' to locate A''; then A'' and B' to locate A''', the last point of contact before striking B. See below.

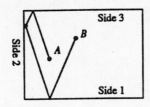

17. Reflect A about road 1 to locate A', and B about road 2 to locate B'. Align A' and B' to locate P and Q. This is an extension of the problem illustrated in Figure 12-31. Reflecting A and B creates the straight-line (i.e., shortest) path $A'B'$, which by construction is equal to the distance (AP + PQ + QB) for the actual roads.

18. The angle of incidence is the same as the angle of reflection. With the mirrors tilted 45°, the object's image reflects to 90° down the tube; then 90° to the eyepiece. The two reflections "counteract" each other, leaving the image upright.

19. (a) ⁻150° rotation about the turtle's starting point.

    (b) Reflection about a vertical line containing the turtle's starting point.

    (c) 45° rotation and slide.

20. (a) Answers may vary.

    (b) The drawing produced in FIG2 is a reflection of the drawing produced by FIG1 through a horizontal line that contains the starting point of the turtle.

    (c) The drawing produced by FIG3 is a reflection to the drawing produced by FIG1 through a vertical line that contains the starting point of the turtle.

21. (a)   TO EQTRI :SIDE
             REPEAT 3 [FORWARD :SIDE RIGHT 120]
            END

    (b)   TO EQTRI2 :SIDE
             REPEAT 3 [FORWARD :SIDE LEFT 120]
            END

    (c)   A reflection in a vertical line through the turtle's home.

    (d)   A half-turn with the turtle's home as center.

22. For a rotation of 360°, all letters. For 180°, see problem 23. No other rotations result in the original letter.

23. H, I, N, O, S, Z.

24. A half-turn about the center of the letter O.

25. (a)   A rotation of any angle about the center of the circle will result in the same circle.

    (b)   Reflections about lines containing diameters.

Problem Set 12-3

1.   (a) and (b). Changing or order of reflection leads to a different final image in both cases. The only case in which the images will not be different is when $l \perp m$.

2. (a)   The translation given by slide arrow $\overrightarrow{NM}$ (N to M).

    (b)   A counterclockwise rotation of 75° about O.

    (c)   A clockwise rotation of 45° about A.

    (d)   A reflection about m and translation $\overrightarrow{BA}$.

    (e)   A second reflection in n.

3. (a)   (4, 3) reflects about m to (4, 1); (4, 1) reflects about n to (2, 1).

    (b)   (0, 1) → (0, 3) → (6, 3)

    (c)   ($^{-}$1, 0) → ($^{-}$1, 4) → (7, 4)

    (d)   (0, 0) → (0, 4) → (6, 4).

4. The scale factor $= \dfrac{A'B'}{AB} = \dfrac{3}{4}$. The center must be the intersection of $\overrightarrow{AA'}$, $\overrightarrow{BB'}$, and $\overrightarrow{CC'}$.

5.   (a)   Slide the small triangle down three units (translation), then complete a size transformation with scale factor 2 using the top right vertex as the center.

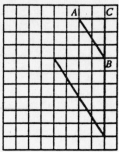

     (b)   Slide right 5, up 1, then complete the size transformation as in (a).

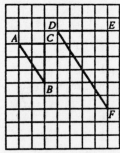

     (c)   Rotate 90° counterclockwise with the lower right vertex of the small triangle as the center of rotation. Then size transformation with scale factor 2 using the same point as center.

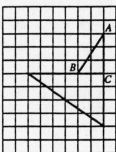

6.

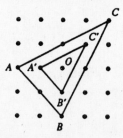

7.   (a)   Translation taking B to B′ followed by a size transformation with center B′ (and scale factor approximately 2).

     (b)   Rotate 90° counterclockwise using center B, translate to take B to B′, and then a size translation with a scale factor of approximately $\frac{1}{2}$.

     (c)   Half-turn with the midpoint of $\overline{AA'}$ as center, followed by a size transformation with scale factor approximately $\frac{1}{2}$ and center A′.

     (d)   Half-turn about C followed by a size transformation with center C and scale factor approximately $\frac{3}{2}$.

1. (a)   (*i*)   Yes. A geometrical figure has line symmetry if it is its own image under a reflection in some line. A line may be drawn through the center circle, either horizontally or vertically, about which the figure is its own image. The line may also be drawn through any of the sets of arrows.

        (*ii*)   Yes. The figure will match the original figure after rotations of 90˚, 180˚, or 270˚.

        (*iii*) Yes. Any figure having 180˚ rotational symmetry has point symmetry about the turn center.

    (b)   (*i*)   Yes. A vertical line through the middle of the bulb is a line of symmetry.

        (*ii*)   No. The figure will not match the original under rotations of less than 360 ˚.

        (*iii*) No. The figure does not have 180˚ rotational symmetry.

    (c)   (*i*)   Yes. A vertical line through the stem is a line of symmetry.

        (*ii*)   No.   (*iii*)   No.

    (d)   (*i*)   Yes. A horizontal line through the middle of the plane is a line of symmetry.

        (*ii*)   No.   (*iii*)   No.

2. Answers may vary, but some possibilites are:

    (a)   The Yellow Pages symbol.   (b)   A regular pentagon (Chrysler symbol).

    (c)   The letter N.

3. Reflect the given portions about *l*.

    (a)   (b)

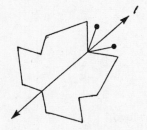   

4. (a)   (*i*)   Switzerland has four lines of symmetry; the diagonals and horizontal or vertical lines through the center.

        (*ii*)   South Korea has no lines of symmetry.

        (*iii*) Israel has two lines of symmetry; horizontally and vertically through the center.

        (*iv*)   Barbados has one line of symmetry; vertically through the center.

4.   (b)   (*i*)   (*iii*)

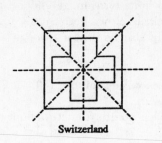

Switzerland

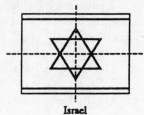

Israel

(*iv*)

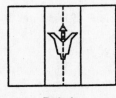

Barbados

5.   (a)   One line of symmetry; vertically through the center.

      (b)   One; vertically through the center.

      (c)   None.

      (d)   One; vertically through the center.

      (e)   Five; one through each vertex and its opposite face.

      (f)   One; vertically through the center.

6.   (a)   A scaline triangle.

      (b)   A strictly isosceles triangle.

      (c)   Not possible.

      (d)   An equilateral triangle.

7.   Answers may vary, but examples include the letter S and the Chevrolet logo.

8.   (a)   Yes. The definition of point symmetry is that it is rotational symmetry of 180°.

      (b)   No. It may have rotational symmetry of other than 180°; an equilateral triangle is an example.

      (c)   Yes. A circle is an example, or the figure in problem 1(a) of this Problem Set.

      (d)   No. Consider the letter Z. (Neither is the converse true.)

      (e)   Yes. Point symmetry implies 180° rotational symmetry.

9. (a)   (b)

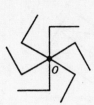

10. (a)   Seven; three through the "peaks", three through the "valleys", and one perpendicular to the others through the width of the figure.

    (b)   Two; one through the middle "peak" and one through the width.

    (c)   Seven; three through the vertices, three through the faces, and one perpendicular to the others through the width of the figure.

    (d)   33; 16 through the peaks, 16 through the valleys, and one through the width.

11. TO TURN.SYM :S :N :A
      REPEAT :N [SQUARE :S RIGHT :A]
    END

    TO SQUARE :S
      REPEAT 4 [FORWARD :S RIGHT 90]
    END

    (a)   Execute TURN.SYM 50 6 60   (b)   Execute TURN.SYM 50 3 120

    (c)   Execute TURN.SYM 50 2 180   (d)   Execute TURN.SYM 50 3 240

    (e)   Execute TURN.SYM 50 6 300

12. TO TURN.SY :S :N :A
      REPEAT :N [EQTRI :S RIGHT :A]
    END

    TO EQUITRI :S
      REPEAT 3 [FORWARD :S RIGHT 120]
    END

    (a)   Execute TURN.SY 50 6 60   (b)   Execute TURN.SY 50 3 120

    (c)   Execute TURN.SY 50 3 240   (d)   Execute TURN.SY 50 6 300

13. (a), (b), and (c): One method is to trace over the figure heavily, then fold at l and trace along the figure (as seen through the paper), copying the image with a "carbon paper" process.

14. (a), (b), and (c): Map the vertices perpendicularly across l and then connect them.

1.   (a)   (b)

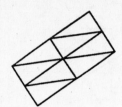

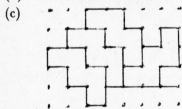

2.   (a)   Perform half-turns about the midpoints of all sides.

     (b)   Yes. If a polygon tessellates the plane, the sum of the angles around every vertex must be 360°.
           Successive 180° turns of a quadrilateral about the midpoints of its sides will produce four congruent
           quadrilaterals around a common vertex, with each of the quadrilateral's angles being represented at
           each vertex. These angles must add to 360°, as angles of any quadrilateral do.

3.   Experimentation by cutting shapes out and moving them about is one way to learn about these types of
     problems.

     (a)

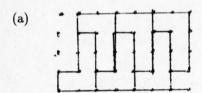

     (b)   Cannot be tessellated.
     (c)

3.   (d)   Tessellate as in (a).

4.   (a)   The dual is another tessellation of squares (congruent to those given).

     (b)   A tessellation of equilateral triangles.

     (c)   The tessellation of equilateral triangles illustrated in the statement of the problem.

5.   Hint: Consider figures like a pentagon formed by combining a square and an equilateral triangle, or
     the figure in Problem 7 on page 669 of the text.

6.   (a)   TO TESSELSQUARE
             PENUP BACK 70 PENDOWN
             REPEAT 9 [SQUARE 20 FORWARD 20]
             PENUP BACK 180 RIGHT 90
             FORWARD 20 LEFT 90 PENDOWN
             REPEAT 9 [SQUARE 20 FORWARD 20]
           END

6. (a)   TO SQUARE :SIDE
             REPEAT 4 [FORWARD :SIDE RIGHT 90]
           END

    (b)   TO TESSELTRI
             PENUP BACK 70 PENDOWN
             REPEAT 9 [TRIANGLE 20 FORWARD 20]
             PENUP BACK 180 RIGHT 60
             FORWARD 20 LEFT 60 PENDOWN
             REPEAT 9 [TRIANGLE 20 FORWARD 20]
           END

           TO TRIANGLE :SIDE
             REPEAT 3 [FORWARD :SIDE RIGHT 120]
           END

    (c)   TO TESSELHEX
             PENUP BACK 70 LEFT 90 PENDOWN
             REPEAT 4 [HEXAGON 20 RIGHT 120 FORWARD 20 LEFT 60 HEXAGON 20
               FORWARD 20 LEFT 60]
           END

           TO HEXAGON :SIDE
             REPEAT 6 [FORWARD :SIDE RIGHT 60]
           END

7. TO TILESTRIP :S
      REPEAT 4 [TILE :S PENUP RIGHT 180 FORWARD 3*:S PENDOWN]
    END

    TO TILE :S
     RIGHT 180
     REPEAT 3 [REPEAT 4 [FORWARD :S LEFT 60] RIGHT 120]
    END

Problem Set 12-6

1. TO WALL3 :XPT :YPT :SIDE
      DRAW
      SETUP :XPT :YPT
      WALLPAPER3 :YPT :SIDE
    END

    TO SETUP :XPT :YPT
     PENUP
     SETXY :XPT :YPT
     PENDOWN
    END

1. TO WALLPAPER :YPT :SIDE
       TRISTRIP :SIDE
       PENUP
       SETUP (:XPT + :SIDE*(SORT 3)/2) :YPT
       PENDOWN
       WALLPAPER3 :YPT :SIDE
    END

    TO TRISTRIP :SIDE
       IF XCOR + :SIDE > 120 TOPLEVEL
       IF (ANYOF (XCOR < −120)
          (XCOR + :SIDE*(SQRT 3)/2 > 120)
          (YCOR < −100)(YCOR + :SIDE > 100))
          STOP
       TRIANGLE :SIDE
       FORWARD :SIDE
       RIGHT 60
       TRIANGLE :SIDE
       LEFT 60
       TRISTRIP :SIDE
    END

    TO TRIANGLE :SIDE
       REPEAT 3 [FORWARD :SIDE RIGHT 120]
    END

2. The conditions are to keep the turtle from drawing off the screen. It forces the boundaries to be as follows:
    −120 < x < 120 and −100 < y < 100.

3. TO WALL4 :XPT :YPT :SIDE
       DRAW
       SETUP :XPT :YPT
       WALLPAPER4 :YPT :SIDE
    END

    TO SETUP :XPT :YPT
       PENUP
       SETXY :XPT :YPT
       PENDOWN
    END

    TO WALLPAPER4 :YPT :SIDE
       MAKE "X XCOR
       HEXSTRIP :SIDE
       PENUP
       SETUP (XCOR + :SIDE*(SQRT 3)) :YPT
       PENDOWN
       WALLPAPER4 :YPT :SIDE
    END

3. TO HEXSTRIP :SIDE
     IF XCOR + :SIDE > 120 TOPLEVEL
     IF (ANYOF (XCOR < −120) (XCOR + :SIDE*(SQRT 3)) > 120)
      (YCOR < −100) (YCOR + :SIDE*3 > 100)) STOP
     HEXAGON :SIDE
     FORWARD :SIDE RIGHT 60 FORWARD :SIDE LEFT 60
     HEXSTRIP :SIDE
    END

    TO HEXAGON :SIDE
     REPEAT 6 [FORWARD :SIDE RIGHT 60]
    END

4. Answers may vary.

5. Yes. Once the figures fit between two parallel lines, then one could make a rubber stamp of the parallel
    lines and the drawings between them and stamp them all across the plane.

6. TO WALL5 :XPT :YPT :SIDE1 :SIDE2
     DRAW
     SETUP :XPT :YPT
     WALLPAPER5 :YT :SIDE1 :SIDE2
    END

    TO SETUP :XPT :YPT
     PENUP
     SETXY :XPT :YPT
     PENDOWN
    END

    TO WALLPAPER5 :YPT :SIDE1 :SIDE2
     RECTANGLESTRIP :SIDE1 :SIDE2
     PENUP
     SETUP (XCOR + :SIDE2) :YPT
     PENDOWN
     WALLPAPER5 :YPT :SIDE1 :SIDE2
    END

    TO RECTANGLESTRIP :SIDE1 :SIDE2
     IF XCOR + :SIDE2 > 120 TOPLEVEL
     IF (ANYOF (XCOR < −120) (XCOR + :SIDE2 > 120) (YCOR < −100) (YCOR + :SIDE1 > 100))
      STOP
     RECTANGLE :SIDE1 :SIDE2
     FORWARD :SIDE1
     RECTANGLESTRIP :SIDE1 :SIDE2
    END

    TO RECTANGLE :SIDE1 :SIDE2
     REPEAT 2 [FORWARD :SIDE1 RIGHT 90 FORWARD :SIDE2 RIGHT 90]
    END

7. TO WALL6 :XPT :YPT :SIDE
     DRAW
     SETUP :XPT :YPT
     WALLPAPER6 :YPT :SIDE
    END

7. TO SETUP :XPT :YPT
    PENUP
    SETXY :XPT :YPT
    PENDOWN
    END

    TO WALLPAPER6 :YPT :SIDE
    CHEVRONSTRIP :SIDE
    PENUP
    SETUP (XCOR + :SIDE) :YPT
    PENDOWN
    WALLPAPER6 :YPT :SIDE
    END

    TO CHEVRONSTRIP :SIDE
    IF XCOR + :SIDE > 120 TOPLEVEL
    IF (ANYOF (XCOR − :SIDE < −120) (XCOR + :SIDE > 120)
      (YCOR − :SIDE*(SQRT 2)/2 < −100) (YCOR + :SIDE > 100)) STOP
    CHEVRON :SIDE
    FORWARD :SIDE
    CHEVRONSTRIP :SIDE
    END

    TO CHEVRONSTRIP :SIDE
    FORWARD :SIDE RIGHT 135
    FORWARD :SIDE*(SQRT 2)/2 LEFT 90
    FORWARD :SIDE*(SQRT 2)/2 RIGHT 135
    FORWARD :SIDE RIGHT 45
    FORWARD :SIDE*(SQRT 2)/2 RIGHT 90
    FORWARD :SIDE*(SQRT 2)/2 RIGHT 45
    END

Chapter 12 Test

1. (a)   (b)

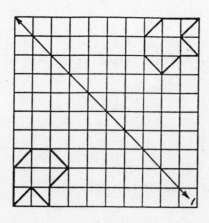
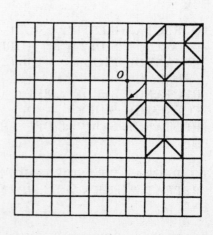

1.   (c)

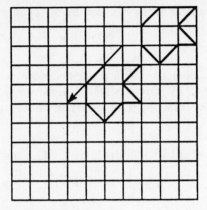

2.   (a), (b), and (c): Construction.

3.   (a)   Four; two diagonals, one each horizontal and vertical.

      (b)   One; the diagonal besecting the central angle.

      (c)   One; the bisector of the point angle.

      (d)   None.

      (e)   Two; horizontal through the points of intersection and vertical through the centers.

      (f)   Two; vertically and horizontally through the center.

4.   (a)   Line and rotational (120° and 240°).

      (b)   Line, rotational, and point.

      (c)   Line: vertically down the middle.

5.   (a)   Infinitely many.

      (b)   Infinitely many.

      (c)   Three; one each cutting the length, width, and height in half.

      (d)   Nine; the three in (c) as well as planes intersecting diagonals of each face.

6.   c, i, l, o, t, v, w, x: line symmetry. l, o, s, x, z: rotational symmetry. l, o, s, x, z: point symmetry.
      (Some variations may occur because of print styles.)

7.   The measure of each exterior angle of a regular octagon is $\frac{360°}{8} = 45°$, so the measure of each interior angle is
      $180 - 45 = 135°$. Because $135 \not| \, 3$ a regular octagon does not tessellate the plane.

8.   C must be equidistant to A and B. Constructing the perpendicular bisector of $\overline{AB}$ locates all such points.
      Either point of intersection of the bisector and the circle may be C.

9. $\overline{BC}$ is formed by the midpoints of $\overline{A'B'}$ and $\overline{A'C'}$.

10.   (a)   Half-turn about X.   (b)   Half-turn about X.

11.   (a)   Each central angle is 60°. BEAU and AUTY are thus 120° apart. A rotation of 120° clockwise will
             take BEAU to AUTY.

11. (b)   Reflection in $\overleftrightarrow{BV}$ followed by a rotation about the center of the hexagon by 60° counterclockwise.

12.   Reflection about $\overline{SO}$.

13.   If $\triangle$ SER was the image of $\triangle$ HOR under a succession of isometries with a size transformation, then $\triangle$ SER would be similar to $\triangle$ HOR which in turn would imply that ER/OR = SR/HR. However, $\frac{ER}{OR} = \frac{2}{3}$ and $\frac{SR}{HR} = \frac{5}{5}$. This contradiction implies that $\triangle$ SER is not the image of $\triangle$ HOR under any succession of isometries with size transformation.

14.   Answers may vary.   Rotate $\triangle$ PIG 180° (half-turn) about the midpoint of $\overline{PT}$, then perform a size transformation with scale factor 2 and center $P'(=T)$.

15.   Answers may vary.

CHAPTER 13 - CONCEPTS OF MEASUREMENT

Problem Set 13-1

1. (a) $AB = 1.0 \text{ cm} - 0.1 \text{ cm} = 0.9 \text{ cm}$ or 9 mm   (b) $DE = 4.5 \text{ cm} - 3.6 \text{ cm} = 0.9 \text{ cm}$ or 9 mm

    (c) $CJ = 10.0 - 2.0 = 8.0 \text{ cm}$ or 80 mm   (d) $EF = 5.0 - 4.5 = 0.5 \text{ cm}$ or 5 mm

    (e) $IJ = 10.0 - 9.3 = 0.7 \text{ cm}$ or 7 mm   (f) $AF = 5.0 - 0.1 = 4.9 \text{ cm}$ or 49 mm

    (g) $IC = 9.3 - 2.0 = 7.3 \text{ cm}$ or 73 mm   (h) $GB = 6.2 - 1.0 = 5.2 \text{ cm}$ or 52 mm

2. (a) $\dfrac{100 \text{ inches}}{36 \text{ inches per yard}} = \dfrac{25}{9} = 2\dfrac{7}{9}$ yards   (b) $(400 \text{ yds}) \cdot (36 \text{ inches per yd}) = 14{,}400$ inches

    (c) $\dfrac{300 \text{ feet}}{3 \text{ feet per yard}} = 100$ yards   (d) $\dfrac{372 \text{ inches}}{12 \text{ inches per foot}} = 31$ feet

3. (a) ———

    (b) _____

    (c) ———

    (d) _____

    (e) ———

    (f) _____

    (g) _____

    (h) ———

4. (a) 98 mm   (b) 9.8 cm

5. (a) Cm; a new pencil measures about 19 cm.   (b) Mm; the diameter is about 21 mm.

    (c) Cm or m; the width is about 120 cm or 1.2 m.

    (d) Cm or mm; the thickness is about 2 cm or 20 mm.

    (e) Cm; about 23 cm.

    (f) M or cm; the height is about 1.9 m or 190 cm.

    (g) M or cm; an average man's height is about 1.75 m (175 cm); an average woman's about 1.65 m (165 cm).

    (h) Cm or mm; about 15-20 cm or 150-200 mm.

6. (a) Inches   (b) Inches

    (c) Feet   (d) Inches

    (e) Inches   (f) Feet

    (g) Feet   (h) Inches

7.   In each case, note that:

From m to cm move decimal point two places to the right.
From cm to mm move decimal point one place to the right.
From mm to cm move decimal point one place to the left.
From cm to m move decimal point two places to the left.

(a)   0.35 m → ⎡35 cm⎤ → 350 mm

(b)   ⎡1.63 m⎤ → 163 cm → 1630 mm

(c)   0.035 m → 3.5 cm → ⎡35 mm⎤

(d)   0.1 m → 10 cm → ⎡100 mm⎤

(e)   ⎡2 m⎤ → 200 cm → 2000 mm

8.   (a)   10.00 mm   (b)   0.770 m

(c)   10.0 m   (d)   15.5 cm

(e)   195.0 cm   (f)   8.100 cm

(g)   40.0 km/hr

9. Convert each to cm: 8cm; 521.8 cm; 245 cm; 9.1 cm; 600 cm; 70 cm. In decreasing order, then, we have:
6 m; 5218 mm; 245 cm; 700 mm; 91 mm; 8 cm.

10.   (a)   E.g., an equilateral triangle with sides of 4 cm or a hexagon with 2 cm sides.

(b)   E.g., a circle with radius about $\frac{5}{8}$ inch.

(c)   E.g., a triangle with sides of 1, $1\frac{1}{2}$, and $1\frac{1}{2}$ inches.

(d)   E.g., a four-point star with 1 inch sides.

11.   (a)   8 cm   (b)   12 cm

(c)   9 cm   (d)   20 cm

12.   (a)   1   (b)   0.17

(c)   0.262   (d)   3000

(e)   0.03   (f)   170

(g)   3500   (h)   0.359

(i)   0.1   (j)   64.7

(k)   1   (l)   5000

(m)   5130

13.   (a), (b), (c).   The sum of the lengths of any two sides of a triangle is greater than the length of the third
side alone.

14. (a) Can be; $23 + 50 > 60$ (b) Cannot be: $10 + 40 \not> 50$

 (c) Cannot be

15. (a) Yes. A rhombus with $120°$ and $60°$ angles satisfies this condition. The shorter diagonal divides the triangle into two equilateral triangles; thus the sides of the rhombus must be the same length as the diagonal.

 (b) No. Either diagonal is the hypotenuse of a right triangle and must be longer than the legs (i.e., the sides of the square). The perimeter has to be less than 4 times the diagonal.

16. Arc length is to circumference as arc measure is to $360°$.

17. (a) The maximum perimeter is attained when the longer sides are part of the perimeter; e.g.:

 (b) The minimum perimeter is attained when the longer sides are not part of it; e.g., the original rectangle.

18. (a) One way is to add four squares to each row to form a 7-square by 2-square rectangle.

 (b) The minimum number of squares for a fixed perimeter is formed when the squares have the maximum number of sides exposed; nine are required.

 (c) Twenty squares forming a 4-square by 5-square rectangle are the maximum possible to achieve a perimeter of 18.

19. Circumference is 2π times the radius ($C = 2\pi r$), so $r = \frac{C}{2\pi}$:

 (a) $r = \frac{12\pi}{2\pi} = 6$ cm. (b) $r = \frac{6}{2\pi} = \frac{3}{\pi} \doteq 0.955$ m.

 (c) $r = \frac{0.67}{2\pi} = \frac{0.335}{\pi} \doteq 0.107$ m. (d) $r = \frac{92\pi}{2\pi} = 46$ cm.

20. $C = 2\pi r$ or πd:

 (a) $C = 6\pi$ cm. (b) $C = 2\pi \cdot 3 = 6\pi$ cm.

 (c) $C = 2\pi\left(\frac{2}{\pi}\right) = 4$ cm. (d) $C = \pi(6\pi) = 6\pi^2$ cm.

21. The circumference doubles; the relationship between the two measures is linear.

22. The arc length of each half-circle is half the circumference of a circle with diameter r, or $L = \frac{1}{2} \cdot \pi \cdot r$. Since there are two half-circles, the total arc length is πr.

23. The height is 3 tennis-ball-diameters. The perimeter is given by the circumference of a tennis ball, πd, and is thus about 3.14 tennis-ball-diameters.

24. (a) 2:1 (b) They are the same.

 (c) If $\triangle ABC \sim \triangle DEF$, with $\frac{DE}{AB} = r$, then $\frac{\text{perimeter } \triangle DEF}{\text{perimeter } \triangle ABC} = \frac{(rAB + rBC + rCA)}{(AB + BC + CA)} = r$.

25. (a) $\left(\frac{300,000 \text{ km}}{\text{sec}}\right)\left(\frac{60 \text{ sec}}{\text{min}}\right)\left(\frac{60 \text{ min}}{\text{hr}}\right)\left(\frac{24 \text{ hr}}{\text{day}}\right)\left(\frac{365 \text{ days}}{\text{year}}\right) \doteq 9.5 \cdot 10^{12}$ km per year.

25. (b)   (4.34 light years)(9.5·10^{12} km per year) $\doteq$ 4.1·10^{13} km.

(c) $\left(\frac{4.1 \cdot 10^{13} \text{ km}}{60,000 \text{ km/hr}}\right) \doteq 6.8 \cdot 10^8$ hours, or about 78,000 years.

(d)   Light travels $(8 \cdot 60 + 19)(300,000) \doteq 1.5 \cdot 10^8$ km in 8 min 19 sec. $\left(\frac{1.5 \cdot 10^8 \text{ km}}{60,000 \text{ km\textbackslash hr}}\right) \doteq 2495$ hours, or about 104 days.

26. (a) $(2.5)(0.344$ km/sec$)(3600$ sec/hr$) \doteq 3096$ km/hr.

(b) $(3)(344$ m/sec$) = 1032$ m/sec.

(c) $\frac{5000 \text{ km/hr}}{0.344 \text{ km/sec} \cdot 3600 \text{ sec/hr}} \doteq 4.04$, or Mach 4.04.

27. Perimeter $= 2 \cdot 19 + 12 + \frac{1}{2} \cdot \pi \cdot 12 = 50 + 6\pi \doteq 68.8$ feet.

28. By definition, 2 "footlongs" = 1 foot.

(a)   1 yard = 3 feet = 6 footlongs.

(b)   1 mile = 5280 feet = 10,560 footlongs.

29. The outer curve has a greater radius and a correspondingly greater distance (i.e., arc length) to run. To compensate for the extra distance, the outer lane is given an apparent head start.

30. Assuming these are unit squares, all perimeters will be even integers six or greater. There are an even number of sides in total. For each side shared by two squares, this means that two sides are not on the perimeter. The even total decreased by the shared pairs yields an even perimeter.

31. A straight line of squares gives minimum area. A square, or the closest thing possible, gives the maximum area; e.g., for perimeter = 22, a 1 by 10 rectangle gives least area while a 5 by 6 rectangle has greatest area.

Perimeter	Minimum Area	Maximum Area
4	1	1
6	2	2
8	3	4
10	4	6
12	5	9
14	6	12
16	7	16
18	8	20
20	9	25
22	10	30
24	11	36
26	12	42
2n	n − 1	*

* Let q be the whole number quotient when 2n is divided by 4. If 2n is a multiple of 4, then the maximum area is q^2; otherwise it is $q(q + 1)$.

Problem Set 13-2

1. (a) cm^2; $in.^2$ (b) cm^2; $in.^2$

(c) cm^2; $in.^2$ (d) m^2, yd^2

1. (e) m^2; yd^2 (f) km^2; mi^2

2. Answers may vary; some possible approximate measures are:

    (a)   1.45 m^2 (b)   1050 cm^2

    (c)   2400 cm^2 (d)   2.97 m^2

3. In each case, note that:
        From m^2 to cm^2, move the decimal point 4 places to the right.
        From cm^2 to mm^2, move the decimal point 2 places to the right.
        From mm^2 to cm^2, move the decimal point 2 places to the left.
        From cm^2 to m^2, move the decimal point 4 places to the left.

    $0.0588 \rightarrow \boxed{588} \rightarrow 58,800$
    $0.000192 \rightarrow 1.92 \rightarrow \boxed{192}$
    $\boxed{1.5} \rightarrow 15,000 \rightarrow 1,500,000$
    $0.01 \rightarrow \boxed{100} \rightarrow 10,000$
    $0.0005 \rightarrow \boxed{5} \rightarrow 500$

4. A 2-m square is a square with all sides 2 m long (an area of 4 m^2); 2 m^2 is the area contained in two 1 m by 1 m squares (in any form; e.g., a 1 m by 2 m rectangle, a 0.5 m by 4 m rectangle, etc.). One is a physical object and the other a characteristic of an object.

5. (a)   444.4   (b)   0.32

    (c)   6400   (d)   130,680

6. (a)   4900   (b)   98

    (c)   0.98

7. (a)   This figure is a triangle with base 3 and height 2, so A = $\frac{1}{2}(3)(2)$ = 3 $units^2$.

    (b)   Total area = $(4)(3)$ = 12 $units^2$.

                            Area A = $\frac{1}{2}(3)(2)$ = 3 $units^2$.
                            Area B = $\frac{1}{2}(2)(1)$ = 1 $unit^2$.
                            Area C = $\frac{1}{2}(3)(2)$ = 3 $units^2$.
                            Area D = $(1)(2)$ = 2 $units^2$.

    So the area of the figure is $12 - (3 + 1 + 3 + 1)$ = 3 $units^2$.

    (c)   This figure is a triangle with base 2 and height 2, so A = $\frac{1}{2}((2)(2)$ = 2 $units^2$.

    (d)   Total area = $(3)(3)$ = 9 $units^2$

                            Area A = $\frac{1}{2}(1)(1)$ = $\frac{1}{2}$ $unit^2$
                            Area B = $(2)(1)$ = 2 $units^2$
                            Area C = $\frac{1}{2}(1)(1)$ = $\frac{1}{2}$ $unit^2$
                            Area D = $\frac{1}{2}((1)(2)$ = 1 $unit^2$

    So the area of the figure is $9 - (\frac{1}{2} + 2 + \frac{1}{2} + 1)$ = 5 $units^2$

7.   (e) 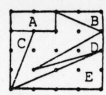   Total area = $(4)(4) = 16$ units^2

Area A = $(2)(1) = 2$ units^2
Area B = $\frac{1}{2}(2)(1) = 1$ unit^2
Area C = $\frac{1}{2}(1)(3) = 1\frac{1}{2}$ units^2
Area D = $\frac{1}{2}(1)(3) = 1\frac{1}{2}$ units^2
Area E = $\frac{1}{2}(4)(2) = 4$ units^2

So the area of the figure is $16 - (2 + 1 + 1\frac{1}{2} + 1\frac{1}{2} + 4) = 6$ units^2

(f)   Total area = $(3)(3) = 9$ units^2

Area A = $\frac{1}{2}(1)(2) = 1$ unit^2
Area B = $\frac{1}{2}(1)(1) = \frac{1}{2}$ unit^2
Area C = $(1)(1) = 1$ unit^2
Area D = $(1)(1) = 1$ unit^2
Area E = $\frac{1}{2}(1)(1) = \frac{1}{2}$ unit^2
Area F = $\frac{1}{2}(1)(1) = \frac{1}{2}$ unit^2

So the area of the figure is $9 - (1 + \frac{1}{2} + 1 + 1 + \frac{1}{2} + \frac{1}{2}) = 4\frac{1}{2}$ units^2

8.   (a) $I = 1; B = 6.$ $A = 1 + \frac{1}{2}(6) - 1 = 3$ units^2.

(b) $I = 2; B = 4.$ $A = 2 + \frac{1}{2}(4) - 1 = 3$ units^2.

(c) $I = 0; B = 6.$ $A = 0 + \frac{1}{2}(6) - 1 = 2$ units^2.

(d) $I = 1; B = 10.$ $A = 1 + \frac{1}{2}(10) - 1 = 5$ units^2.

(e) $I = 3; B = 8.$ $A = 3 + \frac{1}{2}(8) - 1 = 6$ units^2.

(f) $I = 0; B = 11.$ $A = 0 + \frac{1}{2}(11) - 1 = 4\frac{1}{2}$ units^2.

9.   (a) $A = \frac{1}{2}bh = \frac{1}{2}(10)(4) = 20$ cm^2.

(b) $A = \frac{1}{2}(6 \text{ m})(3 \text{ cm}) = \frac{1}{2}(6 \text{ m})(0.03 \text{ m}) = 0.09$ m^2, or $A = \frac{1}{2}(600 \text{ cm})(3 \text{ cm}) = 900$ cm^2.

(c) $A = \frac{1}{2}(3)(5) = 7\frac{1}{2}$ m^2.

(d) Place point D at the intersection of the two dashed lines. Then:
Area $\triangle$ ABD $= \frac{1}{2}(8)(6) = 24$ cm^2; area $\triangle$ CBD $= \frac{1}{2}(10)(3) = 15$ cm^2.
Adding, area $\triangle$ ABC = area $\triangle$ ABD + area $\triangle$ CBD $= 24 + 15 = 39$ cm^2.

(e) Let $\overline{AB}$ be the base; $\overline{BC}$ be the height. Then $A = \frac{1}{2}(30)(40) = 600$ cm^2.

10. All triangles have the same area, since they have a common base and all have the same height; i.e., the distance between l and $\overleftrightarrow{AB}$, which is constant.

11. (a) $A = l^2 = 3^2 = 9$ cm^2.   (b) $A = l \cdot w = (8)(12) = 96$ cm^2.

(c) Using the Pythagorean theorem, the height of the small triangle is $\sqrt{3^2 - 2^2} = \sqrt{5}$. The height of the

large triangle is $\sqrt{5^2 - 2^2} = \sqrt{21}$. The area of the large triangle is thus $\frac{1}{2}(4)(\sqrt{5}) = 2\sqrt{5}$; the area of

the small triangle is $\frac{1}{2}(4)(\sqrt{21}) = 2\sqrt{21}$. The area of the figure, then, is $2\sqrt{21} - 2\sqrt{5} = 2\left(\sqrt{21} - \sqrt{5}\right)$,
or about 256cm^2.

11. (d) $A = b \cdot h = (5)(4) = 20 \text{ cm}^2$

     (e) $A = \frac{1}{2}h(b_1 + b_2) = \frac{1}{2}(7)(10 + 14) = 84 \text{ cm}^2.$

     (f) $A = \frac{1}{2}(6)(27 + 8) = 105 \text{ cm}^2.$

12. (a)   (i) $(1.3)(1.5) = 1.95 \text{ km}^2.$ (ii) $1.95 \text{ km}^2 = 195 \text{ ha}.$

     (b)   (i) $(1300)(1500) = 3{,}097{,}600 \text{ yd}^2 = 0.6295 \text{ mi}^2.$

            (ii) $(1300)(1500) \div 4840 = 402.89 \text{ acres}.$

     (c)   The metric system is easier, requiring only the movement of decimal places.

13. (a)   True.

     (b)   The area would be 60 cm^2 only if the parallelogram were to be a rectangle.

     (c)   The area cannot be more than 60 cm^2, since the height cannot be more than 6 cm (if the base is 10 cm).

     (d)   Since we do not know the height, the area can only be expressed as "less than 60 cm^2."

14. (a)   75 cm^2.

     (b)   Dropping perpendiculars to the lower base from the endpoints of the upper base forms isosceles right triangles whose legs are $\frac{a - b}{2}$. Then using the formula for the area of a trapezoid,

            $$A = \tfrac{1}{2}(a + b)\left[\frac{a - b}{2}\right] = \frac{a^2 - b^2}{4}.$$

15. The diagonals of a rhombus are perpendicular. The height of $\triangle ABC$ in the diagram below is thus $\frac{b}{2}$, and $\triangle ABC$ has area $\frac{1}{2}a(\frac{b}{2}) = \frac{ab}{4}$. Since there are two such triangles, the area of the rhombus is $2 \cdot \frac{ab}{4} = \frac{ab}{2}$.

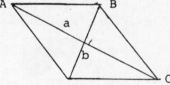

16. (a) $(6.5)(4.5) = 29.25 \text{ m}^2;\ (29.25 \text{ m}^2)(\$13.85/\text{m}^2) = \$405.11.$

     (b) $(15)(11) \div 9 = 18.\overline{3} \text{ yd}^2;\ (18.\overline{3} \text{ yd}^2)(\$30/\text{yd}^2) = \$550.$

17. (a) $A = \pi r^2 = \pi(5^2) = 25\pi \text{ cm}^2.$

     (b) $A = \frac{\theta}{360°} \cdot \pi r^2 = \frac{60}{360} \cdot \pi(4^2) = \frac{8}{3}\pi \text{ cm}^2.$

     (c) $A = \frac{36}{360} \cdot \pi(6^2) = \frac{18}{5}\pi \text{ cm}^2.$

     (d)   Since this is a half-circle, $A = \frac{1}{2}\pi r^2 = \frac{1}{2}\pi(3^2) = \frac{9}{2}\pi \text{ cm}^2.$

     (e)   First find θ. The angle is related to a full circle as the arc length is related to the circumference; i.e., $\frac{\theta}{360} = \frac{\text{arc length}}{2\pi r}$, or $\frac{\theta}{360} = \frac{20}{2\pi(10)}$. Solving, $\theta \doteq 114.59°$. Finally, $A = \frac{114.59}{360} \cdot \pi(10^2) = 100 \text{ cm}^2.$

18. Area of bathroom $= (300)(400) = 12{,}000 \text{ cm}^2.$ Each tile is 100 cm^2; $\frac{12{,}000}{100} = 1200$ tiles.

19. The plot is $(22 \text{ m})(28 \text{ m}) = 616 \text{ m}^2$. It will take $\dfrac{616 \text{ m}^2}{85 \text{ m}^2 \text{ per bag}} = 7.25$ bags (so 8 bags must be bought).

20. (a) (*i*)   12 units, 10 units   (*ii*)   14 units, 10 units

    (*iii*)   62 units, 22 units

    (b) (*i*)   9 units, 5 units   (*ii*)   42 units, 12 units

    (c) $2(n + 1)$ units   (d) $n - 1$ units

21. (a) The area of a regular polygon is given by $A = \frac{1}{2}(\text{apothem})(\text{perimeter})$. Here *a* (the apothem) is $2\sqrt{3}$ and the perimeter is $6 \cdot 4 = 24$. Thus $A = \frac{1}{2}\left(2\sqrt{3}\right)(24) = 24\sqrt{3} \doteq 41.57 \text{ cm}^2$.

    (b) $A = \frac{1}{2}bh = \frac{1}{2}(6)\left(3\sqrt{3}\right) = 9\sqrt{3} \doteq 15.59 \text{ cm}^2$.

22. (a) $r = 4$; $A = 16\pi \text{ cm}^2$.

    (b) $\pi r^2 = s^2$ implies $r = \dfrac{s}{\sqrt{\pi}}$.

23. (a) The radius of the large circle is 2 cm. Its area is $\pi \cdot 2^2 = 4\pi \text{ cm}^2$. Each small circle has area $\pi \cdot 1^2 = \pi \text{ cm}^2$. The shaded area is thus $4\pi - 2\pi = 2\pi \text{ cm}^2$.

    (b) The area of the semicircle is $\frac{1}{2}(\pi r^2) = \frac{1}{2}\pi(1^2) = \frac{1}{2}\pi \text{ cm}^2$. The area of the triangle is $\frac{1}{2}bh = \frac{1}{2}(2)(2) = 2$ cm^2. The shaded area is thus $(\frac{1}{2}\pi + 2) \text{ cm}^2$.

    (c) If the 1 cm radius were extended, it would be the diameter of the large circle, cutting off a small shaded semicircle the same size as the small white semicircle. The shaded area is thus equal to half the large circle, whose radius is 2 cm. The shaded area is thus $\frac{1}{2}(\pi \cdot 2^2) = 2\pi \text{ cm}^2$.

    (d) Consider half the figure, as shown below. Areas $A + B = $ Area C. Areas $A + B = $ Rectangle $-$ Semicircle $= 5 \cdot 10 - \frac{1}{2}(\pi \cdot 5^2) = 50 - \frac{25}{2}\pi$. $A + B + C$ is twice this, or $100 - 25\pi$. Considering both halves of the figure, the total unshaded area is $2(100 - 25\pi) = 200 - 50\pi$. The shaded area is that of the square less the unshaded area, or $10^2 - (200 - 50\pi) = (50\pi - 100) \text{ cm}^2$.

    (e) The square has sides of length 20 cm and area of $20^2 = 400 \text{ cm}^2$. Each circle has area $\pi \cdot 5^2 = 25\pi$ cm^2. The shaded area is thus $400 - 4(25\pi) = (400 - 100\pi) \text{ cm}^2$.

    (f) The two shaded areas form a circle with radius $\frac{r}{2}$, so their area is $\pi(\frac{r}{2})^2 = \dfrac{\pi r^2}{4}$.

    (g) The four shaded areas form two circles each having radius $\frac{r}{4}$, so their area is $2\pi(\frac{r}{4})^2 = \dfrac{\pi r^2}{8}$.

    (h) The eight shaded areas form four circles each having radius $\frac{r}{8}$, so their area is $4\pi(\frac{r}{8})^2 = \dfrac{\pi r^2}{16}$.

24. The flower bed with its encircling sidewalk forms a circle with radius $(3 + 1) = 4$ m. Thus its area is $\pi(4^2) = 16\pi \text{ m}^2$. The flower bed by itself has an area of $\pi(3^2) = 9\pi \text{ m}^2$. The area of the sidewalk is then $16\pi - 9\pi = 7\pi \text{ m}^2$.

25. (a) If we let r = radius of each circle, then the length of the rectangle is 12r and the width is 6r. Thus the area of the rectangle is $72r^2$. The area of each circle is πr^2 and there are 18 circles, so the total area used for lids is $18\pi r^2$. The wasted area is $72r^2 - 18\pi r^2$, and so the ratio of waste to total area

is $\dfrac{72r^2 - 18\pi r^2}{72r^2} = \dfrac{18r^2(4 - \pi)}{72r^2} = \dfrac{4 - \pi}{4}$, or about 21.4%.

(b) (i) The length of the rectangle would be 24r and the width 12r, for an area of $288r^2$. The total area of lids would be $72\pi r^2$. Thus the waste would be:

$$\frac{288r^2 - 72\pi r^2}{288r^2} = \frac{72r^2(4 - \pi)}{288r^2} = \frac{4 - \pi}{4}, \text{ or about } 21.4\% \text{ (as before)}.$$

(ii) Regardless of the radius of the circles, if the rectangle remains the same size the amount of waste will be the same.

26. (a) Rotate the shaded region 180° clockwise about point E. The area of the triangle is the same as the area of the parallelogram. Thus $A = \frac{1}{2}bh$.

(b) Try it!

27. (a) 4:9. $\dfrac{A_1}{A_2} = \dfrac{s_1^2}{s_2^2}$, and $\dfrac{s_1}{s_2} = \dfrac{2}{3}$. Thus $\dfrac{A_1}{A_2} = \left(\dfrac{2}{3}\right)^2 = 4{:}9$.

(b) 4:9. By the Pythagorean theorem, $d^2 = s^2 + s^2 = 2s^2$. If $d_1{:}d_2 = 2{:}3$, then $d_1^2{:}d_2^2 = 4{:}9$ But $d_1^2{:}d_2^2 = 2s_1^2{:}2s_2^2 = s_1^2{:}s_2^2$, or the ratio of areas is 4:9.

28. (a) 4:1   (b) The former is the square of the latter.

(c) For two triangles with corresponding sides in the ratio m:n, the bases and heights have ratios mb:nb. The ratio of areas is then $\frac{1}{2}(mb)(mh){:}\frac{1}{2}(nb)(nh) = m^2(\frac{1}{2}bh){:}n^2(\frac{1}{2}bh) = m^2{:}n^2$.

29. (a) As developed in problems 27 and 28, the ratio of the areas of any two similar objects may be found by squaring the ratio of any corresponding lengths. So for diagonals in the ration 20:27, areas have the ratio $20^2{:}27^2$, or 400:729. This ratio is less than that of the prices (400:600); i.e., there is less area in the smaller screen in comparison to price. The 27-inch set is a better buy.

(b) Let d be the diagonal of the specified set. The areas of the sets have the same ratio as that of the squared diagonals. Thus $20^2{:}d^2 = 1{:}2$, or $\dfrac{400}{d^2} = \dfrac{1}{2}$. Solving, $d \doteq 28.3$ inches.

30. A rectangle ($A = l \cdot w$) is formed. It has length b and width h in relation to the parallelogram; i.e., its area is bh. This must be the same as the original parallelogram.

31. The new figure is a parallelogram that has twice the area of the trapezoid. The area of the parallelogram is $A = \frac{1}{2}(AB + DC)h$, where h is the height of the parallelogram. Thus the area of the trapezoid is $\frac{1}{2}(AB + DC)h$.

32. The total area of the figure is 5 units^2. If we create a trapezoid by connecting a line from P to a point that is 2 units above P and $1\frac{1}{2}$ units to the right of P, we will have an area half that of the figure.

33. One possibility would be to mark off perpendicular diameters, then make arcs with the radius of the circle from the endpoints of the diameters.

34. Draw diameters connecting points of tangency. Then $A = 20 \cdot 16 + 2[\frac{1}{2}(\pi \cdot 8^2)] = (320 + 64\pi) \text{ m}^2$.

35. Removing the same amount from all sides of the original square will form another square. Its area is given by $s^2 = 64$, so $s = 8$ inches. Thus 1 inch should be removed from each side ($10 - 1 - 1 = 8$, or 1 inch from the left and right, top and bottom). Therefore, x = 1.

36. Draw altitudes $\overline{BE}$ and $\overline{DF}$ of triangles BCP and DCP, respectively. $\triangle ABE \simeq \triangle CDF$ by AAS. Thus $\overline{BE} \simeq \overline{DF}$. Because $\overline{CP}$ is a base of $\triangle BCP$ and $\triangle DCP$, and because the heights are the same, the areas must be equal.

37. (a)   10   (b)   104

    (c)   0.35   (d)   40

    (e)   8000   (f)   6.504

38. (a) $4 + \frac{1}{2}(2\pi \cdot 2) = (4 + 2\pi)$ mm.

    (b) $2 + \frac{1}{2}(2\pi \cdot 2) + 1 + 3 + \frac{1}{2}(2\pi \cdot 3) = (6 + 5\pi)$ mm.

39. By construction, $\triangle ABC \simeq \triangle BAC'$. Then congruent alternate interior angles $\angle ABC \simeq \angle BAC'$ and $\angle ABC' \simeq \angle BAC$ imply $\overline{AC} \| \overline{BC'}$ and $\overline{BC} \| \overline{AC'}$; i.e., BCAC' is a parallelogram (by definition).

Problem Set 13-3

1. (a) $x^2 + 8^2 = 10^2 \Rightarrow x^2 + 64 = 100 \Rightarrow x^2 = 36 \Rightarrow x = 6.$

    (b) $2^2 + 2^2 = x^2 \Rightarrow 4 + 4 = x^2 \Rightarrow x^2 = 8 \Rightarrow x = \sqrt{8} = 2\sqrt{2}.$

    (c) $(3a)^2 + (4a)^2 = x^2 \Rightarrow 9a^2 + 16a^2 = x^2 \Rightarrow 25a^2 = x^2 \Rightarrow x = 5a.$

    (d) $x^2 + 5^2 = 13^2 \Rightarrow x^2 + 25 = 169 \Rightarrow x^2 = 144 \Rightarrow x = 12.$

    (e) $x^2 + (\frac{s}{2})^2 = s^2 \Rightarrow x^2 + \frac{s^2}{4} = s^2 \Rightarrow x^2 = \frac{3s^2}{4} \Rightarrow x^2 = \sqrt{\frac{3s^2}{4}} = \frac{s\sqrt{3}}{2}.$

    (f) $x^2 + x^2 = 4^2 \Rightarrow 2x^2 = 16 \Rightarrow x^2 = 8 \Rightarrow x = \sqrt{8} = 2\sqrt{2}.$

    (g) $8^2 + a^2 = 17^2 \Rightarrow 64 + a^2 = 289 \Rightarrow a^2 = 225 \Rightarrow a = 15.$
         $8^2 + b^2 = 10^2 \Rightarrow 64 + b^2 = 100 \Rightarrow b^2 = 36 \Rightarrow b = 6.$
         Thus $x = 15 - 6 = 9.$

    (h) $5^2 + 12^2 = x^2 \Rightarrow 25 + 144 = x^2 \Rightarrow x^2 = 169 \Rightarrow x = 13.$

    (i) $4^2 + 4^2 = (2x)^2 \Rightarrow 16 + 16 = 4x^2 \Rightarrow 32 = 4x^2 \Rightarrow x^2 = 8 \Rightarrow x = 2\sqrt{2}.$

    (j) $3^2 + 6^2 = x^2 \Rightarrow 9 + 36 = x^2 \Rightarrow x^2 = 45 \Rightarrow x = \sqrt{45} = 3\sqrt{5}.$

    (k) $3^2 + 3^2 = d^2 \Rightarrow 9 + 9 = d^2 \Rightarrow d^2 = 18 \Rightarrow d = \sqrt{18}.$
         Then $3^2 + d^2 = x^2 \Rightarrow 9 + 18 = x^2 \Rightarrow x^2 = 27 \Rightarrow x = \sqrt{27} = 3\sqrt{3}.$

    (l) $3^2 + 4^2 = y^2 \Rightarrow 9 + 16 = y^2 \Rightarrow y^2 = 25 \Rightarrow y = 5.$
         Using similar triangles: $\frac{x}{5} = \frac{1}{3} \Rightarrow 3x = 5 \Rightarrow x = \frac{5}{3}.$

2. $x^2 + (2x)^2 = 30^2 \Rightarrow x = 6\sqrt{5}$ and $2x = 12\sqrt{5}.$

3. For the answer to be yes, the numbers must satisfy the Pythagorean theorem (with largest measure = c).

    (a) $10^2 + 16^2 \neq 24^2 \Rightarrow$ not a right triangle.

    (b) $16^2 + 30^2 = 34^2 \Rightarrow$ a right triangle.

3. (c) $\left(\sqrt{2}\right)^2 + \left(\sqrt{2}\right) = 2^2 \Rightarrow$ a right triangle.

   (d) $1^2 + \left(\sqrt{3}\right)^2 = 2^2 \Rightarrow$ a right triangle.

   (e) $\left(\sqrt{2}\right)^2 + \left(\sqrt{3}\right)^2 = \left(\sqrt{5}\right)^2 \Rightarrow$ a right triangle.

   (f) $(\frac{3}{2})^2 + (\frac{4}{2})^2 = (\frac{5}{2})^2 \Rightarrow$ a right triangle.

4. Find the diagonal of a face: $9^2 + 12^2 = x^2 \Rightarrow x = 15$. The diagonal of the prism is then given by: $15^2 + 15^2 = d^2 \Rightarrow d = \sqrt{450}$. The longest segment is thus $\sqrt{450} = 15\sqrt{2}$ cm, the diagonal length of the prism.

5. (a) Based on 4 and $4\sqrt{3}$ leg lengths, this is a 30°-60°-90° triangle with special relationships. Using this knowledge, $x = 8$ and $y = 2\sqrt{3}$. (Otherwise, use the Pythagorean theorem for x and similar triangles for y.)

   (b) Using the special relationship for 45°-45°-90° triangles, $x = \sqrt{2}\left(2\sqrt{2}\right) = 4$. $\sqrt{2}\, y = 2\sqrt{2}$, or $y = 2$.

6. Distances are the legs of a right triangle. $d^2 = 40^2 + 60^2 \Rightarrow d = \sqrt{5200} = 20\sqrt{13}$ km.

7. The distances form the legs of a right triangle. The southbound plane travels $(3.5 \text{ hr})\cdot(376 \text{ km/hr}) = 1316$ km; the westbound plane travels $(3.5 \text{ hr})\cdot(648 \text{ km/hr}) = 2268$ km. The distance apart is given by $d^2 = (1316)^2 + (2268)^2 \Rightarrow d = \sqrt{6{,}875{,}680} \doteq 2622$ km.

8. The boat is 10 mi south and 5 mi east. Using a right triangle, the distance from A is given by: $d^2 = 10^2 + 5^2 \Rightarrow d = \sqrt{125}$ mi.

9. Yes. Knowing that they are right triangles, the third sides (legs) are fixed by the Pythagorean theorem. The triangles are congruent by SSS.

10. $h^2 + 3^2 = 15^2 \Rightarrow h = \sqrt{216} = 6\sqrt{6} \doteq 14.7$ feet above the ground.

11. (a) Drawing radii to consecutive vertices of the hexagon forms an equilateral triangle (central angle is $\frac{1}{6}\cdot 360 = 60°$). Each side of the hexagon is thus 5 cm. Drawing an apothem forms 30°-60°-90° triangles, whose special relationships tell us that the apothem (the longer leg of the 30°-60°-90° triangle in this case) is $(\frac{5}{2})\sqrt{3}$. The area for any regular polygon is $A = \frac{1}{2}(\text{apothem})(\text{perimeter})$, so here $A = \frac{1}{2}[(\frac{5}{2})\sqrt{3}](6\cdot 5) = 37.5\sqrt{3}$ cm^2.

   (b) Substituting r for 5 above gives the area of an inscribed regular hexagon as $A = \frac{1}{2}[(\frac{r}{2})\sqrt{3})(6\cdot r)]$, or $A = \frac{3r^2}{2}\cdot\sqrt{3}$ cm^2.

12. The tall pole stands 10 m above the short one. Draw a horizontal line from the top of the short pole to form a right triangle. Then $d^2 + 10^2 = 14$; solving, $d \doteq 9.8$ m.

13. (a) The altitude forms 30°-60°-90° triangles. Its height is thus $\frac{s}{2}\cdot\sqrt{3}$, and $A = \frac{1}{2}bh = \frac{1}{2}(s)(\frac{s}{2}\cdot\sqrt{3})$, or

   $$A = \frac{s^2\sqrt{3}}{4}.$$

   (b) The triangle is isosceles with height = base = s. $A = \frac{1}{2}(s)(s) = \frac{s^2}{2}$.

14. Draw radius $\overline{OK}$ forming 30°-60°-90° triangle OKC. $\overline{OC} = 0.65$, $\overline{CK} = 0.65 \div \sqrt{3}$, $\overline{OK} = 2(0.65 \div \sqrt{3}) = 0.75 = \overline{OB}$. AB is then $2(0.75) = 1.5$ m.

15. Draw and lable the rhombus as shown:

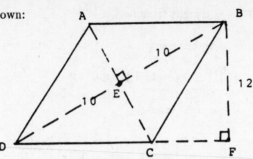

$DF^2 + BF^2 = BD^2$, or $DF^2 + 144 = 400 \Rightarrow DF = 16$. Then $CF = 16 - DC$,
so $(16 - DC)^2 + 12^2 = BC^2$. But $BC = DC$, so $(16 - DC)^2 + 12^2 = DC^2$. Thus
$256 - 32 \cdot DC + DC^2 + 144 = DC^2 \Rightarrow 400 = 32 \cdot DC \Rightarrow DC = 12.5$ cm. $DE^2 + EC^2 = DC^2$,
or $10^2 + EC^2 = 12.5^2 \Rightarrow EC^2 = 56.25 \Rightarrow EC = 7.5$. Thus $AC = 15$ cm.

16. The short leg (opposite the 30° angle) is half the hypotenuse. The longer leg (opposite 60°) is $\sqrt{3}$ times the short leg. The side opposite the 60° angle in this case is then $\frac{c}{4} \cdot \sqrt{3}$.

17. From the "special triangles" section, the hypotenuse of any 45°-45°-90° triangle is $\sqrt{2}$ times a leg. Thus here, $c = \sqrt{2} \cdot l$, or $l = \frac{c}{\sqrt{2}}$.

18. (a) Make sides the length of the given diagonal, which is $\sqrt{2} \cdot s$. The area is $(\sqrt{2} \cdot s)^2 = 2s^2$, or twice the original area.

     (b) Make sides half the length of a diagonal, or $\frac{\sqrt{2} \cdot s}{2}$; the area is $\left(\frac{\sqrt{2} \cdot s}{2}\right)^2 = \frac{1}{2}s^2$.

19. The sides of squares made in this fashion will always be hypotenuses of right triangles (as shown in (a)). As such, the relationship $s^2 = a^2 + b^2$ must hold, with a and b whole numbers, since they are given by spaces between dots. Only numbers representable this way can be areas of such squares (since s^2 is the area of a square).

     (a) Here $1^2 + 2^2 = 5 = s^2$, so the relationship exists.

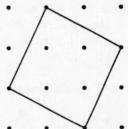

     (b) Not possible.

     (c) Here $2^2 + 2^2 = 8 = s^3$, so the relationship exists.

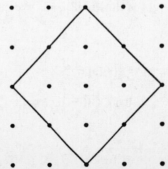

     (d) Not possible.   (e) Not possible.

20. $\triangle$ ACD $\simeq$ $\triangle$ ABC; AC/AB = AD/AC implies b/c = x/b which implies $b^2 = cx$.
$\triangle$ BCD $\simeq$ $\triangle$ ABC; AB/CB = CB/DB implies c/a = a/y which implies $a^2 = cy$.
$a^2 + b^2 = cx + cy = c(x + y) = cc = c^2$.

21. The included angle between sides of length c is 90°. Adding the areas of the three triangles gives
$A = \frac{1}{2}ba + \frac{1}{2}ab + \frac{1}{2}cc = ab + \frac{1}{2}c^2$. Using the formula for area of a trapezoid gives

$A = \frac{1}{2}(a + b)(a + b) = \frac{1}{2}(a^2 + 2ab + b^2)$. These represent the same area, so

$ab + \frac{1}{2}c^2 = \frac{1}{2}(a^2 + 2ab + b^2) \Rightarrow 2ab + c^2 = a^2 + 2ab + b^2 \Rightarrow c^2 = a^2 + b^2$.

22. Yes.

23. (a) Yes.

    (b) The area of an equilateral triangle with side s is $\frac{s^2}{4} \cdot \sqrt{3}$. Let the sides of the right triangle be a, b, and

    c, with c the hypotenuse. The areas of the equilateral triangles are thus $\frac{a^2}{4} \cdot \sqrt{3}$, $\frac{b^2}{4} \cdot \sqrt{3}$, and $\frac{c^2}{4} \cdot \sqrt{3}$.

    We must now answer the question, "Does $\frac{a^2}{4}\sqrt{3} + \frac{b^2}{4}\sqrt{3} = \frac{c^2}{4}\sqrt{3}$?" Multiplying both sides by $\frac{4}{\sqrt{3}}$ gives

    $a^2 + b^2 = c^2$, which must be true since the triangle is right.

24. The area of the large square is equal to the sum of the areas of the smaller square and the four triangles.
Thus $(a + b)^2 = c^2 + 4(ab/2) \Rightarrow a^2 + 2ab + b^2 = c^2 + 2ab \Rightarrow a^2 + b^2 = c^2$.

25. There is a 6 foot (or meter) vertical rise in a horizontal distance of 100 feet (or meters).

26. $\triangle$ ABC is a right triangle with hypotenuse (diameter) $\overline{AB}$. Then $AB^2 = AC^2 + BC^2 \Rightarrow BC = 8$ cm.

27. The brace will be a hypotenuse. Then $3^2 + 5^2 = x^2$, or $x = \sqrt{34}$. This must be the diagonal distance of the bracing board. Its length is given by $(0.5)^2 + l^2 = x^2$, or $l \doteq 5.81$ feet. The excess length is $8 - 5.81$, or 2.19 feet.

28. $d^2 = 90^2 + 90^2$, or $d \doteq 127.28$ feet.

29. Form a right triangle with a diameter, height, and length of spaghetti (the hypotenuse) that just fits.
Then $d^2 + h^2 = s^2$, or $4^2 + 10^2 = h^2 \Rightarrow h = \sqrt{116} \doteq 10.77$ inches.

30. 0.032 km, 322 cm, 3.2 m, 3.020 mm.

31. (a) Change all measurements to mm and draw horizontal lines to form three rectangles. The rectangles will have dimensions 75 mm by 25 mm, 25 mm by 30 mm, and 35 mm by 20 mm. The areas are 1875 mm², 750 mm², and 700 mm², for a total of 3325 mm² = 33.25 cm².

    (b) The area is $\frac{1}{2}(10)(6) = 30$ cm².

    (c) Change 600 cm to 6 m. The area is then $\frac{1}{2}(6 + 10)(4) = 32$ m².

32. (a) $\boxed{5 \text{ cm}}$ 10 10π 25π

    (b) 12 $\boxed{24 \text{ cm}}$ 24π 144π

    (c) $\sqrt{17}$ $2\sqrt{17}$ $2\pi\sqrt{17}$ $\boxed{17\pi \text{ m}^2}$

    (d) 10   20 $\boxed{20\pi \text{ cm}}$ 100π

33.   The area has a circumference of 10 m; i.e., $2\pi r = 10$. Then $r = \frac{10}{2\pi} = \frac{5}{\pi}$. The area is πr^2, or
      $\pi\left(\frac{5}{\pi}\right)^2 = \frac{25}{\pi}$ m^2.

Problem Set 13-4

1.   (a)   SA of a cube $= 6e^2$ (where $e =$ the length of each edge). SA $= 6(4)^2 = 96$ cm^2.

      (b)   SA of a right circular cylinder $= 2\pi r^2 + 2\pi rh$ (where r is the radius of the top and bottom circles and
            h is the height of the cylinder). SA $= 2\pi(6)^2 + 2\pi(6)(12) = 72\pi + 144\pi = 216\pi$ cm^2.

      (c)   SA of a right triangular prism $= ph + 2B$ (where p is the perimeter, h is the height, and B is the area
            of the base). $p = 2l + 2w = 2(8) + 2(5) = 26$ cm; B $= lw = (8)(5) = 40$ cm^2. h $= 6$ cm.
            SA $= (26)(6) + 2(40) = 156 + 80 = 236$ cm^2.

      (d)   SA of a sphere $= 4\pi r^2$ (where r is the radius). SA $= 4\pi(4)^2 = 64\pi$ cm^2.

      (e)   SA of a right circular cone $= \pi r^2 + \pi rl$ (where r is the radius of the base and l is the slant height from
            any point on the base to the vertex of the cone). To find l, use the Pythagorean theorem:

            $l = \sqrt{4^2 + 3^2} = 5$ cm. SA $= \pi(3)^2 + \pi(3)(5) = 9\pi + 15\pi = 24\pi$ cm^2.

      (f)   SA of a right square pyramid $= B + \frac{1}{2}pl$ (where B is the area of the base, p is the perimeater of the
            base, and l is slant height from the base to the apex). B $= b^2$ (where b is the length of a face of the
            base) $= 5^2 = 25$ cm^2; p $= 4b = 4(5) = 20$ cm. SA $= 25 + \frac{1}{2}(20)(6.5) = 25 + 65 = 90$ cm^2.

      (g)   The width of the slanted roof is given by: w $= \sqrt{8^2 + 15^2} = 17$ feet. Roof area is then given
            by $2(17\cdot40) = 1360$ ft^2. The triangular area is $2(\frac{1}{2})(30)(8) = 240$ ft^2. The side wall area is
            $2(20\cdot30) + 2(20\cdot40) = 2800$ ft^2. The base area is $(30)(40) = 1200$ ft^2.
            Total surface area is $1360 + 240 + 2800 + 1200 = 5600$ ft^2.

      (h)   Hemispherical area is $\frac{1}{2}(4\pi r^2) = \frac{1}{2}(4\pi\cdot10^2) = 200\pi$ ft^2.
            Base area is $\pi r^2 = \pi(10^2) = 100\pi$ ft^2.
            Lateral area of cylinder $= 2\pi rh = 2\pi(10)(60) = 1200\pi$ ft^2.
            Total surface area $= 200\pi + 100\pi + 1200\pi = 1500\pi$ ft^2.

      (i)   Slant height is given by: $l = \sqrt{4^2 + 8^2} = 4\sqrt{5}$ cm. Conical area $= \pi rl = \pi(4)\left(4\sqrt{5}\right) = 16\sqrt{5}\pi$ cm^2.
            Hemispherical area $= \frac{1}{2}(4\pi r^2) = \frac{1}{2}(4)\pi(4)^2 = 32\pi$ cm^2.

            Total surface area $= \left(32 + 16\sqrt{5}\right)\pi$ cm^2.

2.   Area of walls $= 2(6)(25) + 2(4)(2.5) = 50$ m^2. Paint needed $= 50\div20 = 2.5$ L.

3.   Change all units to mm. The ring then has an inner radius of 20 mm and a height of 30 mm.
      The outer ring has a radius of 22 mm and a height of 30 mm; SA $= 2\pi rh = 2\pi(22)(30) = 1320\pi$ mm^2.
      The inner ring has a radius of 20 mm and a height of 30 mm; SA $= 2\pi(20)(30) = 1200\pi$ mm^2.
      The area of the top and bottom rings is each the area of a circle with radius 22 mm minus the area of a
          circle with radius 20 mm.
      There are two base rings, so SA $= 2[\pi(22^2) - \pi(20^2)] = 2[484\pi - 400\pi] = 168\pi$ mm^2.
      The total surface area $= 1320\pi + 1200\pi + 168\pi = 2688\pi$ mm^2, or 26.88π cm^2.

4.   SA $= 4\pi(6370)^2 = 162,307,600\pi$ km^2.

5.   SA (large cube) $= 6e^2 = 6(6)^2 = 216$ cm^2.   SA (small cube) $= 6(4^2) = 96$ cm^2.
Ratio of surface areas $= \frac{96}{216} = \frac{4}{9} = 4:9$.
Note that the ratio of the surface areas is the ratio of the squares of the sides.

6.   (a)   Lateral surface area (first cylinder) $= 2\pi \text{rh} = 2\pi(2)(6) = 24\pi$ m^2.
           Lateral surface area (second cylinder) $= 2\pi(6)(2) = 24\pi$ m^2.

     (b)   SA (first cylinder) $= 2\pi r^2 + 2\pi \text{rh} = 2\pi(2^2) + 24\pi = 32\pi$ m^2.
           SA (second cylinder) $= 2\pi(6^2) + 24\pi = 96\pi$ m^2.
           The cylinder with the larger radius has the larger surface area.

7.   SA of a right pyramid $= B + \frac{1}{2}pl$, where B is the area of the base, p is the perimeter of the base, and l is the slant height from the base to the apex.
$B = \frac{1}{2}ap$, where a is the apothem. Since a hexagon is composed of equilateral triangles about the center, the distance from each vertex to the center is the same as each edge. Thus

$$a = \sqrt{12^2 - 6^2} = \sqrt{108} = 6\sqrt{3}. \text{ Then } B = \tfrac{1}{2}\left(6\sqrt{3}\right)(6 \cdot 12) = 216\sqrt{3}.$$

Since the apothem is $6\sqrt{3}$ and the altitude is 9, $l = \sqrt{9^2 + \left(6\sqrt{3}\right)^2} = \sqrt{189} = 3\sqrt{21}$.

Finally, SA $= 216\sqrt{3} + \frac{1}{2}(6 \cdot 12)\left(3\sqrt{21}\right) = \left(216\sqrt{3} + 108\sqrt{21}\right)$ m^2.

8.   (a)   Since surface area of a cube is proportional to the square of the length of each edge, when length is tripled area is increased by a factor of 9.

     (b)   Surface area of a cylinder is proportional to the height, so if the height is doubled the surface area is doubled.

9.   For any figure, if all dimensions have the same percentage change, the change of the area is the square of the change in a side. Thus:

     (a)   The surface area is quadrupled.   (b)   The surface area is multiplied by 9.

     (c)   The surface area is multiplied by k^2.

10.   (a)   Lateral surface area is proportional to slant height, so if slant height is tripled lateral surface area is tripled.

      (b)   Lateral surface area is proportional to the radius of the base, so when it is tripled lateral surface area is tripled.

      (c)   Lateral surface area is proportional to the product of slant height and base radius, so when they are each tripled lateral surface area is multiplied by 9.

11.   (a)   SA of a sphere is proportional to the square of the radius, so if radius is doubled SA is increased by a factor of 4.

      (b)   The SA is multiplied by 9.

12.   (a)   SA of the given structure is 40 units^2. Adding one cube could increase area by 4 units^2 (adding 5 faces but eliminating one). Maximum SA is then 44 units^2.

      (b)   Placing a cube in the hole eliminates 4 faces while adding only 2; minimum SA $= 38$ units^2.

      (c)   Yes, by arranging five cubes in a C shape. Filling the hole with a sixth cube would add no surface area.

12. (d)   A 2 by 2 by 3 rectangular prism gives minimum SA of 32 units^2.

13.   Answers may vary. One possibility is to form a regular square pyramid with base sides of 2 cm and triangle slant heights of 1.5 cm. Then SA $= B + \frac{1}{2}pl = 2^2 + \frac{1}{2}(8)(1.5) = 4 + 6 = 10$ cm^2.

14.   The two extremes are a regular square pyramid and one in which the apex is directly above a vertex of the base. The surface areas then would vary from $\left(\sqrt{5} + 1\right)s^2$ to $\left(2 + \sqrt{2}\right)s^2$, respectively (where s is the side of the cube).

15.   A good estimate could be made by using the method in problem 3 (the napkin ring).

16. $l = 1.5$ m; the circumference of the base $= \frac{240}{360}[2\pi(1.5)] = 2\pi$ m $\Rightarrow 2\pi r = 2\pi$, or r = 1.

(a)   Lateral surface area $= \pi(1)(1.5) = 1.5\pi$ m^2.

(b)   SA $= 1.5\pi + \pi(1^2) = 2.5\pi$ m^2.

17.   Using $\frac{\theta}{360}(\pi r^2)$ for the area of a sector, $270 = \frac{270}{360}(\pi r_s^2)$. r_s is the radius of the sector which, when rolled up, will become the slant height of the cone, l. Solving, we obtain $\frac{360}{\pi} = r_s^2 \Rightarrow r_s = \frac{60}{\sqrt{\pi}} = l$.

The arc length of the sector $= \frac{\theta}{360}(2\pi r) = \frac{270}{360}\left(2\pi \cdot \frac{60}{\sqrt{\pi}}\right) = \frac{90\pi}{\sqrt{\pi}}$. This will become the circumference of the base of the cone.
Using r_b as the radius of the base, $2\pi r_b = \frac{90\pi}{\sqrt{\pi}}$, or $r_b = \frac{45}{\sqrt{\pi}}$ cm.

(a)   Area $= \pi r_b^2 = \pi\left(\frac{45}{\sqrt{\pi}}\right)^2 = 202.5$ cm^2.

(b)   Form a right triangle with r_b, l, and h (cone height). Then $r_b^2 + h^2 = l^2$, or $\left(\frac{45}{\sqrt{\pi}}\right)^2 + h^2 = \left(\frac{60}{\sqrt{\pi}}\right)^2$.

Solving gives h$^2 = \frac{3600}{\pi} - \frac{2025}{\pi} = \frac{1575}{\pi}$, or h $= \sqrt{\frac{1575}{\pi}}$ cm.

18.   SA of a sphere $= 4\pi r^2$; SA of a cylinder $= 2\pi r^2 + 2\pi rh = 2\pi r^2 + 2\pi r(2r) = 6\pi r^2$.
The areas are in the ratio 2:3.

19.   27 rounds represents the entire lawn; 27 rounds require 2(27) = 54 passes along the length and width, so the width is 54(3) = 162 feet. The rectangle left after the first 12 rounds has width $162 - 2 \cdot 12 \cdot 3 = 90$ feet and length $l - 2 \cdot 13 \cdot 3 = l - 72$. This rectangle has half the total area, or $90(l - 72) = \frac{1}{2}(162 \cdot l)$. Solving, we find $l = 720$ feet. The field is then 162 by 720 feet.

20.   SA $= B + \frac{1}{2}pl$, where $B = 100$; $p = 4\sqrt{100} = 40$; and $l = \sqrt{20^2 + 5^2} = 5\sqrt{17}$. SA $= (100 + 100\sqrt{17})$ cm^2.

21.   (a)   The figure will be a cone with base radius 10 cm and height 20 cm.

SA $= \pi r^2 + \pi rl = \pi(10^2) + \pi(10)\left(\sqrt{20^2 + 10^2}\right) = 100\pi + 10\pi(10\sqrt{5}) = 100\pi(1 + \sqrt{5})$ cm^2.

(b)   The figure will be a right circular cylinder with base radius 15 cm and height 30 cm.
SA $= 2\pi r^2 + 2\pi rh = 2\pi(15^2) + 2\pi(15)(30) = 450\pi + 900\pi = 1350\pi$ cm^2.

(c)   The figure will be a truncated cone, with large end radius 25 cm and small end radius 15 cm. If one considers the given area as part of a triangle, as shown, then using similar triangles:

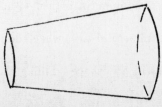

21. (c) $\frac{35}{10} = \frac{x}{25}$, where x is the hypotenuse of the large triangle. Solving, x = 87.5. The triangle, when rotated, will form a cone with slant height 87.5 and radius 25 cm, having
SA = $\pi r^2 + \pi r l = \pi(25^2) + \pi(25)(87.5) = 625\pi + 2187.5\pi = 2812.5\pi$ cm^2.
Cutting off the top eliminates the lateral surface area $\pi r l = \pi(15)(87.5 - 35) = 787.5$ cm^2 and adds the circular area $\pi r^2 = \pi(15^2) = 225\pi$ cm^2. The resulting SA is
$(2812.5 - 787.5 + 225)\pi = 2250\pi$ cm^2.

22. (a)   SA = $6e^2$; e = $\sqrt{\dfrac{10,648}{6}} \doteq 42$ cm.

     (b)   Diagonal of face = $\sqrt{42^2 + 42^2} \doteq 59.4$ cm. Corner-corner diagonal = $\sqrt{59.4^2 + 42^2} \doteq 73$ cm.

23. A regular tetrahedron is made of 4 equilateral triangles. The area of an equilateral triangle is $\frac{s^2\sqrt{3}}{4}$.

With total surface area = 400 cm^2, each triangle is 100 cm^2, or $\frac{s^2\sqrt{3}}{4} = 100$. Then s = $\sqrt{\dfrac{400}{\sqrt{3}}} \doteq 15.2$ cm.

24. With h = height of completed cone, $\frac{h}{100} = \frac{h - 40}{60}$, or h = 100. The slant height is then $100\sqrt{2}$. Slant

height of the missing piece is $60\sqrt{2}$. As in problem 21(c), final surface area is

$\pi(100^2) + \pi(100)\left(100\sqrt{2}\right) - \pi(60)\left(60\sqrt{2}\right) + \pi(60^2) = (6400\sqrt{2}\pi + 13,600\pi)$ cm^2.

25. The cross section is shown:

Then $\frac{10}{x} = \frac{40}{25}$ $\Rightarrow$ x = 6.25. This is the radius of the cylinder.
Lateral surface area is $2\pi rh = 2\pi(6.25)(30) = 375\pi$ cm^2.

26. (a)   100,000   (b)   1.368

     (c)   500   (d)   2,000,000

     (e)   1   (f) 10^6

27. d = $\sqrt{10^2 + 20^2} = 10\sqrt{5}$ cm.

28. $(\frac{1}{2}d)^2 + 20^2 = 30^2$, or d = $\sqrt{2000} = 20\sqrt{5}$ cm.

29. (a)   Change 0.6 m to 60 cm. The hypotenuse is then $\sqrt{60^2 + 80^2} = 100$ cm. The perimeter is
           60 + 80 + 100 = 240 cm, or 2.4 m.

           Area is $\frac{1}{2}$bh = $\frac{1}{2}(60)(80) = 2400$ cm^2, or 0.24 m^2.

     (b)   Drawing an altitude to the end point of the top base forms a 45°-45°-90° isosceles triangle. The bottom base must be 5 cm longer on each side than the top; i.e., one leg of the isosceles triangle is 5 cm, so the height is also 5 cm. Using the Pythatorean theorem, the slanted segments on each side of the trapezoid are each $5\sqrt{2}$ cm. The perimeter is thus $20 + 10 + 2(5\sqrt{2}) = (30 + 10\sqrt{2})$ cm.

           Area = $\frac{1}{2}(10 + 20)(5) = 75$ cm^2.

30. Use the technique of Problem Set 13-3, problem 15, to find the length of the sides to be 25 cm and the length of diagonal $\overline{AD}$ to be 30 cm.

1. (a)   8000. 1 m^3 = 1000 dm^3 since (1 m)^3 = (10 dm)^3.

    (b)   0.0005. 1 cm^3 = 0.000001 m^3, since (1 cm)^3 = (0.01 cm)^3.

    (c)   0.000675. 1 m^3 = 0.000000001 km^3, since (1 m)^3 = (0.001 km)^3.

    (d)   3,000,000. 1 m^3 = 1,000,000 cm^3.

    (e)   7. 1 mm^3 = 0.001 cm^3.

    (f)   2000.

    (g)   0.00857. $\dfrac{400 \text{ in}^3}{x \text{ yd}^3} = \dfrac{(36^3) \text{ in}^3}{1 \text{ yd}^3}$.

    (h)   675. 1 yd^3 = 27 ft^3.

    (i)   345.6. 1 ft^3 = 144 in^3.

    (j)   0.69.

2. Answers may vary, but although unit squares or unit cubes can be stacked to form other squares and cubes, this cannot be done with unit spheres.

3. (a)   V = $l$wh = (4)(4)(4) = 64 cm^3.

    (b)   V = $l$wh = (8)(5)(3) = 120 cm^3.

    (c)   V = Bh (where B is the area of the triangle and h is its height).
          B = $\frac{1}{2}$bh = $\frac{1}{2}$(6)(6) = 18 cm^2; h = 12. Thus V = (18)(12) = 216 cm^3.

    (d)   V = $\frac{1}{3}$Bh (where B is the area of the base and h is the height) = $\frac{1}{3}$(5^2)(6) = 50 cm^3.

    (e)   V = $\frac{1}{3}$πr^{2}h = $\frac{1}{3}$π(3^2)(7) = 21π cm^3.

    (f)   V = πr^{2}h = π(6^2)(12) = 432π cm^3.

    (g)   V = $\frac{4}{3}$πr^3 = $\frac{4}{3}$π(10^3) = $\frac{4000}{3}$π cm^3.

    (h)   V of triangular prism portion = Bh = $\frac{1}{2}$(30(8)(40) = 4800 cm^3.
          V of rectangular prism portion = $l$wh = (30)(40)(15) = 18,000 cm^3.

          Total volume = 4800 + 18,000 = 22,800 ft^3.

    (i)   V of hemispherical portion = $\frac{1}{2}$($\frac{4}{3}$πr^3) = $\frac{1}{2}$($\frac{4}{3}$)π(10^3) = $\frac{2000}{3}$π ft^3.
          V of circular cylinder = πr^{2}h = π(10^2)(60) = 6000π ft^3.

          Total volume = 6000π + $\frac{2000}{3}$π = $\frac{20,000}{3}$π ft^3.

    (j)   V of triangular prism portion = $\frac{1}{2}$(10)(6)(60) = 1800 ft^3.
          V of trapezoidal prism portion = $\frac{1}{2}$(8)(10 + 50)(60) = 14,400 ft^3.
          V of rectangular prism portion = (50)(60)(20) = 60,000 ft^3.

          Total volume = 1800 + 14,400 + 60,000 = 76,200 ft^3.

3. (k)   V of hemispherical portion $= \frac{1}{2}(\frac{4}{3}\pi \cdot 4^3) = \frac{128}{3}\pi$ cm^3.

V of conical portion $= \frac{1}{3}\pi(4^3)(8) = \frac{128}{3}\pi$ cm^3.

Total volume $= \frac{256}{3}\pi$ cm^3.

4.
(a)	2000	2	2	2000
(b)	500	0.5	0.5	500
(c)	1500	1.5	1.5	1500
(d)	5000	5	5	5000
(e)	750	0.750	0.750	750
(f)	4800	4.8	4.8	4800

5. (a)   200.0 mL   (b)   0.320 L

(c)   1.0 L   (d)   5.00 mL

6. Converting all measurements to mm, the radius of the inner circle is 20 mm and the height is 20 mm.
V (outer cylinder) $= \pi r^2 h = \pi(22^2)(20) = 9680\pi$ mm^3.
V (inner cylinder) $= \pi(20^2)(20) = 8000\pi$ mm^3.
V (napkin ring) $= (9680 - 8000)\pi = 1680\pi$ mm^3.

7. $V_1 = 4^3 = 64$; $V_2 = 6^3 = 216$. $V_1:V_2 = 64:216 = 8:27$. If all lengths of the two objects have the ratio m:n, then their volumes will have the ratio m^3:n^3.

8. The volume of a sphere is proportional to the cube of the radius. If the radius is doubled, then volume is increased by a factor of 2^3, or 8.

9. For each right rectangular prism, V $= l$wh. Then:

(a)	20 cm	10 cm	10 cm	2000	2	2
(b)	10 cm	2 dm	3 dm	6000	6	6
(c)	2 dm	1 dm	2 dm	4000	4	4 L
(d)	15 cm	2 dm	2.5	7500	7.5 dm^3	7.5

10. $V = \pi r^2 h = \pi(6.5^2)(6) = 253.5\pi$ m^3. Since 1m^3 = 1000 L, V = 253,500π L.

11. Volume is proportional to the cube of the radius. Thus a sphere with 4 times the radius of another has $4^3 = 64$ times its volume.

12. $V = l$wh $= (18)(18)(5) = 1620$ cm^3. 1000 cm^3 = 1 L, so V = 1.62 L.

13. $V = l$wh $= (50)(25)(2) = 2500$ m^3. 1 m^3 = 1000 L, so V = 2,500,000 L.

14. There are $(60)(24)(30) = 43,200$ minutes in a 30-day month.
There would be $(15)(43,200) = 648,000$ drops in 30 days.

There would be $\frac{648,000}{20} = 32,400$ mL = 32.4 L of water wasted.

15. The radius of the straw is 2 mm = 0.2 cm. $V = \pi r^2 h = \pi (0.2^2)(25) = \pi$ cm$^3 = \pi$ mL.

16. (a) $V = \pi (5^2)(1000) = 25{,}000\pi$ cm$^3 = 25\pi$ L.

    (b)   The pipe must hold $\frac{1{,}000{,}000}{25\pi} \doteq 12{,}732$ times as much water. The pipe should be
    $(10)(12{,}732)$ m = 127.32 km long.

17. No. The volume of a pyramid is $\frac{1}{3}Bh$, compared to Bh for the box. Thus the pyramid provides only $\frac{1}{3}$ the
    popcorn for $\frac{1}{2}$ the price.

18. Volume of the 5 cm grapefruit is $\frac{4}{3}\pi (5^3) \doteq 523.6$ cm^3; cost/cm$^3 = \frac{22}{523.6} = 4.2\cancel{c}$. Similarly, the cost for the
    6 cm grapefruit is $3.4\cancel{c}$ per cm^3. The larger fruit is the better buy.

19. The circumference of a circle $= 2\pi r$, or $r = \frac{C}{2\pi}$. Thus the radius of the larger melon is $\frac{60}{2\pi} \doteq 9.55$ cm;
    similarly, the radius of the smaller melon is about 7.96 cm. The ratio of the radii is thus $\frac{9.55}{7.96} \doteq 1.2$. Since
    the volume of a sphere is proportional to the cube of the radius, the volume of the larger cantalope is 1.2^3,
    or about 1.7 times that of the smaller. The larger melon is the better buy; its volume is 1.7 times that of
    the smaller but its price is only 1.5 times as much.

20. Perimeter = 16 implies that each side = 4 m. $V = \frac{1}{3}Bh = \frac{1}{3}(4^2)(3) = 16$ m^3.

21. $V_{prism} = AB \cdot BC \cdot AP$. $V_{pyramid} = \frac{1}{3}(AB \cdot BC \cdot AX) = \frac{1}{3}(AB \cdot BC \cdot 3AP) = AB \cdot BC \cdot AP$.
    The volumes are the same.

22. 1 L = 1000 cm^3. $V = \pi r^2 h$, so $1000 = \pi (12^2)h$. Solving, h $\doteq 2.2$ cm.

23. Let r be the radius of each of the cans and h be the height of the box and the cans. The dimensions of the
    base of the box are 6r by 4r.
    $V_{box} = (6r)(4r)(h) = 24r^2 h$. $V_{6\ cans} = 6\pi r^2 h$. $V_{wasted} = 24r^2 h - 6\pi r^2 h = 6r^2 h(4 - \pi)$.

    The portion wasted is $\frac{6r^2 h(1 - \pi)}{24r^2 h} = \frac{4 - \pi}{4} \doteq 21.5\%$.

24. (a)   Answers may vary, but one design would be a square base with sides 5 m and height 12 m.

    (b)   There are infinitely many factors s and h such that $\frac{1}{3}s^2 h = 100$; thus there are infinitely many
    pyramids.

25. Assume a regular pyramid. Then let s = length of a side = height. The slant height of the pyramid is the
    hypotenuse of the right triangle with height s and base $\frac{s}{2}$, or

    $\sqrt{s^2 + \left(\frac{s}{2}\right)^2} = \sqrt{s^2 + \left(\frac{s^2}{4}\right)} = \sqrt{\frac{5s^2}{4}} = \frac{\sqrt{5}s}{2}$. The area of each of the four triangles in the lateral surface

    of the pyramid is $\frac{1}{2}bh = \frac{1}{2} \cdot s \cdot \frac{\sqrt{5}s}{2} = \frac{\sqrt{5}s^2}{4}$. There are four sides, so the lateral surface area is $4 \cdot \frac{\sqrt{5}s^2}{4} = \sqrt{5}s^2$.

    If lateral surface area is 2 m^2, then $\sqrt{5}s^2 = 2$ and $s = \sqrt{\frac{2}{\sqrt{5}}}$. $V = \frac{1}{3}Bh = \frac{1}{3}s^2 s = \frac{1}{3}s^3 = \frac{1}{3}\left(\sqrt{\frac{2}{\sqrt{5}}}\right)^3$, or

    $V = 0.28$ m^3.

26. (a)   Dimensions are 160 cm by 160 cm by 20 cm; volume is 512,000 cm^3.

    (b) $l = w = y - 2x$; h = x. $V = x(y - 2x)^2$.

27. Let two square pyramids have sides and heights of s, h, s_1, and s_2. If the pyramids are similar, then

$$\frac{s}{s_1} = \frac{h}{h_1} = k(\text{the common ratio}). \quad \frac{V}{V_1} = \frac{\frac{1}{3}s^2h}{\frac{1}{3}s_1^2h_1} = \left(\frac{s}{s_1}\right)^2 \cdot \frac{h}{h_1} = k^2k = k^3.$$

28. (a)   There will be 20 oranges, each of radius 1.5 inch. $V_{total} = 20(\frac{4}{3}\pi 1.5^3) = 90\pi$ in^3.

    (b)   The oranges would be stacked in a regular triangular pyramid (i.e., a tetrahedron) to satisfy these conditions. The equilateral base has sides 12 inches; the height is less than 12 inches (4 oranges high), since sides "mesh". The approximation of height may vary, although mathematically h = 9. Using

    $$s = 12 \text{ and } h = 9, \text{ then } V = \frac{1}{3}\left(\frac{s^2\sqrt{3}}{4}\right)h = \frac{1}{3}\left(36\sqrt{3}\right)(9) \doteq 187 \text{ in}^3.$$

29. $h_{stack} = 20 \cdot \frac{1}{16}$ in = 1.25 inch; outer radius = 3.5 inch; and inner radius = 0.75 inch.
    Volume of outer radius cylinder = $\pi r^2h = \pi(3.5^2)(1.25) \doteq 15.3\pi$ in^3.
    Volume of inner radius cylinder = $\pi(0.75^3)(1.25) \doteq 0.7\pi$ in^3.
    Volume of record stack = $(15.3 - 0.7)\pi = 14.6\pi \doteq 45.9$ in^3.

30. Depending on amount of irregularity and size, possible methods could include:
    (i)   Liken it to some regular figure and find the volume of that.
    (ii)   Calculate the volume of water in some regular container; submerse the object and recalculate the volume. The difference would be the volume of the object.

31. A cord is a box-shaped stack 4 by 4 by 8 feet. V = (4)(4)(8) = 128 ft^3.

32. For the ice cream, r = 5 and $V = \frac{4}{3}\pi(5^3) = \frac{500}{3}\pi$ cm^3.
    For the cone, r = 5, h = 10, and $V = \frac{1}{3}\pi(5^2)(10) = \frac{250}{3}\pi$ cm^3.
    The cone needs twice its present volume to hold the ice cream; since volume is proportional to height, it would need to be 20 cm high.

33. Volume is proportional to the cube of the radius; i.e., radius is proportional to the cube root of volume. If

    volume is halved, radius is decreased by a factor of $\sqrt[3]{0.5} \doteq 0.794$.

34. (a) $2B + ph = 2(\frac{1}{2})(30)(40) + (120)(120) = 15,600$ cm^3.

    (b) $B + \frac{1}{2}pl = 10^2 + \frac{1}{2}(40)(10\sqrt{2}) = (100 + 200\sqrt{2})$ cm^3.

    (c) $2B + ph = 2\left(9 \cdot 8 + \frac{9^2 \cdot \sqrt{3}}{4}\right) + (43)(35) \doteq 1719$ m^3.

35. (a)   Change 1.3 m to 130 cm. Then the other side of the rectangle is given by $w^2 = 130^2 - 120^2$, or w = 50 cm. P = 2w + 2l = 2(120) + 2(50) = 340 cm.

    (b)   A = lw = (120)(50) = 6000 cm^2.

36. Let b = 2. Then $h = \sqrt{3^2 - 1^2} = 2\sqrt{2}$. $A = \frac{1}{2}(2)(2\sqrt{2}) = 2\sqrt{2}$ m^2.

37. The height of the printed material is 74 − (12 + 12) = 50 cm.
    The width of the printed material is w − (6 + 6) = w − 12.
    The area of the printed material is 50(w − 12) = 2500, or, solving, w = 62 cm.

1. (a) A car would weigh in thousands of pounds, so use kilograms or metric tons.

   (b) A woman could weigh 130 pounds, so use kilograms.

   (c) Juice would weigh in ounces, so use grams.

   (d) Metric tons.   (e) Grams.

   (f) Grams.   (g) Metric tons.

   (h) Grams or kilograms.   (i) Grams or kilograms.

2. (a) Milligrams.   (b) Kilograms.

   (c) Milligrams.   (d) Grams.

   (e) Grams.   (f) Milligrams.

3. (a) 15   (b) 8

   (c) 36   (d) 0.072

   (e) 4.23   (f) 3.007

   (g) 5750   (h) 5.75

   (i) 30   (j) $2.6 \cdot 16 = 41.6$

   (k) $25 \cdot \frac{1}{16} = 1\frac{9}{16}$ (l) $50 \cdot \frac{1}{16} = 3\frac{1}{8}$

   (m) $3.8 \cdot 16 = 60.8$

4. (a) No. 1,000,000 g = 1000 kg.   (b) Possibly. 100,000 g = 100 kg.

   (c) Yes. 10,000 g = 10 kg.   (d) Yes. 1000 g = 1 kg.

   (e) Yes.

5. $V = lwh = (40)(20)(20) = 16,000 \text{ cm}^3$. 1 g = 1 cm^3 of water; 16,000 cm^3 = 16,000 g = 16 kg.

6. 400 g = 0.04 kg. Cost is (0.04)(5.80) = \$2.32.

7. 1 g = 0.001 kg; cost is (0.001)(20) = \$0.02 = 2¢ per g.

8. $\frac{\$4.60}{0.4 \text{ kg}}$ = \$11.50/kg. Abel made the better buy at \$9/kg.

9. (a) $C = \frac{5}{9}(F - 32) = \frac{5}{9}(10 - 32) = \frac{5}{9}(^-22) \doteq {}^-12° \text{ C.}$

   (b) $C = \frac{5}{9}(0 - 32) \doteq {}^-18° \text{ C.}$

   (c) $C = \frac{5}{9}(30 - 32) \doteq {}^-1° \text{ C.}$

   (d) $C = \frac{5}{9}(100 - 32) \doteq 38° \text{ C.}$

   (e) $C = \frac{5}{9}(212 - 32) = 100° \text{ C.}$

9. (f) $C = \frac{5}{9}(^-40 - 32) = {}^-40°$ C (this is the only temperature at which F and C have the same value).

10. (a)   Probably not; this is 68° F.   (b)   No; this is 79° F.

    (c)   No; 37° C = 98.6° F.   (d)   Probably; 39° C is 102.2° F.

    (e)   No; this is 104° F.   (f)   Yes; this is 95° F.

    (g)   Yes, if it has been cold for long.   (h)   Chilly; this is 61° F.

    (i)   Hot. 30° C is 86° F.

11. (a) $F = \frac{9}{5}C + 32 = \frac{9}{5}(10) + 32 = 50°$ F.

    (b) $F = \frac{9}{5}(0) + 32 = 32°$ F.

    (c) $F = \frac{9}{5}(30) + 32 = 86°$ F.

    (d) $F = \frac{9}{5}(100) + 32 = 212°$ F.

    (e) $F = \frac{9}{5}(212) + 32 \doteq 414°$ F.

    (f) $F = \frac{9}{5}(^-40) + 32 = {}^-40°$ F.

12. (a)   Perimeter $= \frac{1}{2}(2\pi \cdot 6) + 2\left(\sqrt{6^2 + 8^2}\right) = (6\pi + 20)$ cm. Area $= \frac{1}{2}(\pi \cdot 6) + 6 \cdot 8 = (18\pi + 48)$ cm^2.

    (b)   Perimeter $= \frac{1}{2}(2\pi \cdot 20) + 2[\frac{1}{2}(2\pi \cdot 10)] = 40\pi$ cm. Area $= \frac{1}{2}(\pi \cdot 20^2) - 2[\frac{1}{2}(\pi \cdot 10^2)] = 100\pi$ cm^2.

    (c)   Perimeter $= 3 + 10 + 11 + 3 + 5 + 7 + 6 + 5 = 50$ m.
           Area $= 2[\frac{1}{2}(3)(4)] + (4)(7) + (4)(10) = 80$ m^2.

13. (a)   35   (b)   0.16

    (c)   400,000   (d)   5,200,000

    (e)   5200   (f)   0.0035

14. (a)   Yes. $1^2 + \left(\sqrt{2}\right)^2 = \left(\sqrt{3}\right)^2$.

    (b)   No.   (c)   Yes.

    (d)   No. Sides are $\sqrt{10}$, $\sqrt{17}$, and 5.

15. The person has walked a total of 6km north and 5 km east, forming the legs of a right triangle.

    $d = \sqrt{6^2 + 5^2} = \sqrt{61}$ km.

16. (a)   Volume $= \frac{1}{3}\pi(30^2)(40) = 12{,}000\pi$ cm^3. SA $= \pi(30^2) + \pi(30)(50) = 2400\pi$ cm^2.

    (b)   Volume $= \frac{1}{2}(65)(33)(40) = 42{,}900$ cm^3.

           SA $= 2[\frac{1}{2}(65)(33)] + (33 + 65 + \sqrt{5314})(40) = (6065 + 4\sqrt{5314})$ cm^2.

1. (a) It draws a circle five times. The circumference is $\frac{1}{5}$ of the circumference of CIRCLE 1.

   (b) It draws the same size circle as CIRCLE1 but draws it to the left.

2.
```
TO FCIRCLE :N :S
  REPEAT :N [FD :S RT 360/:N]
END
```

3. (a)
```
TO ARC :S :D
  REPEAT :D [FD :S RT 1]
END
```

   (b)
```
TO ARCRAD :R :D
  REPEAT :D [FD 2*3.14159*R/360 RT 1]
END
```

4. Answers may vary.

5. (a)
```
TO CIRCS :RAD
  HT
  CIRCLE :RAD
  ARCRAD :RAD/2 180
END

TO CIRCLE :R
  VCIRCLE 2*3.14159*R/360
END

TO VCIRCLE :S
  REPEAT 360 [FD :S RT 1]
END

TO ARCRAD :R :D
  REPEAT :D [FD 2*3.14159*R/360 RT 1]
END

TO LARCRAD :R :D
  REPEAT :D [FD 2*3.14159*R/360 LT 1]
END
```

   (b)
```
TO EYES :RAD
  HT
  CIRCLE :RAD
  CIRCLE :RAD/2
  CIRCLE :RAD/4
  LCIRCLE :RAD
  LCIRCLE :RAD/2
  LCIRCLE :RAD/4
  ARCRAD (:RAD + 0.6*:RAD) 90
  LT 180
  LARCRAD (:RAD + 0.6*:RAD) 90
  RT 180
  LARCRAD (:RAD + 0.6*:RAD) 90
  HT
END
```

5. (b)   TO LCIRCLE :RAD
                LVCIRCLE 2*3.14159*:RAD/360
            END

            TO LVCIRCLE:S
              REPEAT 360 [FD :S LT 1]
            END

    (c)   TO SEMIS :R
              ARCRAD :R 180
              RT 90 FD :R*2 RT 90
              ARCRAD :R/2 180
              RT 180
              ARCRAD :R/2 180
            END

            TO ARCRAD :R :D
              REPEAT :D [FD 2*3.14159*:R/360 RT 1]
            END

    (d)   TO CONCIRC :R
              HT CIRCLE :R
              PU LT 90 FD :R/2 RT 90 PD
              CIRCLE :R + :R/2
              PU LT 90 FD :R/2 RT 90 PD
              CIRCLE :R*2
            END

            TO CIRCLE :R
              VCIRCLE 2*3.14159*:R/360
            END

            TO VCIRCLE :S
              REPEAT 360 [FD :S RT 1]
            END

    (e)   TO FRAME SIZE
              SQUARE :SIZE
              FD :SIZE/2
              CIRCLE :SIZE/2
            END

            TO SQUARE :S
              REPEAT 4 [FD :S RT 90]
            END

6. TO SYMBOL :R
      PU LT 90 FD 140 RT 90 PD
      REPEAT 3[CIRCLE :R PU RT 90 FD 9*:R/4 LT 90 PD]
      PU LT 90 FD :R*45/8 LT 90 FD :R RT 180 PD
      REPEAT 2[CIRCLE :R PU RT 90 FD 9*:R/4 LT 90 PD]
      HIDETURTLE
    END

6. ```
   TO CIRCLE :R
    HT
    VCIRCLE 2*3.14159*:R/360
    ST
   END

   TO VCIRCLE :S
    REPEAT 360 [FD :S RT 1]
   END
   ```

7. ```
   TO FLOWER :RAD
    REPEAT 6[PETAL :RAD 60 RT 60]
   END

   TO PETAL :RAD :DEG
    HT ARCRAD :RAD :DEG
    RT 180 — :DEG
    ARCRAD :RAD :DEG
    RT 180 — :DEG
    ST
   END

   TO ARCRAD :R :D
    REPEAT :D [FD 2*3.14159*:R/360 RT 1]
   END
   ```

8. ```
   TO DIAMCIRC :R
    REPEAT 360 [FD 2*3.14159*:R/360  RT 1]
    RT 90
    FD 2*:R
   END
   ```

9. ```
   TO MASTERCARD :W
    CARD 3* :W 5* :W CARD 3*:W/2 RD 90 FD :W LT 90 PD
    CIRCLES :W
   END

   TO CARD :W :L
    REPEAT 2 [FD :W RT 90 FD :L RT 90]
   END

   TO CIRCLES :R
    CIRCLE :R PU
    RT 90
    FD :R
    LT 90 PD
    CIRCLE :R
   END

   TO CIRCLE :R
    VCIRCLE 2*3.14159*:R/360
   END

   TO VCIRCLE :S
    REPEAT 360 [FD :S RT 1]
   END
   ```

10.   0.416666

Chapter 13 Test

1.   (a)   50,000   5000   50 $\boxed{0.05}$

     (b)   3200 $\boxed{320}$ 3.2   0.0032

     (c) $\boxed{260,000,000}$ 26,000,000   260,000   260

     (d)   190,000   19,000 $\boxed{190}$ 0.19

2.   (a)   Millimeter   (b)   Centimeter

     (c)   Millimeter   (d)   Kilometer

     (e)   Centimeter   (f)   Meter

3.   (a)   Find the area of $\triangle$ ADC ($A = \frac{1}{2}AC \cdot AE$) and double it.

     (b)   Use the formula for a parallelogram: $A = bh = AB \cdot BF$.

4. $\frac{1}{2}(4)(11) - \frac{1}{2}(4)(3k) = 16$ units^2.

5.   Using Pick's theorem (Problem Set 13-2, problem 8), $A = I + \frac{1}{2}B - 1$.

     (a) $I = 7$, $B = 5$. $A = 7 + \frac{1}{2}(5) - 1 = 8\frac{1}{2}$ cm^2.

     (b) $I = 5$, $B = 5$. $A = 5 + \frac{1}{2}(5) - 1 = 6\frac{1}{2}$ cm^2.

     (c) $I = 2$, $B = 12$. $A = 2 + \frac{1}{2}(12) - 1 = 7$ cm^2.

6.   Sum the areas of the four triangles: $A = 252$ cm^2.

7.   Rearranging as shown gives a rectangle with width $\frac{h}{2}$ and length $A'B' = b_2 + b_1$. Its area is $A = lw = \frac{h}{2}(b_1 + b_2)$, which must be the area of the initial trapezoid.

8.   (a) $A = \frac{1}{2}ap$, where $a = 3\sqrt{3}$ and $p = 6 \cdot 6 = 36$. $A = \frac{1}{2}(3\sqrt{3})(36) = 54\sqrt{3}$ cm^2.

     (b) $A = \pi r^2$, where $r = 6$. $A = \pi(6^2) = 36\pi$ cm^2.

9.   (a) $A = \pi(4^2) - \pi(2^2) = 12\pi$ cm^2.

     (b)   Semicircle: $A = \frac{1}{2}(\pi \cdot 3^2) = 4.5\pi$ cm^2. Triangle: $A = \frac{1}{2}(6)(4) = 12$ cm^2.
          Shaded area: $A = (4.5\pi + 12)$ cm^2.

     (c) $A = (6)(4) = 24$ cm^2.

     (d) $A = \frac{1}{2}(2)(3) + (12)(3) + (3)(7) + \frac{1}{2}(3)(3) = 64.5$ cm^2.

     (e) $A = (8)(18) + \frac{1}{2}(3)(18 + 5) = 178.5$ cm^2.

     (f) $A = \frac{40}{360}(\pi \cdot 6^2) = 4\pi$ cm^2.

10. (a) Yes. $5^2 + 12^2 = 13^2$.

    (b) No. $40 + 60 < 104$. Cannot represent any triangle.

11. (a) $SA = B + \frac{1}{2}pl$, where $l = \sqrt{4^2 + 6^2} = 2\sqrt{13}$. $SA = 8^2 + \frac{1}{2}(32)(2\sqrt{13}) = (64 + 2\sqrt{13})$ cm^2.

         $V = \frac{1}{3}Bh = \frac{1}{3}(8^2)(6) = 128$ cm^3.

    (b) $SA = \pi r^2 + \pi r l$, where $l = \sqrt{6^2 + 8^2} = 10$. $SA = \pi(6^2) + \pi(6)(10) = 96\pi$ cm^2.

         $V = \frac{1}{3}\pi r^2 h = \frac{1}{3}\pi(6^2)(8) = 96\pi$ cm^3.

    (c) $SA = 4\pi r^2 = 4\pi(5^2) = 100\pi$ m^2.

         $V = \frac{4}{3}\pi r^3 = \frac{4}{3}\pi(5^3) = \frac{500}{3}\pi$ m^3.

    (d) $SA = 2\pi r^2 + 2\pi rh = 2\pi(3^2) + 2\pi(3)(6) = 54\pi$ cm^2.

         $V = \pi r^2 h = \pi(3^2)(6) = 54\pi$ cm^3.

    (e) $SA = sB + ph = 2(4)(10) + (28)(8) = 304$ m^2.

         $V = lwh = (10)(4)(8) = 320$ m^3.

12. $l = \sqrt{12^2 + 5^2} = 13$. Lateral area $= \pi r l = \pi(5)(13) = 65\pi$ m^2.

13. The graph really shows an eight-fold growth. With both lengths changed, volume is proportional to the cube of length, so if lengths are doubled volume is increased by a factor of 8.

14. (a) Metric tons   (b) 1 cm^3

    (c) 1 gram   (d) 1 L = 1 dm^3

    (e) 25 L   (f) 2000

    (g) 51,800   (h) 10,000,000

    (i) 50,000   (j) 5.830

    (k) 25,000   (l) 75,000

    (m) 52.813   (n) 4.8

15. (a) $\frac{50}{3} = 16.\overline{6}$ (b) $\frac{947}{1760} \doteq 0.538$

    (c) $\frac{9800}{9} = 1088.\overline{8}$ (d) 2176

    (e) 486   (f) 1382.4

    (g) 60.8   (g) $\frac{49}{16} = 3.0625$

    (h) 82.4   (i) 35

    (j) 35

16. $h_1^3 : h_2^3 = V_1 : V_2$

17. (a) $V = (1)(2)(3) = 6 \text{ m}^3 = 6{,}000{,}000 \text{ cm}^3 = 6{,}000{,}000 \text{ g} = 6{,}000 \text{ kg}$.

(b) $V_{sphere} = \frac{4}{3}\pi(30^3) = 36{,}000\pi \doteq 113{,}097 \text{ cm}^3$. Consider the height increase from the sphere, changing length and width to cm: $V = 113{,}097 = (100)(200)h$, or $h = 5.65$ cm (rise from the sphere). The tank was half full (i.e., $h = 1.5$ m); with a rise of 5.65 cm = 0.0565 the new height is 1.5565 m.

(c) Half the volume of the tank is 3,000,000 cm^3. A sphere with this volume would have dimensions: $\frac{4}{3}\pi r^3 = 3{,}000{,}000$; $r = \sqrt[3]{\dfrac{3 \cdot 3{,}000{,}000}{4\pi}} \doteq 89.5$ cm. A sphere of this radius, however, will not fit in the tank; the largest sphere is the largest that will fit in the container; i.e., one with r = 50 cm.

18. (a) liters   (b) kilograms

(c) grams   (d) grams

(e) kilograms   (f) metric tons

(g) milliliters

19. (a) Unlikely. $15°$ C = $59°$ F.   (b) Likely. $26°$ C = $79°$ F.

(c) Unlikely. $0°$ C is the freezing point of water.

(d) Unlikely. $100°$ C is the boiling point of water.

(e) Unlikely. Water will not freeze until it lowers to $0°$ C.

20. (a) 2000   (b) 1000

(c) 3   (d) 0.0042

(e) 0.0002

CHAPTER 14 - COORDINATE GEOMETRY

Problem Set 14-1

1. (a) The major perpendicular streets could be the zero lines represented by the axes. Other streets would use them as a reference in terms of north, south, east, and west.

   (b) S = School
   C = Church
   H = City Hall
   M = Museum
   U = College

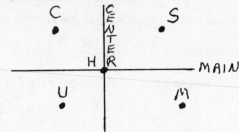

2. (a) A(2, 2), B(5, 0), C(4, ⁻3), D(0, ⁻3), E(⁻2, ⁻3), F(⁻4, 0), G(⁻4, 3), H(0, 3).

   (b) Any point with ordinate ⁻3 is collinear with E, D, and C; e.g., (5, ⁻3).

3. (a) I   (b) III

   (c) II   (d) IV

   (e) Between I and II

4. (a) Quadrant I = {(x, y) | x > 0 and y > 0}.

   (b) Quadrant II = {(x, y) | x < 0 and y > 0}.

   (c) Quadrant III = {(x, y) | x < 0 and y < 0}.

   (d) Quadrant IV = {(x, y) | x > 0 and y < 0}.

5. D should be located at (4, ⁻2). Its x-value must be the same as that of C and its y-value that of A.

6. Answers may vary. Some examples are (5, ⁻1), (6, ⁻2), (1, 3), etc. You will find that all points will be on the line y = 4 − x.

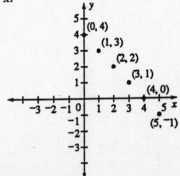

7. (a) P(3, 4) and Q(6, 1)   (b) M(⁻1, ⁻1) and N(⁻1, 4)

8. (a) P′(2, ⁻2), Q′(2, ⁻5), R′(4, ⁻2)   (b) P′(⁻2, 2), Q′(⁻5, 2), R′(⁻2, 4)

   (c) P′(4, 2), Q′(4, 5), R′(6, 2)

9. (a) A reflection in the x-axis causes the y-coordinates to change sign. Thus:
   (0, 1) → (0, ⁻1); (1, 0) → (1, 0) (This point is on the x-axis and cannot reflect); (2, 4) → (2, ⁻4);
   (⁻2, 4) → (⁻2, ⁻4); (⁻2, ⁻4) → (⁻2, 4); (2, ⁻4) → (2, 4)

9. (b) A reflection in the y-axis causes the x-coordinates to change sign. Thus:
  (0, 1) → (0, 1) (This point is on the y-axis and cannot reflect); (1, 0) → (⁻1, 0); (2, 4) → (⁻2, 4);
  (⁻2, 4) → (2, 4); (⁻2, ⁻4) → (2, ⁻4); (2, ⁻4) → (⁻2, ⁻4)

  (c) Under 90° counterclockwise rotation, the x- and y-coordinates are interchanged and the x′-coordinate changes sign. Thus:
  (0, 1) → (⁻1, 0); (1, 0) → (0, 1); (2, 4) → (⁻4, 2); (⁻2, 4) → (⁻4, ⁻2); (⁻2, ⁻4) → (4, ⁻2);
  (2, ⁻4) → (4, 2)

  (d) A half-turn causes the x-and y-coordinates to both change sign. Thus:
  (0, 1) → (0, ⁻1); (1, 0) → (⁻1, 0); (2, 4) → (⁻2, ⁻4); (⁻2, 4) → (2, ⁻4); (⁻2, ⁻4) → (2, 4);
  (2, ⁻4) → (⁻2, 4)

  (e) Each point will change its x- and y-coordinate by the same value that the coordinates of point A change from those of point O; i.e., we add 0 to the x-coordinate and ⁻4 to the y-coordinate of each point. Thus:
  (0, 1) → (0, ⁻3); (1, 0) → (1, ⁻4); (2, 4) → (2, 0); (⁻2, 4) → (⁻2, 0); (⁻2, ⁻4) → (⁻2, ⁻8;)
  (2, ⁻4) → (2, ⁻8)

10. (a) A′(⁻2, ⁻5), B′(2, ⁻6), C′(5, ⁻1)   (b) A′(2, 5), B′(⁻2, 6), C′(⁻5, 1)

  (c) A′(2, ⁻5), B′(⁻2, ⁻6), C′(⁻5, ⁻1)

11. (a) P(2, 4) → P′(⁻2, 4) after reflection in the y-axis; P′(⁻2, 4) → P″(⁻2, ⁻4) after reflection in the x-axis

  (b) P(a, b) → P″(⁻a, ⁻b)

12. These are reflections about the line y = x, causing the x- and y-coordinates to be interchanged. Thus:
  A′(0, 1), B′(2, 2), C′(1, 3), D′(⁻1, 3), E′(b, a).

13. (a) Since P and its center of rotation both have x-value *a*, the radius of rotation is b; i.e., P′ will be b units away from the center, on the x-axis (with y-value 0). Thus P(a, b) → P′(a − b, 0).

  (b) As in 9(c), P(a, b) → P′(⁻b, a).

14. (a) $\overline{AB} = \sqrt{(0 - 0)^2 + (7 - 3)^2} = \sqrt{16} = 4$

  (b) $\overline{AB} = 4$ (c) $\overline{AB} = 5$

  (d) $\overline{AB} = 5$ (e) $\overline{AB} = \sqrt{52} = 2\sqrt{13}$

  (f) $\overline{AB} = 5$ (g) $\overline{AB} = \sqrt{\frac{365}{4}} \doteq 4.78$

  (h) $\overline{AB} \doteq \sqrt{15.13} \doteq 3.89$ (i) $\overline{AB} = 5$

  (j) $\overline{AB} = \sqrt{68} = 2\sqrt{17}$

15. $\overline{AB} = \sqrt{(⁻4 - 0)^2 + (⁻3 - 0)^2} = \sqrt{16 + 9} = \sqrt{25} = 5$

  $\overline{AC} = \sqrt{(⁻5 - 0)^2 + (0 - 0)^2} = \sqrt{25} = 5$

  $\overline{BC} = \sqrt{(⁻5 - ⁻4)^2 + (0 - ⁻3)^2} = \sqrt{(⁻1)^2 + (3)^2} = \sqrt{10}$

  So the perimeter of the triangle = 5 + 5 + $\sqrt{10}$ = 10 + $\sqrt{10}$.

16. The sides have lengths $\sqrt{45}$, $\sqrt{180}$, and $\sqrt{225}$. Since $\left(\sqrt{45}\right)^2 + \left(\sqrt{180}\right)^2 = \left(\sqrt{225}\right)^2$, the triangle is a right triangle

17. Using the distance formula, we find: $\overline{AB} = 5$, $\overline{AC} = 7\sqrt{2}$, and $\overline{BC} = 5$. Since $\overline{AB} = \overline{BC}$, the triangle is isosceles.

18. $\sqrt{(x-1)^2 + (9-3)^2} = 10$. Solving, we find $(x-1)^2 + 6^2 = 100$, or $x = \{9, ^-7\}$.

19. (a) $\left(\frac{^-3 + 3}{2}, \frac{1 + 9}{2}\right) = (0, 5)$ (b) $\left(\frac{4 + 5}{2}, \frac{^-3 + ^-1}{2}\right) = (\frac{9}{2}, ^-2)$

    (c) $\left(\frac{1.8 + 2.2}{2}, \frac{^-3.7 + 1.3}{2}\right) = (2, ^-1.2)$

    (d) $\left[\frac{(1+a) + (1-a)}{2}, \frac{(a-b) + (b-a)}{2}\right] = (1, 0)$

20. The center is the midpoint of the diameter; i.e., $\left(\frac{x + 3}{2}, \frac{y + ^-1}{2}\right) = (^-2, 5)$. Solving, the coordinates of the other endpoint are $x = ^-7$, $y = 11$.

21. Let point X be the midpoint of $\overline{AB}$, Y be the midpoint of $\overline{AC}$, and Z be the midpoint of $\overline{BC}$. Then:

    (a) $X = \left(\frac{0 + ^-4}{2}, \frac{0 + 6}{2}\right) = (^-2, 3)$; $Y = \left(\frac{0 + 4}{2}, \frac{0 + 2}{2}\right) = (2, 1)$; $Z = \left(\frac{^-4 + 4}{2}, \frac{6 + 2}{2}\right) = (0, 4)$

    (b) The medians are $\overline{CX}$, $\overline{BY}$, and $\overline{AZ}$. The distance formula gives:

    $$\overline{CX} = \sqrt{(^-2 - 4)^2 + (3 - 2)^2} = \sqrt{37}$$

    $$\overline{BY} = \sqrt{(^-4 - 2)^2 + (6 - 1)^2} = \sqrt{61}$$

    $$\overline{AZ} = \sqrt{(0 - 0)^2 + (4 - 0)^2} = 4$$

22. (a) $(x - 3)^2 + (y - 2)^2 = 4$ (b) $(x + 3)^2 + (y + 4)^2 = 25$

    (c) $(x + 1)^2 + y^2 = 4$ (d) $x^2 + y^2 = 9$

23. Substitute the given coordinates in the equation $x^2 + y^2 = 9$. If the value $= 9$, the point is on the circle. If the value is less than 9, the point is inside the circle. If the value is greater than 9, the point is outside the circle.

    (a) $3^2 + (^-3)^2 > 9$; exterior.   (b) $2^2 + (^-2)^2 < 9$; interior.

    (c) $1^2 + 8^2 > 9$; exterior.   (d) $3^2 + 1982^2 > 9$; exterior.

    (e) $5.1234^2 + (^-3.7804)^2 > 9$; exterior.   (f) $\left(\frac{1}{387}\right)^2 + \left(\frac{1}{1983}\right)^2 < 9$; interior.

    (g) $\left(\frac{^-1}{2}\right)^2 + \left(\frac{35}{2}\right)^2 > 9$; exterior.   (h) $0^2 + 3^2 = 9$; on the circle.

24. $r = \sqrt{(^-3 - 0)^2 + (5 - 0)^2} = \sqrt{34}$; $C = (0, 0)$. Thus $x^2 + y^2 = 34$.

25. The equations will be of the form $(x - 4)^2 + (y + 3)^2 = r^2$. Use the distance formula to find r.

    (a) $r = \sqrt{(4 - 0)^2 + (^-3 - 0)^2} = 5$; $(x - 4)^2 + (y + 3)^2 = 25$.

    (b) $r = \sqrt{(5 - 4)^2 + (^-2 - ^-3)^2} = \sqrt{2}$; $(x - 4)^2 + (y + 3)^2 = 2$.

26. Center $= \left(\frac{^-8 + 4}{2}, \frac{2 - 6}{2}\right) = (^-2, ^-2)$; $r = \sqrt{(^-2 - 4)^2 + (^-2 + 6)^2} = \sqrt{52}$.

    The equation is $(x + 2)^2 + (y + 2)^2 = 52$.

27. (a) 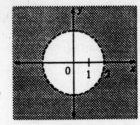   (b)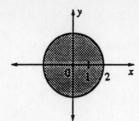

(c) 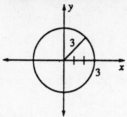   (d)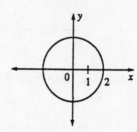

(e)   The graph is the empty set.   (f)   Same as (d).

28. Since the circle is on the x-axis, its center is at (x, 0). The distance from the center to (0, 0) and to (5, 2) is the same (i.e., it is the radius), or:

$$\sqrt{(x - 0)^2 + (0 - 0)^2} = \sqrt{(x - 5)^2 + (0 - 2)^2}.$$ Solving, $x^2 = (x - 5)^2 + 4$, and $x = \frac{29}{10}$.

Thus the center is at $\left(\frac{29}{10}, 0\right)$ with $r = \frac{29}{10}$. The equation is $\left(x - \frac{29}{10}\right)^2 + y^2 = \left(\frac{29}{10}\right)^2$

29. Yes, Dividing both sides of the equation by 2 gives $x^2 + y^2 = \frac{1}{2}$. This is a circle with center (0, 0) and radius $\sqrt{\frac{1}{2}}$.

30. If A($^-$1, 5), B(0, 2), and C(1, $^-$1) are collinear, $\overline{AB} + \overline{BC} = \overline{AC}$. Using the distance formula, $\overline{AB} = \sqrt{10}$, $\overline{BC} = \sqrt{10}$, and $\overline{AC} = 2\sqrt{10}$. The points are collinear.

31. It is necessary to show that AM = BM = OM. $M = \left(\frac{0 + a}{2}, \frac{b + 0}{2}\right) = \left(\frac{a}{2}, \frac{b}{2}\right)$. Thus:

$$AM = \sqrt{\left(a - \frac{a}{2}\right)^2 + \left(0 - \frac{b}{2}\right)^2} = \sqrt{\frac{a^2}{4} + \frac{b^2}{4}}.$$ Similarly, $BM = OM = \sqrt{\frac{a^2}{4} + \frac{b^2}{4}}$.

Thus the midpoint of the hypotenuse is equidistant from the vertices of the triangle.

32. Linda arrives back home.

33. On a 5 by 5 grid, there are 25 coordinate pairs. Thus there is a $\frac{1}{25}$ chance of Professors Carlson and Lazzell choosing identical coordinates.

Problem Set 14-2

1. Both graphs have slope $^-$1, so they are parallel. One has y-intercept = 0 and the other has y-intercept = 3.

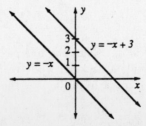

2. Both are parallel to the given line (slopes are equal). (a) has y-int. = 3, while (b) has y-int. = $^-$3.

3.   One method of graphing is to plot the y-intercept and draw a line through that point with the given slope.

(a)   The y-intercept is at $(0, 3)$. A line with slope $= \frac{\text{rise}}{\text{run}} = \frac{^-3}{4}$ goes down 3 units (negative rise) and to the right 4 units (positive run) from $(0, 3)$, as shown:

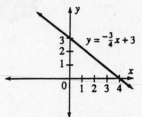

(b)   This line has zero slope (i.e., it is horizontal) and passes through all points where $y = {}^-3$.

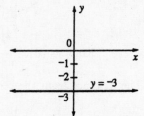

(c)   The y-intercept is at $(0, {}^-30)$. The slope is 15 (i.e., a rise of a positive 15 for a run of a positive 1). Checking $(0, 0)$ in $y \geq 15x - 30$ gives $0 \geq 0 - 30$, which is a true statement; thus the half-plane containing $(0, 0)$ is the graph of the inequality. The line $y = 15x - 30$ is part of the solution, so it is a solid line.

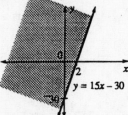

(d)   This line has an undetermined slope (i.e., is vertical) and passes through the point $x = {}^-2$.

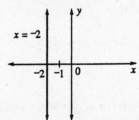

(e)   The y-intercept is at $(0, {}^-3)$; the slope is 3.

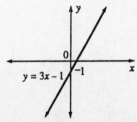

(f)   The y-intercept is at $(0, 0)$; the slope is $\frac{1}{20}$. Since the line passes through the origin, we cannot check the point $(0, 0)$; let us use $(0, 1)$ instead. Checking, we have $1 \leq 0 \cdot \frac{1}{20}$. This is not a true statement, so the half-plane on the other side of $y = \frac{1}{20}x$ from $(0, 1)$ is the solution set. See page 285.

3.   (f)

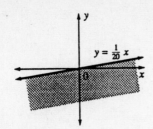

$y = \frac{1}{20}x$

4.   x-intercept   y-intercept

      (a)   (4, 0)   (0, 3)

      (b)   None   (0, ⁻3)

      (c)   (2, 0)   (0, ⁻30)

      (d)   (⁻2, 0)   None

      (e)   ($\frac{1}{3}$, 0)   (0, ⁻1)

      (f)   (0, 0)   (0, 0)

5.   (a)   The slope is $\frac{9}{5}$; the y-intercept is 32:

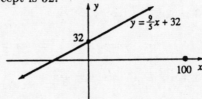

      (b) $y = \frac{5}{9}x - 17\frac{7}{9}$; the slope is $\frac{5}{9}$ and the y-intercept is $^-17\frac{7}{9}$:

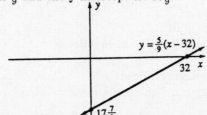

      (c)   The graphs intersect at (⁻40, ⁻40). ⁻40° is the temperature at which both scales are numerically equal. To the right of the intersection, the Fahrenheit graph is higher; to the left the Celsius graph is higher.

6.   (a) $y = \frac{1}{3}x$ (b) $y = ^-x + 3$

      (c) $y = \frac{^-4}{3}x + 4$ (d) $y = \frac{3}{4}x + \frac{7}{4}$

      (e) $y = \frac{1}{3}x$ (f) $y = x$

7.   Slope is given by: $m = \frac{y_2 - y_1}{x_2 - x_1}$.

      (a) $m = \frac{0 - 3}{5 - 4} = \frac{^-3}{^-9} = \frac{1}{3}$ (b) $m = \frac{2 - ^-1}{5 - ^-4} = \frac{1}{9}$

      (c) $m = \frac{2 - 2}{1 - \sqrt{5}} = 0$ (d) $m = \frac{198 - 81}{^-3 - ^-3} \Rightarrow$ no slope (vertical line)

      (e) $m = \frac{12 - 10}{1.0001 - 1} = \frac{2}{0.0001} = 20,000$ (f) $m = \frac{b - a}{b - a} = 1$

8.   (a) $y = {}^-x - 1$ (b) $y = \frac{1}{2}x$

     (c) $y = 1$ (d) $x = 2$

     (e) $y = x - \frac{1}{2}$ (f) $y = 0$

9.   Use the point-slope form of the line.

     (a) $y - 0 = \frac{^-1}{2}(x - {}^-3) \Rightarrow y = \frac{^-1}{2}(x + 3) \Rightarrow y = \frac{^-1}{2}x - \frac{3}{2}$

     (b) $y - {}^-3 = \frac{2}{3}(x - 1) \Rightarrow y + 3 = \frac{2}{3}x - \frac{2}{3} \Rightarrow y = \frac{2}{3}x - \frac{2}{3} - 3 \Rightarrow y = \frac{2}{3}x - \frac{11}{3}$

     (c) $y + 3 = 0(x - 2) \Rightarrow y + 3 = 0 \Rightarrow y = {}^-3$

     (d) $y + 5 = \frac{^-5}{7}(x + 1) \Rightarrow y + 5 = \frac{^-5}{7}x - \frac{5}{7} \Rightarrow y = \frac{^-5}{7}x - \frac{5}{7} - 5 \Rightarrow y = \frac{^-5}{7}x - \frac{40}{7}$

10.   (a)   Parallel; $m = 2$ (b)   Parallel; $m = \frac{3}{4}$

     (c)   Parallel; $m = 2$ (d)   Not parallel; $m_1 = \frac{^-4}{3}$, $m_2 = \frac{4}{3}$

11.   Find the slope (m) of the given line and then use it in the point-slope form of the desired line.

     (a) $y = {}^-2x \Rightarrow m = {}^-2$
           $y - 3 = {}^-2(x + 2) \Rightarrow y - 3 = {}^-2x - 4 \Rightarrow y = {}^-2x - 1$

     (b) $3y + 2x + 1 = 0 \Rightarrow 3y = {}^-2x - 1 \Rightarrow y = \frac{^-2}{3}x - \frac{1}{3} \Rightarrow m = \frac{^-2}{3}$

           $y - 3 = \frac{^-2}{3}(x + 2) \Rightarrow y - 3 = \frac{^-2}{3}x - \frac{^-4}{3} \Rightarrow y = \frac{^-2}{3}x + \frac{5}{3}$

     (c) $x = 0 \Rightarrow$ vertical line (slope undetermined)
           A vertical line passing through $({}^-2, 3)$ has equation $x = {}^-2$

     (d) $y = {}^-1 \Rightarrow$ horizontal line ($m = 0$)
           A horizontal line passing through $({}^-2, 3)$ has equation $y = 3$

     (e) $x = 3 \Rightarrow$ vertical line (slope undetermined)
           A vertical line passing through $({}^-2, 3)$ has equation $x = {}^-2$

     (f) $y = {}^-4 \Rightarrow$ horizontal line ($m = 0$)
           A horizontal line passing through $({}^-2, 3)$ has equation $y = 3$

     (g) $x + y = 2 \Rightarrow y = {}^-x + 2 \Rightarrow m = {}^-1$
           $y - 3 = {}^-1(x + 2) \Rightarrow y - 3 = {}^-x - 2 \Rightarrow y = {}^-x + 1$

     (h) $\frac{x}{2} + \frac{y}{3} = 1 \Rightarrow 3x + 2y = 6 \Rightarrow y = \frac{^-3}{2}x + 3 \Rightarrow m = \frac{^-3}{2}$

           $y - 3 = \frac{^-3}{2}(x + 2) \Rightarrow y - 3 = \frac{^-3}{2}x - 3 \Rightarrow y = \frac{^-3}{2}x$

12.   (a)   Perpendicular; $m_1 = \frac{1}{3}$, $m_2 = {}^-3$ (b)   Parallel; $m_1 = m_2 = \frac{1}{2}$

     (c)   Perpendicular; vertical and horizontal   (d)   Neither; $m_1 = {}^-1$, $m_2 = \frac{1}{2}$

13.   Rise is 4 feet. $m = \frac{\text{rise}}{\text{run}} = \frac{1}{10}$. Thus $\frac{4}{x} = \frac{1}{10}$ and $x = 40$ feet. Length $= \sqrt{40^2 + 4^2} = \sqrt{1616} = 4\sqrt{101}$ ft.

14.   Slopes of $\overline{AB}$ and $\overline{CD}$ are both 4 which implies $\overline{AB} \| \overline{CD}$. Slopes of $\overline{AD}$ and $\overline{BC}$ are both $\frac{1}{2}$ which implies $\overline{AD} \| \overline{BC}$. Thus opposite sides are parallel and it is a parallelogram.

15. Three points can be collinear only if the slopes of line segments joining them are the same. Label the given coordinates: $A(0, ^-1)$, $B(1, 2)$, $C(^-1, ^-4)$. Then:

$m_{\overline{AB}} = \frac{2 - ^-1}{1 - 0} = 3$ and $m_{\overline{BC}} = \frac{^-4 - 2}{^-1 - 1} = 3$. Since the slopes are the same, the points must be collinear.

16. For the x-intercept, $y = 0$; thus $\frac{x}{a} = 1$ and $x = a$. Similarly, at the y-intercept, $y = b$.

17. (a) Since all points reflected in the x-axis have the signs of their y-coordinates changed, replace y by ^-y in the equation:
$^-y = 3x + 1 \Rightarrow y = ^-3x - 1$

(b) Reflecting about the y-axis changes the signs of the x-coordinates. Thus replace x with ^-x:
$y = 3(^-x) + 1 \Rightarrow y = ^-3x + 1$

(c) Reflecting about the line $y = x$ reverses the coordinates. Thus replace x with y and y with x:
$x = 3y + 1 \Rightarrow y = \frac{1}{3}x - \frac{1}{3}$

18. (a) The slope of $\overleftrightarrow{BC}$ is $m = \frac{^-2 - 2}{^-3 - 1} = 1$. The slope of the perpendicular is thus $^-1$.

The equation is $y + 1 = ^-1(x - 1) \Rightarrow y = ^-x$

(b) The slope of $\overleftrightarrow{AC}$ is $\frac{3}{2}$. The slope of the perpendicular is thus $\frac{^-2}{3}$. The equation is $y = \frac{^-2}{3}x + \frac{8}{3}$.

19. A triangle is right if two of its sides (legs) are perpendicular.

(a) $m_{\overline{AB}} = \frac{5 - 3}{^-3 - ^-2} = ^-2$; $m_{\overline{AC}} = \frac{6 - 3}{4 - ^-2} = \frac{1}{2}$. $\overline{AB}$ and $\overline{AC}$ are perpendicular; the triangle is right.

(b) $m_{\overline{AB}} = 1$; $m_{\overline{AC}} = 0$; $m_{\overline{BC}} = \frac{^-1}{3}$. No sides are perpendicular; the triangle is not right.

20. The midpoint of both diagonals is $(\frac{a}{2}, \frac{a}{2})$. They therefore meet at each other's midpoint; i.e., they bisect each other. $m_{\overline{AC}} = ^-1$; $m_{\overline{OB}} = 1$, so they are perpendicular.

21. Answers may vary.

(a) The points are on the line $y = 2$. Others are $(^-3, 2)$, $(5, 2)$, ...

(b) The points are on the line $x = ^-1$. Others are $(^-1, 7)$, $(^-1, ^-5)$, ...

(c) The points are on the line $y = 0$ (i.e., the x-axis). Others are $(2, 0)$, $(4, 0)$, ...

(d) The points are on the line $x = 0$ (i.e., the y-axis). Others are $(0, ^-1)$, $(0, 6)$, ...

(e) Same as (d)

(f) The points are on the line $y = x$ [all points are of the form (a, a)]. Others are $(3, 3)$, $(1, 1)$, ...

22. (a) $x = ^-2$; y may have any real value.   (b) $y = 1$; x may vary.

(c) $x > 0$; $y < 0$.

23. The rectangle has dimensions 2 by 4. The area is thus $2 \cdot 4 = 8$; the perimeter is $2(2) + 2(4) = 12$.

24. (a) 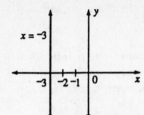   (b)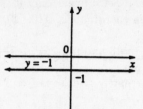

(c) 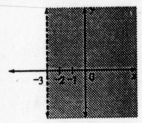   (d)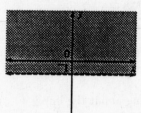

(e) 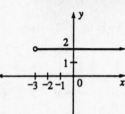   (f)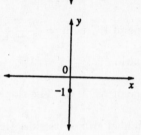

25. (a) This is a vertical line through (3, 0); its equation is x = 3.

(b) This is a horizontal line through (0, ⁻2); its equation is y = ⁻2.

(c) A horizontal line through (⁻4, 5); its equation is y = 5.

(d) A vertical line through (⁻4, 5); its equation is x = ⁻4.

26. (a) 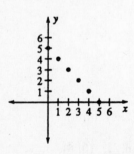   (b)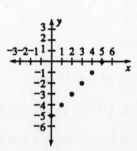

(c)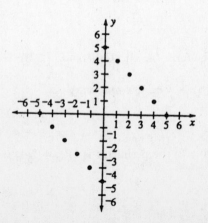

27.   The points to be graphed are:

(a)   (0, 2), (1, 3), (2, 4), (3, 5), (4, 6).

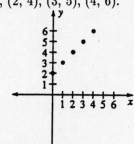

(b)   (⁻1, 0), (0, 1), (1, 2), (2, 3), (3, 4).

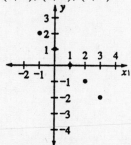

(c)   Both x and y must be integers for a point to be classified as a lattice point.
       Points are (3, 0), (⁻3, 0), (0, 3), (0, ⁻3).

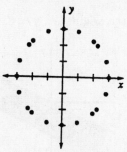

(d)   (⁻4, 16), (⁻3, 9), (⁻2, 4), (⁻1, 1), (0, 0), (1, 1), (2, 4), (3, 9), (4, 16).

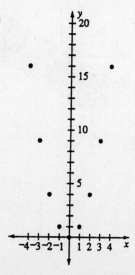

27.   (e)   (1, 5), (⁻1, ⁻5)

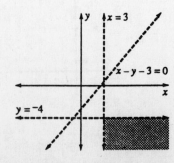

28.   (a) $\{(x, y) \mid {}^{-}1 \leq x \leq 1 \text{ and } {}^{-}1 \leq y \leq 1\}$

      (b) $\{(x, y) \mid x \leq 1 \text{ and } y \leq 1\}$

      (c) $\{(x, y) \mid {}^{-}1 \leq x \leq 2 \text{ and } {}^{-}1 \leq y \leq 1\}$

      (d) $\{(x, y) \mid x \geq 0 \text{ and } y \leq 1\}$

29.   (a)   The line reflects upon itself and is still x = 3.

      (b)   The line reflects to the left of the y-axis, becoming x = ⁻3.

      (c)   The vertical line becomes horizontal, still 3 units from the origin; i.e., y = 3.

30.   (a)   (b)

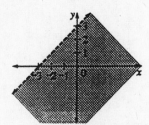   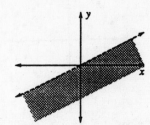

      (c)   (d)

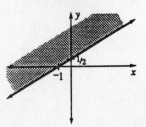   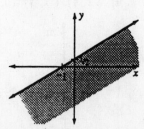

31.   Plot on the same graph the sets of inequalities as described in problem 3 of this section. The solution set is
      that which is common to all the graphs.

      (a)   (b)

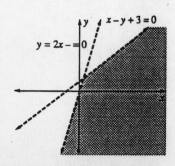   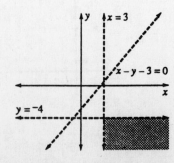

31. (c)

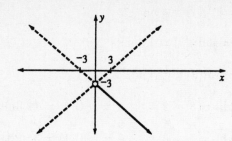

32. (a) $y = {}^-x$ (b) $y = {}^-x$

     (c) $x = 0$ (d) $y = {}^-x$

     (e) $y = x$ (f) $y = x - 3$

     (g) $y = x + 3$

     (h)   The graphs are reflections of each other over the x-axis.

     (i)   Same as (h).

33. (a)   y-coordinates change signs; $x - ({}^-y) = 1 \Rightarrow y = {}^-x + 1$.

     (b)   x-coordinates change signs; $({}^-x) - y = 1 \Rightarrow y = {}^-x - 1$.

     (c)   Coordinates are interchanged; $y = x + 1$.

     (d)   Both coordinates change signs; $({}^-x) - ({}^-y) = 1 \Rightarrow y = x + 1$.

34. (a)   (b)

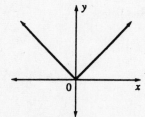   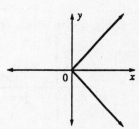

     (c)

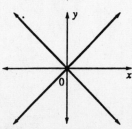

35. The graph of an equation or inequality having no solutions is empty. Some examples are: $|x - 3| = {}^-7$;
     $7 < x < 5$, etc.

36. (a) $y = {}^-8$ (b) $x = {}^-7$

37. (a)   The points are on the line $y = {}^-2$; others include $(3, {}^-2), (0, {}^-2), \ldots$

     (b)   Move from P to Q right 10 units and up 12 (i.e., add 10 to x and 12 to y). To obtain other points,
            continue the pattern: $(3 + 10, 4 + 12) = (13, 16), (13 + 10, 16 + 12) = (23, 28), \ldots$

38. There are three possible locations for D: $(12, 0), (0, 12),$ or $(4, {}^-8)$.

39. (a)   Base (along the x-axis) = 3; height = 1. A = $\frac{1}{2}(3)(1) = \frac{3}{2}$ units^2.

(b)   Base (along the x-axis) = 10; height = 3. A = $\frac{1}{2}(10)(3) = 15$ units^2.

(c)   Base (along the y-axis) = 5; height = 3. A = $\frac{1}{2}(5)(3) = \frac{15}{2}$ units^2.

(d)   Base (along the line y = 2) = 5 − 1 = 4; height = 8 − 2 = 6. A = $\frac{1}{2}(4)(6) = 12$ units^2.

(e)   Base (along the line y = 1) = 7 − 1 = 6; height = 1 − 0 = 1. A = $\frac{1}{2}(6)(1) = 3$ units^2.

Problem Set 14-3

1. (a)   Solutions may be found by selecting any value of x or y and then solving algebraically for the other. E.g., if y = 1, then 2x − 3(1) = 5 $\Rightarrow$ 2x = 8 $\Rightarrow$ x = 4; thus one solution is (4, 1). It may be easier to first solve the equation for x or y; i.e., $^-3y = {}^-2x + 5 \Rightarrow y = \frac{2}{3}x - \frac{5}{3}$. Now, for any value of x that is chosen, the corresponding value of y may be quickly found. E.g., for x = 3, $y = \frac{2}{3}(3) - \frac{5}{3} = \frac{1}{3}$. There are an infinite number of solutions, but some possibilities include (4, 1), (7, 3), or (1, $^-$1).

(b)   2x − 3y = 5 is a straight line. To graph the specified portion, find its endpoints [(2, $\frac{^-1}{3}$), ($^-$2, $^-$3)] by substituting x = 2 and x = $^-$2 into the equation. Connecting these points gives the graph below.

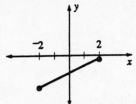

(c)   Use y = 0 and y = 2 to obtain endpoints (2.5, 0) and (5.5, 2). See below.

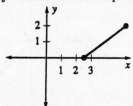

2. (a)   (2, 5) is a unique solution.

(b)   Elimination yields 0 = 1; thus there are no solutions.

(c)   (1, $^-$5) is a unique solution.

(d)   Elimination yields 0 = 258; thus there are no solutions.

(e)   (0, 0) is a unique solution.

(f) $(\frac{4}{11}, \frac{1}{11})$ is a unique solution.

3. (a)   Given: y = x + 3
                3x − 4y + 1 = 0
     Then, by substitution, 3x − 4(x + 3) + 1 = 0 $\Rightarrow$ 3x − 4x − 12 + 1 = 0 $\Rightarrow$ x = $^-$11.
     If x = $^-$11, y = ($^-$11) + 3 $\Rightarrow$ y = $^-$8.
     The solution set is ($^-$11, $^-$8).

3.   (b)   Given: $\frac{x}{3} - \frac{y}{4} = 1$

$\frac{x}{5} - \frac{y}{3} = 2$

Eliminating fractions gives the equivalent equations:
$$4x - 3y = 12$$
$$3x - 5y = 30$$

Multiplying the first equation by $^-5$ and the second by 3 yields:
$$^-20x + 15y = ^-60$$
$$9x - 15y = 90$$

Adding the equations to eliminate y gives:
$$^-11y = 30 \Rightarrow y = \frac{^-30}{11}.$$ Then substituting into one of the equivalent equations:

$$3x - 5\left(\frac{^-30}{11}\right) = 30 \Rightarrow x = \frac{^-84}{11}.$$ The solution set is $\left(\frac{^-84}{11}, \frac{^-30}{11}\right)$.

Using either substitution or elimination techniques, as demonstrated above, gives other solutions as follows:

(c) $\left(\frac{13}{3}, \frac{43}{12}\right)$ (d) $(0, 0)$

(e) $\left(^-1 + 3\sqrt{2}, 3 - \sqrt{2}\right)$ (f) $\left(\frac{^-6}{5}, \frac{^-4}{5}\right)$

4.   (a)   (*i*)   Slopes are $\frac{^-2}{3}$ and 1, respectively.

(*ii*)   Both slopes equal 1.

(*iii*)   Both slopes equal $^-4$.

(b)   (*i*)   One solution

(*ii*)   No solution (with the same slope and different y-intercepts, the lines are parallel).

(*iii*)   An infinite number of solutions (dividing the first equation by 2 shows that both represent the same line.

(c)   If the slopes represented by the two equations are different, there is a unique solution to the system. If the slopes are the same and the intercepts are the same, there is an infinite number of solutions. If the slopes are the same and the intercepts are different, there is no solution.

5.   (a)   Solving each equation for y gives $y = \frac{3}{4}x - \frac{5}{4}$ and $y = \frac{5}{3}x - 5$. The slopes are different ($\frac{3}{4}$ and $\frac{5}{3}$), so there is a unique solution.

(b)   The slope of both equations is $\frac{3}{4}$, while the y-intercepts ($^-1$ and $^-5$) are different. There are no solutions; the lines are parallel.

(c)   Solving each equations for y yields $y = \frac{2}{3}x + 5$. The lines are the same, therefore, and there are an infinite number of solutions.

(d)   These are the lines x = 0 and y = 0; i.e., the x- and y-axes. The slopes are therefore different and there is a unique solution.

6.   The equations of the three line segments are $y = 8x - 40$, $y = \frac{^-4}{7}x + \frac{40}{7}$, and $y = \frac{1}{2}x$. Equating each pair gives the common solution $\left(\frac{16}{3}, \frac{8}{3}\right)$ for all pairs.

7. Solve each of the equations for y.
   Equation 1: $^-3y = ^-x - 3 \Rightarrow y = \frac{1}{3}x + 1$. Equation 2: $2y = ^-x + 2 \Rightarrow y = \frac{^-1}{2}x - 4$.
   These equations represent two adjacent sides. Their parallels must have the same slopes and go through the point $(0, ^-4)$; i.e., since $(0, ^-4)$ is not a solution for either of the given equations. Thus we can use the point-slope form of the equation of a line, knowing the respective slopes and a point on each.

   Parallel line 1: $y - (^-4) = \frac{1}{3}(x - 0) \Rightarrow y = \frac{1}{3}x - 4$ is the equation of one side.

   Parallel line 2: $y - (^-4) = \frac{^-1}{2}(x - 0) \Rightarrow y = \frac{^-1}{2}x - 4$ is the equation of the other side.

8. The three possible pairs of equations have solutions $(\frac{2}{3}, \frac{13}{3})$, $(3, 9)$, and $(3, 2)$. These are the triangle's verteces. The base, along $x = 3$, is $9 - 2 = 7$ units long and the height is $3 - \frac{2}{3} = \frac{7}{3}$ units. The area is thus $\frac{1}{2}(7)(\frac{7}{3}) = \frac{49}{6}$ units^2.

9. (a) The slope of $\overline{AC} = \frac{1}{6}$; thus the slope of $\overline{BP}$ (its perpendicular) is $^-6$. The equation of $\overline{BP}$ [with $m = ^-6$ and passing through the point $(2, 5)$] is thus $y - 5 = ^-6(x - 2)$, or $y = ^-6x + 17$.

   The slope of $\overline{BC} = ^-1$; thus the slope of $\overline{AP} = 1$. The equation of $\overline{AP}$ is $y - 0 = 1(x - 0)$, or $y = x$.

   By substitution, $x = ^-6x + 17$, or $x = \frac{17}{7}$. Since $y = x$, then $y = \frac{17}{7}$. The point of intersection is $(\frac{17}{7}, \frac{17}{7})$.

   (b) The slope of $\overline{AB} = \frac{5}{2}$; the line perpendicular to $\overline{AC}$ through C (the third altitude) thus has equation

   $y - 1 = \frac{^-2}{5}(x - 6)$, or $y = \frac{^-2}{5}x + \frac{17}{5}$. $(\frac{17}{7}, \frac{17}{7})$ is a solution of this equation; i.e., the line passes through P.

10. $x + y = \frac{3}{4}$ and $y - y = \frac{7}{9}$ implies $x = \frac{55}{72}$ and $y = \frac{^-1}{72}$.

11. Write one equation for the contents of the truck (where G is the number of gallons of gasoline and K is the number of gallons of kerosene): $G + K = 5000$. Write another for the profit: $0.13G + 0.12K = 640$.
    Multiplying the first equation by $^-12$ and the second by 100 yields
       $^-12G - 12K = ^-60,000$
       $13G + 12K = 64,000$.
    Eliminating K and solving for G, we have $G = 4000$ gallons of gasoline. Substituting and solving for K finds $K = 1000$ gallons of kerosene.

12. With C = cashew granola and G = golden granola:
       $C + G = 200$
       $1.8C + 1.2G = 1.6(200)$
    Solving gives $C = 133\frac{1}{3}$ pounds and $G = 66\frac{2}{3}$ pounds.

13. Let A and B be the amounts of the two solutions. Write one equation for the amount of the solution and another for the amount of acid:
       $A + B = 150$
       $0.6A + 0.9B = 0.8(150)$
    Solving gives $A = 50$ liters of 60% solution and $B = 100$ liters of 90% solution.

14. If F is the first stock and S is the second, then:
       $F + S = 80,000$
       $0.15F + 0.20S = 15,000$
    Solving gives $20,000 at 15%; $60,000 at 20%.

15. (a) In eight months, $80 interest was earned. Since it is simple interest, this is $10 per month; thus in the first ten months (10 months)·($10 per month) = $100 was earned. The original balance was $2100 - 100 = 2000.

15. (b)   Interest = (Principal)·(Rate)·(Time), or $100 = (2000)$·(Rate)·$(\frac{10}{12})$. Solving gives R = 0.06 = 6%.

16. $5w = 4l$, or $w = \frac{4}{5}l$. $2w + 2l = 270 \Rightarrow w = 60$ inches and $l = 75$ inches.

17.   Write one equation for the number of coins and another for their value (where D is the number of dimes and Q is the number of quarters).

   $D + Q = 27$
   $0.10D + 0.25Q = 5.25$.

   Solving gives D = 10 dimes and Q = 17 quarters.

18. (a)   All solutions are $(^-1, 2)$.

   (b)   Answers will vary; one set would be $9x + 10y = 11$ and $12x + 13y = 14$. One would expect the solution to be $(^-1, 2)$

   (c)   All systems of the form $ax + (a + 1)y = (a + 2)$ and $(a + 3)x + (a + 4)y = (a + 5)$ will have $(^-1, 2)$ as a solution since $^-1(a) + 2(a + 1) = {}^-a + 2a + 2 = a + 2$.

19.   The sides have slopes $\frac{c}{b}$, $\frac{c}{b-a}$, and 0. The slopes of the altitudes are thus $\frac{^-b}{c}$, $\frac{a-b}{c}$, and undefined. The altitudes pass through (a, 0), (0, 0), and (b, c), respectively, and thus have equations:

   $$y - 0 = \frac{^-b}{c}(x - a), \text{ or } y = \frac{^-b}{c}x + \frac{ab}{c} ,$$

   $$y - 0 = \frac{a-b}{c}(x - 0), \text{ or } y = \frac{a-b}{c}x , \text{ and}$$

   $$x = b.$$

   Substituting for y with the first two gives $\frac{^-b}{c}x + \frac{ab}{c} = \frac{a-b}{c}x$, or $\frac{ab}{c} = \frac{a}{c}x$, implying that x = b and matching the third equation.
   The three altitudes are then concurrent at the point $(b, \frac{ab - b^2}{c})$.

20.   b (hyperbola) and c(half-plane) do not represent lines.

21.   Write equations in the form y = mx + b (i.e., solve for y) to most easily find the slope and y-intercept.

   (a) $6y + 5x = y \Rightarrow y = \frac{^-5}{6}x + \frac{7}{6}$. Thus $m = \frac{^-5}{6}$ and $b = \frac{7}{6}$.

   (b) $\frac{2}{3}x + \frac{1}{2}y = \frac{1}{5} \Rightarrow y = \frac{^-4}{3}x + \frac{2}{5}$. $m = \frac{^-4}{3}$ and $b = \frac{2}{5}$.

   (c) $0.2y - 0.75x - 0.37 = 0 \Rightarrow y = 3.75x + 1.85$. m = 3.75 and b = 1.85.

   (d)   y = 4 is equivalent to y = 0x + 4; m = 0 and b = 4.

22. (a) $m = \frac{9}{10} \Rightarrow y - 7 = \frac{9}{10}(x - 4)$, or $y = \frac{9}{10}x + \frac{17}{5}$.

   (b) $m = \frac{5}{3} \Rightarrow y - 7 = \frac{5}{3}(x - 4)$, or $y = \frac{5}{3}x + \frac{1}{3}$.

   (c) $m = 0 \Rightarrow y = {}^-8$.

23.   Graph by either determining intercepts (i.e., let x and then y equal 0 for y- and x-intercpts, respectively) or by following the slope from the y-intercepts. For inequalities, shade the half-plane containing the solution set. See graphs on page 296.

23.   (a) 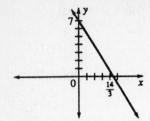   (b)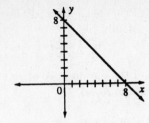

      (c) 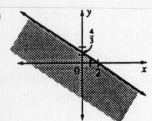   (d)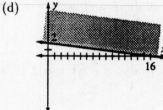

24.   (a) $m = \frac{1}{2}$ (b) $m = \frac{^-1}{2}$

      (c) $m = 0$ (d)   undetermined slope

25.   Solve the system of equations to locate the point of intersection:

   $$3x + 5y = 7 \;\Rightarrow\; 3x + 5y = 7$$
   $$2x - y = {}^-4 \;\Rightarrow\; 10x - 5y = {}^-20$$

   Eliminating y and solving for x yields $x = {}^-1$; substituting, $y = 2$. The solution is $({}^-1, 2)$.

   A line parallel to the x-axis has slope $m = 0$ and is of the form $y = a$; here, $y = 2$.

Problem Set 14-4

1.   The answer will vary depending upon the version of Logo used.

2.   The figures generated by the MEDIAL.TRI procedures are similar.

3.   TO AXES
   SETXY 0 120
   SETXY 0 (-120)]
   SETXY 0 0
   SETXY 130 0
   SETXY -130 0
   SETXY 0 0
   END   (In LCSI, use SETPOS LIST instead of SETXY.)

4.   There are three possible squares that can be constructed.

5.   TO FILL.RECT
   REPEAT 50 [SETY 30 SETY 0 RT 90 FD 1 LT 90]
   END

6.   TO CCIRCLE :XCEN :YCEN :RAD
   PU SETXY :XCEN :YCEN
   FD :RAD RT 90
   PD
   CIRCLE :RAD
   END

6. ```
   TO  CIRCLE :R
     VCIRCLE  2*3.14159*R/360
   END

   TO  VCIRCLE :S
     REPEAT  360  [FD :S  RT  1]
   END
   ```

7. ```
   TO  QUAD :X1 :Y1 :X2 :Y2 :X3 :Y3 :X4 :Y4
     PU  SETXY :X1 :Y1  PD
     SETXY :X2 :Y2
     SETXY :X3 :Y3
     SETXY :X4 :Y4
     SETXY :X1 :Y1
   END    (In LCSI, use SETPOS LIST instead of SETXY.)
   ```

8. (a) Use the QUAD procedures from problem 7 and the following:

   ```
   TO  MEDIAL.QUAD :X1 :Y1 :X2 :Y2 :X3 :Y3 :X4 :Y4
     QUAD :X1 :Y1 :X2 :Y2 :X3 :Y3 :X4 :Y4
     MIDPOINT :X1 :Y1 :X2 :Y2
     MIDPOINT :X2 :Y2 :X3 :Y3
     MIDPOINT :X3 :Y3 :X4 :Y4
     MIDPOINT :X4 :Y4 :X1 :Y1
     MIDPOINT :X1 :Y1 :X2 :Y2
   END    (In LCSI, use SETPOS LIST instead of SETXY.)

   TO  MIDPOINT :X1 :Y1 :X2 :Y2
     SETXY  (:X1 + :X2)/2 (:Y1 + :Y2)/2
   END
   ```

   (b) The medial quadrilateral is a parallelogram.

9. Use the QUAD procedure from problem 7 and the following:

   ```
   TO  MEDIAL.QUADS :NUM :X1 :Y1 :X2 :Y2 :X3 :Y3 :X4 :Y4
     IF :NUM = 0 STOP
     QUAD :X1 :Y1 :X2 :Y2 :X3 :Y3 :X4 :Y4
     MEDIAL.QUADS :NUM − 1 (:X1 + :X2)/2 (:Y1 + :Y2)/2 (:X2 + :X3)/2 (:Y2 + :Y3)/2
         (:X3 + :X4)/2 (:Y3 + :Y4)/2 (:X4 + :X1)/2 (:Y4 + :Y1)/2
   END    (In LCSI, replace STOP with [STOP] and use SETPOS LIST instead of SETXY.)
   ```

10. ```
    TO  SAS :S1 :A :S2
      BK :S1
      RT :A
      FD :S2
      HOME
    END
    ```

11. ```
    TO  R.ISOS.TRI :LEN
      FD :LEN
      RT 90
      FD :LEN
      RT 135
      FD (SQRT 2)*:LEN
    END
    ```

12. TO CIRC50
    PU
    SETXY (-20) (-40)
    PD
    REPEAT 360 [FD 2*3.14159*:R/360 RT 1]
    END   (In LCSI, use SETPOS LIST instead of SETXY.)

13. TO GENCIRC :X :Y :R
    PU
    SETXY :X :Y
    PD
    REPEAT 360 [FD 2*3.14159*:R/360 RT 1]
    END   (In LCSI, use SETPOS LIST instead of SETXY.)

14. TO MEDIAL.TRIS :NUM :X1 :Y1 :X2 :Y2 :X3 :Y3
    IF :NUM = 0 STOP
    TRI :X1 :Y1 :X2 :Y2 :X3 :Y3
    MEDIAL.TRIS :NUM − 1 (:X1 + :X2)/2 (:Y1 + :Y2)/2 (:X2 + :X3)/2 (:Y2 + :Y3)/2
        (:X3 + :X1)/2 (:Y3 + :Y1)/2
    END

    TO TRI :X1 :Y1 :X2 :Y2 :X3 :Y3
    PU
    SETXY :X1 :Y1
    PD
    SETXY :X2 :Y2
    SETXY :X3 :Y3
    SETXY :X1 :Y1
    END   (In LCSI, replace STOP with [STOP] and use SETPOS LIST instead of SETXY.)

Chapter 14 Test

1. Use the distance formula to find $\overline{AB} = 5$, $\overline{BC} = 5$, and $\overline{AC} = 6$. The perimeter is $5 + 5 + 6 = 16$.

2. Label the points X(4, 2), Y(0, ¯1), and Z(¯4, ¯4). The points are collinear if:
   (*i*)   The slope from X to Y equals that from Y to Z. The slopes are both $\frac{3}{4}$; the lines are collinear.
   (*ii*) XY + YZ = XZ. $5 + 5 = 10$; the lines are collinear.

3. (a)

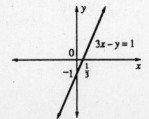

   (b)

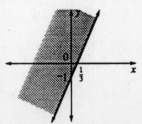

   (c)

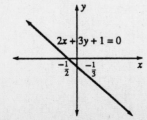

4.   (a) $y - (^-3) = \frac{^-4}{3}(x - 2) \Rightarrow y = \frac{^-4}{3}x - \frac{1}{3}$.

       (b) $x = {^-}3$ (c) $y = 3$

5.   (a)   Lines parallel to $\overline{AB}$ have the same slope; $m = \frac{4}{3}$. Use the point-slope form with $m = \frac{4}{3}$ and the point (2, 5) to find $y = \frac{4}{3}x + \frac{7}{3}$.

       (b)   This is a horizontal line; $y = 5$.

       (c) $\overline{AB}$ has equation $y = \frac{4}{3}x + 4$. The lines will cross where $y = 5$; substituting, find $x = \frac{3}{4}$ when $y = 5$. The lines intersect at $(\frac{3}{4}, 5)$.

6.   Solving for y, we find that the given line has slope $m = \frac{^-2}{3}$ and y-intercept $(0, \frac{^-1}{3})$. The perpendicular has slope $m = \frac{3}{2}$. Use the point-slope form to find $y = \frac{3}{2}x - \frac{1}{3}$.

7.   (a)   Using the elimination method, find the solution to be (4.2, $^-$0.6). Since the slopes of the lines are different, (4.2, $^-$0.6) is a unique solution.

       (b)   Using the elimination method, find the (unique) solution to be $(\frac{10}{9}, \frac{4}{3})$.

       (c)   The lines have the same slope and different y-intercepts; they are parallel and there is no solution.

8.   Solve the equations $R + 3D = 170$ and $2R + 1.5D = 205$ to find $R = 80$ regular containers and $D = 30$ deluxe containers.

9.   (a)   Use the midpoint formula to find $(1, \frac{^-1}{2})$.

       (b)   Solve $\left(\frac{^-3 + x}{2}, \frac{5 + y}{2}\right) = (^-5, 4)$ to find $x = ^-7$ and $y = 3$. The endpoint is $(^-7, 3)$.

10.   (a)   (b)

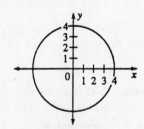
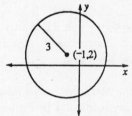

      (c)

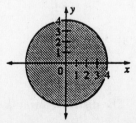

11.   The equation will have the form $(x + 3)^2 + (y - 4)^2 = r^2$. Use the distance formula to find r, the distance between (0, 0) and ($^-$3, 4), to be $r = 5$. The equation is $(x + 3)^2 + (y - 4)^2 = 25$.

12.   (a)   (b)

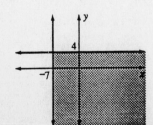
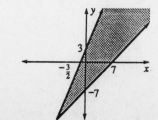

13. Solve the equations $R + B = 12$ and $R + B = 2(R - B)$ to find $R = 9$ red jelly beans and $B = 3$ black jelly beans.

14. If F is the number of students in the freshman class and S is the number of students in the sophomore class, then $F = S - 225$ and $S = 2F - 50$. Solving gives 500 sophomores and 275 freshmen.

15. Let R be the number of Roosevelt's votes and H the number of Hoover's votes. Then:
    $R = H + 6,563,988$, and
    $H + \frac{1}{5}R = R - \frac{1}{5}R + 2,444,622$.
    Solving, $R = 22,521,525$ votes and $H = 15,957,537$ votes.

16. (a) $m_{\overline{OB}} = 4$; $\overline{OB}$'s perpendicular bisector then has slope $\frac{-1}{4}$ and passes through the point $(\frac{1}{2}, 1)$. The equation is thus $y = \frac{-1}{4}x + \frac{17}{8}$. Similarly, the perpendicular bisector of $\overline{BC}$ is $y = x - 1$. Their intersection is the point $(2.5, 1.5)$.

    (b) The third bisector is $x = 2.5$, which passes through the point $(2.5, 1.5)$.

    (c) $\sqrt{(2.5 - o)^2 + (1.5 - o)^2} \doteq 2.9$.

         $\sqrt{(2.5 - 1)^2 + (1.5 - 4)^2} \doteq 2.9$.

         $\sqrt{(2.5 - 5)^2 + (1.5 - 0)^2} \doteq 2.9$.

    (d) The point of intersection found in (a) is the center of the circumscribed circle with radius $\doteq 2.9$. The equation is then $(x - 2.5)^2 + (y - 1.5)^2 = (2.9)^2 = 8.5$.

17. The closest point will be on the perpendicular line through the origin. The slope of the given line is $^-1$; a line perpendicular to it will have slope 1. The line through the origin with slope 1 is $y = x$. The desired point is where the lines intersect, or $(\frac{3}{2}, \frac{3}{2})$.

18. The distance is that from $(1, 0)$ to the point of intersection of $y = 2x$ and the line perpendicular to it through $(1, 0)$. The perpendicular line is $y = \frac{-1}{2}x + \frac{1}{2}$. The point of intersection is $(\frac{1}{5}, \frac{2}{5})$. Using the distance formula, we find $d = \frac{2}{5}\sqrt{5}$.

19. Distance must be measured perpendicularly. To get two points between which to measure distance, find the points where a perpendicular line intersects each; e.g., $y = \frac{1}{2}x$ is perpendicular to both. The intersection of $y = \frac{1}{2}x$ and $y = ^-2x + 1$ is $(\frac{2}{5}, \frac{1}{5})$. Similarly, $y = \frac{1}{2}x$ and $y = ^-2x + 3$ intersect at $(\frac{6}{5}, \frac{3}{5})$. The distance between these points is $\frac{2}{5}\sqrt{5}$.

20. (a) $(5, 3, 0)$ (b) $(0, 3, 8)$

    (c) $(5, 0, 8)$

    (d) The z-coordinate of both points $= 0$; thus may be disregarded. The distance formula yields $\sqrt{13}$.

    (e) A is 7 units directly above $(5, 3, 1)$

    (f) Since the x-coordinate is the only one changed, $d = 5 - ^-5 = 10$.